Feders'
THE ART AND SCIENCE OF EVALUATION IN THE ARTS THERAPIES

ABOUT THE AUTHORS

Robyn Flaum Cruz, Ph.D., BC-DMT studied dance/movement therapy at New York University, and received her doctorate in educational psychology specializing in measurement and methodology from The University of Arizona. Her work as a methodologist has spanned quantitative and qualitative research in many fields, including dance/movement therapy, psychology, psychiatry, and neurology. Her work has been published in professional journals, such as *Brain*, *Neuropsychologia*, *Psychiatric Services*, *Archives of Neurology*, and *American Journal of Dance Therapy*. She was co-editor of the *American Journal of Dance Therapy* from 1998 to 2001. She is core faculty in the Expressive Therapies Ph.D. Program, Lesley University, Cambridge, MA, and Editor-in-Chief of *The Arts in Psychotherapy*. She is a Past President of American Dance Therapy Association.

Bernard Feder received his Ph.D. from New York University in 1957, and has taught education and psychology at NYU, Adelphi, Hofstra, and the University of Sarasota. Among his books are *The Complete Guide to Taking Tests* (Prentice-Hall) and (with David Stutz, M.D.) *The Savvy Patient: How to Be an Active Participant in Your Medical Care* (Consumer Reports Books). In addition, he has edited a medical directory and guide and written numerous articles for general and professional journals. In 1990, he was invited to present a history of the arts therapies at the National Library of Medicine of the NIH.

Elaine Feder was a dance/movement therapist. Her background included study with such pioneers in modern dance as Martha Graham, Jose Limon, and Doris Humphrey; wide experience in teaching, performing, and choreographing; a degree in expressive arts therapies; and extensive graduate study in the psychotherapies and movement analysis. She was a member of the American Dance Therapy Association and the Laban Institute of Movement Studies.

The Feders wrote *The Expressive Arts Therapies: Art, Music and Dance as Psychotherapy* (Prentice-Hall, 1981, 1984), and wrote jointly for *Psychology Today*, *Human Behavior*, *The New York Times*, *The Chicago Tribune*, and other general and professional publications.

IN MEMORIAM

Elaine Feder
April 28, 1926 – May 22, 2010
She danced her way through life

Second Edition

Feders' THE ART AND SCIENCE OF EVALUATION IN THE ARTS THERAPIES

How Do You Know What's Working?

By

ROBYN FLAUM CRUZ, PH.D., BC-DMT

and

BERNARD FEDER, PH.D.

With Contributions by Donna Betts, PH.D., ATR-BC,
and Barbara L. Wheeler, PH.D., MT-BC

CHARLES C THOMAS • PUBLISHER, LTD.
Springfield • Illinois • U.S.A.

Published and Distributed Throughout the World by

CHARLES C THOMAS • PUBLISHER, LTD.
2600 South First Street
Springfield, Illinois 62704

ISBN 978-0-398-08852-1 (hard)
ISBN 978-0-398-08853-8 (paper)
ISBN 978-0-398-08854-5 (ebook)

Library of Congress Catalog Card Number: 2012032279

First Edition, 1998
Second Edition, 2013

With THOMAS BOOKS *careful attention is given to all details of manufacturing and design. It is the Publisher's desire to present books that are satisfactory as to their physical qualities and artistic possibilities and appropriate for their particular use.* THOMAS BOOKS *will be true to those laws of quality that assure a good name and good will.*

Printed in the United States of America
SM-R-3

Library of Congress Cataloging-in-Publication Data

Cruz, Robyn Flaum.
Feders' the art and science of evaluation in the arts therapies / by Robyn Flaum Cruz and Bernard Feder ; with contributions by Donna Betts and Barbara L. Wheeler. -- 2nd ed.
p. cm.
Includes bibliographical references and index.
ISBN 978-0-398-08852-1 (hard) -- ISBN 978-0-398-08853-8 (pbk.) -- ISBN 978-0-398-08854-5 (ebook)
1. Art therapy. 2. Music therapy. 3. Dance therapy. 4. Mental illness--Treatment--Evaluation. 5. Psychodynamic psychotherapy. 6. Psychotherapist and patient. I. Feder, Bernard. II. Betts, Donna J. III. Wheeler, Barbara L. IV. Title. V. Title: Art and science of evaluation in the arts therapies.

RC489.A7F426 2013
616.89'1656--dc23

2012032279

CONTRIBUTORS

Donna Betts, Ph.D., ATR-BC, is an assistant professor in the George Washington University Graduate Art Therapy Program, Washington, DC. Dr. Betts has served on the Board of Directors of the American Art Therapy Association and the Art Therapy Credentials Board. She is a member of the advisory editorial board of *The Arts in Psychotherapy* international journal, and the editorial board of the *Journal of Art for Life.* A leading authority on art therapy assessment and rating procedures, Dr. Betts is founder and Director of the International Art Therapy Research Database, www.arttherapyresearch.com, an expanding archive of art-based data to inform practice and facilitate research.

Barbara L. Wheeler, Ph.D., MT-BC, retired in 2011 as Professor of Music Therapy and University Professor at the University of Louisville, where she began the music therapy program in 2000. She holds the designation of Professor Emerita from Montclair State University, where she taught from 1975–2000. She frequently presents and teaches in the U.S. and internationally. Her clinical work has been with a variety of clientele, most recently as Neurologic Music Therapist at several facilities. Barbara edited *Music Therapy Research: Quantitative and Qualitative Perspectives* and *Music Therapy Research,* Second Edition, and is coauthor of *Clinical Training Guide for the Student Music Therapist.* She has published numerous articles and chapters. She is a past president of the American Music Therapy Association and was recently Interview Co-Editor for *Voices: A World Forum for Music Therapy.*

PREFACE

This second edition follows the tradition of the first edition as both an introductory text and a handbook in evaluation and assessment in the creative arts therapies. It was written to be useful both for graduate students in arts therapies training programs, doctoral programs, and for practitioners in the field who want guidelines for developing and implementing evaluation programs.

The first section of the book deals with fundamentals and principles that apply to all evaluation, qualitative as well as quantitative. This general treatment is followed by chapters that deal with specific approaches to evaluation: psychometric, clinical or intuitive, and behavioral. The last section focuses on evaluation procedures in art therapy, dance/movement therapy, and music therapy, contributed by individuals who have specific expertise in those areas.

It is quite an honor to be asked to revise and update someone else's work, especially when the original work was a labor of love. The evidence of that love and the love that characterized their long relationship is clearly communicated in Bernard and Elaine Feder's introduction to the first edition which is included in this volume. In revising, I have tried to keep Bernard's lively presentation and wonderful grasp of the historical underpinnings and development of evaluation in the last century while presenting more current advancements. I am grateful for my colleagues and contributors, Barbara Wheeler and Donna Betts. Their chapters on evaluation in music therapy and art therapy, respectively, add immeasurably to the book. Wonderfully, as I worked on this revised book, it became apparent that the arts therapies professions have grown and developed even more than I had realized. I write this with the hope that this volume will be useful to current and future generations of arts therapies professionals. Creative arts therapists bring much needed humanity to caring for those in need, and we do this because of our understanding of the centrality of the arts to life.

R.F.C.

INTRODUCTION TO THE FIRST EDITION

There are two basic themes around which this book is organized. First, we believe that the argument over whether therapy is an art or a science is not only fruitless but counterproductive; it can only perpetuate divisions in a field in which both artistic creativity and scientific validation are necessary. Second, we contend that the therapeutic endeavor has little meaning if therapists cannot formulate defensible ways of ascertaining whether what they do makes a difference.

Let's begin with an overview of our first proposition.

"Art is I," wrote Claude Bernard (1813–1878); "science is we." In Isaac Newton's words, the scientist, seeking to uncover the laws that govern the operation of the universe, stands "on the shoulders of giants." Science is collaborative, incremental, and cumulative. Each scientist adds a bit of understanding to the body of knowledge, to enhance or to correct what had been discovered before. In this sense, even competitors are collaborators. What has been supplanted is either rendered obsolete or is incorporated into the revised perception of the reality of the world around us.

In contrast, the hallmark of art is independence and autonomy, the freedom to break from what was done before, and to create the new. Artists, of course, are not completely free agents; to some degree, they are in bondage to the technology of art, to the limitations of their materials, and to the demands of tradition. More easily than scientists, artists can break with tradition. However, unlike the scientist, the artist doesn't add to the body of knowledge so much as he or she transforms what has already been learned to create a unique statement. This statement does not necessarily detract from what came before. Michelangelo's masterpieces are not diminished by the works of van Gogh, or Monet, or Jackson Pollock.

While the cultures of art and science appear to be distinct, there is an interplay, and there are vast areas of overlap. Discoveries about the properties of clay or glass or marble, improvements in the quality of pigments or oils or tempera, the development of new materials for the manufacture of musical instruments, advances in the production of varnishes, all open up vistas for artists and provide them with the means by which they can conceive, and create, and execute their personal statements. Historian and former Librarian of Congress Daniel J. Boorstin (1994) writes of the symbiotic relationship between what he calls the culture of discovery and the culture of creation during an age in which both flourished:

> Renaissance belief in the inspired unique creator elevated the painter, equipped with the newly discovered science of perspective, from craftsman to artist. . . . The technique that Giotto had applied by rule of thumb became a science in the hands of da Vinci or Duren. (pp. 24, 29)

It would be a mistake to think of the artist only as the beneficiary of the fruits of scientific labor. During this age of exuberant discovery and creativity, we must remember, the quintessential Renaissance man was simultaneously discoverer and creator.

In da Vinci's notebooks, we find questions and more questions, and we would be hard-pressed to know if these are the questions of an artist or a scientist. How does a bird fly? How does a man walk? How can the trajectory of a mortar shell be described? What does each of the ten ways he could draw a foot reveal about its structure and function? In these notebooks, we find a bewildering assortment of drawings: pumps, a self-locking worm gear, an air hose, a steam engine, a parachute, an airplane, a submarine, roller bearings, sprocket chains, a machine gun. Was this a man who used science to master the skills of the artist? Or a scientist who used art to probe the worlds of anatomy, and geology, and mechanics, and hydraulics?

While we cannot find many Leonardos, for whom creativity and discovery are indivisible, there is a constant interplay between the worlds of art and science. Just as the artist owes much to the discoveries of the scientist, there are significant bodies of scientific knowledge that have been induced by questions posed by artists. The field of "projective geometry," dealing with the images that figures create when they are viewed from different angles, was developed by mathematicians in the seventeenth century as a result of prompting by artists.

Modern psychotherapy owes much to both cultures. From art, it draws on the artistic creative impulse driven by intuitive insight, the ability to discern relationships, to develop the personal empathetic bond between therapist and patient that acts as catalyst in the interpretive and healing processes. From science, it derives the recognition that the creative proposition must conform with what has been discovered about the ways humans actually function, so that we can distinguish between a principled proposition and a whim.

The relationship between art and science in the modern practice of psychotherapy is a restless and disturbed one. With the increasing specialization of occupation, artist and scientist frequently speak in different tongues and have difficulty understanding each other. From what should be a harmonious chorus often comes a disturbing and dissonant cacophony.

Science seeks underlying principles and the natural order of things. The scientist wants to find the common elements that make humans human; that provide the grand structure of human nature. The individual who deviates from this order is literally the victim of a "disorder." The scientist wants to identify the nature of the disorder so that he or she can bring the victim back to normality – that is, conformity with the statistical norm, the natural order of things. The scientifically minded psychologist asks: What can we learn about depression or psychoses from studying the myriad of people who suffer from these disorders? Are we doomed to see each problem as floating in a vast void, unrelated to similar problems?

Art seeks the unique, the individual, the things that set humans apart. Why and how, the artist asks, is this human different from all other humans? How has this individual created his or her personal reality and structured his or her own world? The key to understanding the individual is to peer into that private world, to find the expression of his or her individuality. This ability to find the unique core of the individual constitutes the art of the therapist.

This thread – the uneasy relationship between the therapist as artist and the therapist as scientist – runs through this book.

The divergences may never be resolved, but they should be understood, because the elements of both art and science are essential to a meaningful practice of therapy. Without science, therapy can degenerate into the practice of superstitious ritual, in which each practitioner owes allegiance only to his or her personal myth of existence. Without art, it can lose the very humanity it seeks to examine.

This brings us to the second issue at hand: How can individual arts therapists ascertain the appropriate treatment for their patients or clients, and how can they know whether what they do works?

When we began this book, we lived in the small university city of Athens, Georgia. As we drove from Interstate 85, we would pass a large billboard that proclaimed: PRAY. IT WORKS.

It was difficult for us to pass this sign without comment. Occasionally, we would refer to the experience of Hans J. Eysenck, a psychologist at the University of London's Institute of Psychiatry, who had raised questions about whether psychotherapy "works." Almost a half-century ago, Eysenck published a number of articles in which he questioned the efficacy of psychotherapy, concluding that no method worked better than any other, and that no form of therapy improved on the recovery rate obtained through ordinary life experiences and nonspecific treatment.

Eysenck's conclusions were the subject of intense debate among both clinicians and researchers. We have no wish here to become embroiled in the substance of his studies, which were badly flawed in a number of respects. What was most interesting about the whole affair was the furor his work created at the time in the psychotherapeutic community. The very act of testing the effectiveness of psychotherapy, he reported, aroused emotional responses that he compared with those of a true believer against a blasphemer who had attempted a statistical test of the efficacy of prayer.

Since Freud's day, debate has raged over the effectiveness of psychotherapy. The debate has often been tumultuous and, at times, acrimonious. At one end of the debate stand clinicians who are impressed with improvements they see (or claim to see) in their patients, and are understandably eager to attribute such change to their efforts. At the other end stand the researchers who demand objective evidence that real change has actually taken place and that any such change is the result of the therapeutic intervention.

This book is designed for the individual arts therapist, for whom the issue is not whether there is a change in his or her patients. Change will occur whether a patient is in therapy or not. The central issues are to recognize and identify the nature of the change, and to know with some assurance the degree to which such change is the result of the therapy, and not coincidental with it.

Much has changed in the decades since Eysenck figuratively nailed his theses to the doors of the psychotherapeutic institution. Increasing numbers of both verbal and nonverbal therapists have come to accept the need for more than faith, zeal, and uncorroborated anecdotal reports of cures in considering the effectiveness of their work.

This book explores a variety of approaches, both theoretical and methodological. Our purpose is not to provide formulas, which can be found in any basic textbook on psychological testing, or recipes, which abound in professional journals. It is to help therapists to relate their evaluation program to their goals, to identify what they are interested in evaluating, and to design the kind of evaluation program that can do what the therapist wants it to do.

In the actual development of this book, Bernard was the designated writer. He was assigned the task of putting into words the ideas on which we had agreed during extended discussions. After each draft, we argued. Elaine, the intuitive enthusiast, and Bernard, the analytic skeptic, would spend hours debating points of contention until we arrived at a consensus. The one position on which we agreed from the beginning was that the arts therapies cannot legitimately lay claim to being professions until arts therapists can establish a credible method for evaluating (literally, ascertaining the value of) their services, and until they can develop ways of knowing that what they do makes a difference to the troubled individuals with whom they work.

We believe that arts therapists are painfully aware of this problem. In large part, the problem has been brought to their attention through the demands of outsiders, such as insurance companies. In part, it is the result of the maturation process in a field undergoing an awkward adolescence. In recent years, virtually every professional conference includes panels and seminars on assessment, evaluation, and research in the therapies. Yet, it is sobering to recognize how few arts therapies programs offer instruction either in research or in evaluation. The major problem now is not the resistance to assessment that Eysenck encountered in the 1960s, but the uncritical zeal with which many practitioners have come to embrace methods and instruments that offer the illusion of certainty, and often without any real understanding of their functions and limitations.

In this connection, it may be instructive to read the words of Oscar Buros, half-a-century ago. In the introduction to *Tests in Print* (1961), he wrote:

> At present, no matter how poor a test may be, if it is nicely packaged and if it promises to do all sorts of things which no test can do, the test will find many gullible buyers.
>
> . . . [Test users] seem to have an unshakable will to believe the exaggerated claims of test authors and publishers. If these test users were better informed regarding the merits and limitations of their testing instruments, they would probably be less happy . . . in their work. The test user who has faith – however unjustified – can speak with confidence in interpreting test results and in making recommendations. The well-informed test user cannot do this; he knows that the best of our tests are still highly fallible instruments which are extremely difficult to interpret with accuracy in individual cases. Consequently, he must interpret test results cautiously and with so many reservations that others wonder whether he really knows what he is talking about. (Buros, 1961, p. xxix)

A decade later, Buros apparently found that little had changed since his earlier comments, and he wrote in apparent exasperation that "at least half of the tests currently on the market should never have been published. Exaggerated, false, or unsubstantiated claims are the rule rather than the exception" (Buros, 1972, p. xxvii).

We believe that assessment procedures will improve only if the creators and users of these procedures become more knowledgeable about evaluation and assessment than are most therapists today. It is our hope that this book will make some contribution in this regard.

For a number of reasons, this book is not a comprehensive primer on evaluation or a survey of assessment in the arts therapies.

First of all, practical considerations made it infeasible to try to develop a complete guide to evaluation. Such a book would have been prohibitively long and intimidating expensive.

In addition, the writing of such a book would have involved us in in-depth research in areas in which we were not comfortable, mainly because we were not familiar with their practical application. At the invitation of several faculty members of the University of Georgia, we considered applying for a grant to involve doctoral students in various areas in which we ourselves were deficient, but we decided that such an endeavor would have been too time-consuming and would have added only marginally to the book.

As a result, we chose to delimit the work in two major areas. The first decision was to deal only with the assessment of individual clients and patients, and to refer fleetingly to the vast areas of couple, group, and family therapy. While there are some tangential points between the assessment of individuals and the assessment of families and groups, there are compelling reasons to view these areas as distinct categories in the field of the therapies.

The second decision, after a good deal of painful consideration, was to abandon the work we had already begun in examining such areas as psychodrama, drama therapy, and poetry therapy. Because these therapies are fundamentally verbal, evaluation procedures tend to rely heavily on approaches that have been developed either in individual psychotherapy or in couple, family, or group therapies.

We are obligated to those arts therapists who shared with us the evaluation procedures on which they had worked or were working. Many offered comments on their experiences, their philosophies, and their frustrations.

We owe a particular debt of gratitude to those who agreed to review and comment on the chapters in which they had particular expertise and interest. These include friend and former colleague, Dr. John W. French, who had coordinated College Board research at the Educational Testing Service; Dr. Richard Graham, Director of the School of Music at the University of Georgia and former editor of the *Journal of Music Therapy;* Dr. Jerry Gale of the University of Georgia, whose area of interest is qualitative evaluation; Dr. Charles R. Martin of the Center for Applications of Psychological Types; and the numerous arts therapists, psychiatrists, psychologists, psychometricians, and scholars in a variety of fields who offered criticisms and suggestions.

Bernard and Elaine Feder

CONTENTS

Feders'
THE ART AND SCIENCE OF EVALUATION IN THE ARTS THERAPIES

Chapter 1

PURPOSES OF EVALUATION

Most arts therapists in the U.S. have some notion of the value of evaluation. This is due in part to changes in training programs, the development of doctoral programs specific to arts therapists, and developments in the arts therapies literature. While not all are comfortable with evaluation as part of research, the recognition of the need for research has been regularly documented in the literature, and across art, music, and dance/movement therapies specific texts on research are now widely available (see for example, Cruz & Berrol, 2012; Kapitan, 2010; Wheeler, 2005). In addition to acknowledgment of the need for research to promote the arts therapies, several developments have spurred arts therapists to generate plans for assessing the needs of their patients and clients and for evaluating the results of their efforts. These activities have been motivated in part by a growing culture of accountability that characterizes modern healthcare.

Increasing demand by third-party payers that claims for services specify the diagnosis of the patient or client has certainly played a role in shaping arts therapies practice. Arts therapists in private practice and who work within clinics, frequently hold state licenses that allow them to submit claims for treatment to insurance companies, Medicare, and other third-party payers. This often requires practitioners to couch goals and assessments in specific claims language, and to use diagnostic classification systems such as the *Diagnostic and Statistical Manual of Mental Disorders (DSM)* developed by the American Psychiatric Association. Arts therapies training programs in states where graduates can apply for state licensing even include brief training on the *DSM* in the curriculum.

Another development is the expansion of the arts therapies beyond their original base in psychiatric settings into schools, various community programs, wellness centers, and medical treatment settings. In addition, concerns with the aging population in the U.S. and social activism have been significant factors in the expanded settings where arts therapists can be found.

Increasing numbers of arts therapists were drawn into school systems as a result of the enactment of Public Law 94–142 in 1975, and have continued to work in schools. This law, Individuals with Disabilities Education Act (IDEA), mandated the establishment of programs to serve the needs of children with physical, development, or emotional problems, and revisions to the law over the years have preserved this feature. Schools have been required to develop a host of services addressed to the problems of exceptional children. Arts therapists in these settings are involved as teachers, therapists, or consultants and are required to ascertain the developmental, physical, neurological, or emotional problems of exceptional children, to identify their disabilities, and to develop individual educational plans (IEPs) designed to remediate or ameliorate these deficiencies. Similarly, in other treatment settings, arts therapists are involved with identification of disabilities and issues with an eye to planning and delivering treatment to address perceived and reported client needs.

As an example of one of the more recent expansions of arts therapies, in medical settings, arts therapists are increasingly working with the medically ill accompanied by greater acceptance that "creative expression can make a powerful contribution to the healing process" (Stuckey & Nobel, 2010). Similarly, arts therapies for community activism and wellness (see for example, Ho, Tsao, Bloch, & Zeltzer, 2011) as well as illness continue to grow in acceptance and application around the world.

In many of the array of settings in which arts therapists now work, there are standard formats for assessing individual progress such as the Minimum Data Set, a clinical assessment mandated for use with all residents in Medicare or Medicaid certified nursing homes in the U.S. However, in settings where there is no mandated overall assessment or where an assessment lacks relevant psychosocial or mood components, arts therapists must assist in developing assessments or assessment components that are relevant for the arts therapies and the particular population treated in the program.

The approaches to evaluation are as varied as the many philosophical approaches to the arts therapies. But, regardless of approach, the problem is the same: without some meaningful criteria for evaluation, we have no way of knowing whether a patient or client is receiving treatment that is appropriate for his or her problem; whether the treatment is helping, or has helped the client; whether a therapist should augment, abandon, or change a method or an approach; whether a program is doing what it was set up to do; and whether it should be maintained or modified or abandoned.

There is no single best way to evaluate. Evaluation may be formal or informal, based on statistics or on intuition. Information may be gathered through the use of tests and measurement scales, through observation of patient/client behavior or by asking individuals about their thoughts and activities, through a qualitative assessment of an individual's drawing or movements or music-making, or through a convergence of impressionistic data. But, in terms of the definition of evaluation on which this book rests, they have a common denominator. Evaluation, for the purposes described in this volume, is a method for collecting information on which to base decisions. And for some situations and for some purposes, some forms of evaluation are far more appropriate than others. Much of the skill of the evaluator rests on knowing the differences among forms of evaluation.

FUNCTIONS OF EVALUATION

There are five basic functions of evaluation:

1. to ascertain the problems and needs of a person (a patient/client or a staff member), a program, or an institution;
2. to predict future behavior;
3. to monitor change;
4. to learn how to improve treatment methods or techniques; and
5. to know when to stop or discontinue treatment.

These functions are not independent and mutually exclusive. For example, without a baseline to establish the patient's status and need, monitoring is useless, since there is no way of knowing what change has taken place. Unless a therapist can predict a patient's behavior with some accuracy, there is no way to monitor change in any meaningful way, or to know when to terminate treatment, since any change that is noted might have been the result of the treatment, or it might simply have been a reflection of the natural course of the disorder.

All of these functions serve one fundamental purpose: to guide and direct treatment. Any evaluation that does not contribute to planning or improving treatment, and any program whose purpose is merely to label individuals or to pigeonhole them, serve no useful purpose and may actually do considerable harm.

In addition, an assessment or evaluation is likely to be of little value unless the evaluator has a clear idea of why he or she is undertaking it. Purposes can vary widely from choosing an appropriate course of treatment to assessing suicide risk or understanding why a specific treatment is not working. Each of these examples suggests a particular direction for the assessment procedure or even a different procedure.

The terms evaluation and assessment are often used interchangeably, and readers will find that to be true even in this text. Both evaluation and assessment are used to refer to value judgments that are used as a basis for decision making. However, many use the term assessment to describe the entire process of identifying a patient's or client's problems, and for monitoring his or her progress, and use evaluation to refer to examining the efficacy of the program or course of treatment. Interestingly, assessment comes from a Latin root with the meaning "to sit beside." In healthcare, assessment frequently refers only to the initial determination of the patient's problems or needs, while evaluation describes the dual processes of monitoring patient progress and making judgments about the course of treatment.

DIAGNOSIS AND ASSESSMENT

In spite of the fact of the expansion of creative arts therapies practice over the last 20 years into many different settings, its early roots were in psychiatry. In addition, many arts therapists see themselves as psychotherapists or counselors and the continued concentration of art therapists in mental health settings make diagnosis and assessment relevant and important issues for arts therapies practice.

In medical settings, the initial assessment of a patient's problem is usually referred to as diagnosis, derived from the Greek words meaning "to separate" and "to know." It is the act of recognizing a disease by distinguishing it from others; in modern medicine, this process is sometimes referred to as differential diagnosis. The diagnostic function in psychotherapy rests squarely on the medical or illness model of mental distress and is often referred to as psychodiagnosis.

Diagnosis as a Guide to Decision Making

Years ago, the diagnosis of patients was not as critical as it is today in identifying mental disturbances, mainly because there were few treatment options. During the Middle Ages and the Renaissance, mental illness was attributed to possession by demons (Zilboorg, 1941) or was perceived as retribution for sin. The standard treatment consisted of exorcism or prayer. Court records dating as far back as the thirteenth century indicate that judges used mental status examinations to distinguish between the mentally retarded or "natural fools" and the mentally ill, or "lunatics" (Neugebauer, 1979, p. 481). The reason for the distinction, apparently, was to identify lunatics who might pose a danger to the community, and who were locked out of sight, with no real attempt at therapy (from the Greek words for "to nurse" or "to cure").

With the advent of psychoanalysis, the "talking cure" constituted both diagnosis and treatment. Fundamentally, all patients were offered the same treatment, in the course of which their particular problems would emerge. While such drugs as opium and morphine had been used for over a century in mental institutions, they were used almost exclusively to sedate patients, to keep them quiet, docile, and manageable, rather than to treat them (Brandt, 1975, p. 39). Even in the 1950s, when new drugs were found that could treat psychotic symptoms, the need for accurate diagnosis was not recognized for some time. As more pharmacologic agents were developed, it became increasingly apparent that many of them were not only useless but could be harmful if they were prescribed for the wrong disorder, or even for the right disorder, but during the wrong phase of that disorder. It was learned that different drugs acted quite differently on disorders whose symptoms seemed similar, like schizophrenia and some phases of manic depression, and that there were even metabolic differences between patients with different types of depression that caused them to react very differently to drugs (Ayd, 1976, p. 146).

While the movement for greater precision in diagnosis was inspired by the advent of the psychiatric drugs, a good deal of information has now accumulated to drive the endeavor to hone the diagnostic process. Researchers have found that patients who exhibit similar symptoms may be suffering from very different problems, requiring different forms of treatment. Moreover, even people with the same general disorder may respond very differently to a particular treatment. As a result, differential diagnosis has become a basic principle in choosing the appropriate therapeutic methods and procedures.

A Nosological or a Classification Label

The term nosology is often defined as taxonomy, a system for classifying diseases as a basis for diagnosis. However, some writers contend that, while nosology and taxonomy are related, they refer to different concepts. Paul Pruyser and Karl Menninger (1976) stated that a nosology has to do with the way we conceptualize a disease – as a biochemical imbalance, for example, or a psychological response to stress. Nosology involves creating theoretical constructs for disorders, erecting boundaries and parameters to distinguish these concepts from others. The bases for these conceptualizations range from the philosophical to the empirical. At one time, it was thought that what we now call hebephrenia (inappropriately "silly" behavior), catatonia (extreme changes in muscular tension), and paranoia (delusions centered on suspiciousness) were distinct disorders. Around the early 1900s, the German psychiatrist Emil Kraepelin recognized from his clinical observations that the three were more similar than they were different and that, in fact, individuals could manifest symptoms of one or the other at different times. He conceived the nosological concept of a single disease that he called dementia praecox, meaning an early (precocious) form of dementia, or mental deterioration, to differentiate it from senile dementia. The Swiss psychiatrist Eugene Bleuler (1911) coined the name schizophrenia (splitting of mental functions) for the disorder, from the Greek words for "division" and "mind," and he added a fourth subtype, simple schizophrenia, characterized by "negative" or "nonpsychotic" symptoms (inattentiveness, flattening of affect, loss of appetite). Therefore, nosology refers to the concept of the disease in terms of its attributes or characteristics.

A taxonomy or classification, in this view, refers to the ways psychiatrists organize the categories of the disorders and, usually, the diagnostic criteria or symptoms by which each may be recognized. The *Di-*

agnostic and Statistical Manual (DSM) of the American Psychiatric Association, first published in 1952, is a taxonomy, or classification system. The *DSM* provides the names (and numbers) of categories and subcategories by which psychiatrists and therapists identify mental disorders, as well as the diagnostic criteria for each.

The description of the symptoms on which the classification system rests often reveals the underlying nosological constructs. For example, the revisions of the *DSM* in the 1970s and 1980s defined schizophrenia largely in terms of "positive" symptoms, such as hallucinations and delusions; the 1994 revision reintroduced Bleuler's and Kraepelin's notion of "negative" or "nonpsychotic" symptoms, such as loss of drive, loss of ability to experience pleasure, and loss of emotional expression (Andreasen, 1994, pp. 345–346). While both the American *DSM* and the World Health Organization's *International Category of Diseases (ICD)* may use the same names for mental disorders, the lists of symptoms sometimes reveal differences in underlying concepts. In both systems, the classification label is simply a name that is used to describe a group of observable behaviors.

The *DSM* does not suggest either the cause of the problem or the indicated treatment. Efforts to explicitly operationalize diagnostic criteria were made in the 1980 *DSM-III* to address interrater reliability, and "Although efforts have been made . . . to make this [*DSM-IV*] classification more empirically based, diagnostic classification remains . . . a typological or conceptual system, rather than a taxonomic or empirical system" (Cruz, 1995, p. 27). *DSM-5* (the old Roman numerals were abandoned) scheduled for publication in 2013 was in development for several years, and some major revisions were proposed, many of which aroused fierce controversy in the mental health community (and from the prestigious British Psychological Society) because of the proliferation of disorders and an apparent emphasis on medication. And again, while scientific evidence was used in updating, and while *DSM-5* was conceptualized as a "living document" to allow emerging evidence to be incorporated as it is validated (Bernstein, 2011) – the fact remains that psychiatric diagnosis is a typology, rather than a taxonomic system.

Diagnostic labels, aside from psychopharmacology, don't do much to offer guidance in the choice of treatment. What does a therapist who faces a patient diagnosed as manic depressive know about the patient's suicide risk, his or her cognitive style, or affective level, or capacity for insight, or preferred activity? All of this information must be assessed in addition to diagnosis.

A Point of View

The diagnosis that suggests the etiology, or causes, of a problem, will inevitably reflect the assumptions that the diagnostician makes about the origin of disorders. "The obscurity of etiology in mental illness," said Modlin (1976), "vivifies several unverified hypotheses, such as organic, neurochemical, psychodynamic, behavioral, interaction, and social explanations for our patient's deviations from theoretically constructed norms" (p. 153). Points of view may be influenced not only by theoretical allegiances but by the country or culture in which the diagnostician practices. For *DSM-5*, Bernstein (2011) noted that collaboration between the *DSM-5 Task Force* and the *International Advisory Group* revising *ICD-10* hoped to bring the two systems closer to agreement. However, documented biases based on racial and ethnic differences between diagnostician and patient that have fueled research on healthcare disparities in the U.S. will need quite another solution.

The Diagnostic Babel

Compounding the ambiguities of diagnosis are the confusions surrounding the language of psychiatric diagnosis. The classification systems and the names of the disorders themselves are riddled with inconsistencies. There is no single unified conceptual scheme for organizing or naming disorders. The constructs on which diagnostic labels are based may change with time, and constructs are formulated to fit theories. Moreover, old diagnostic terms tend to persist long after the constructs on which they are based have been abandoned. For example, the term neurosis, referring to a neurological disorder, is still in common use, although it was dropped from the *DSM* in the 1980s.

Because of the complexity of disorders, and the many-sided nature of most mental problems, *DSM-III* (1980) provided for multiaxial diagnoses that touch upon various manifestations of a problem, and the multiaxial system has continued in subsequent *DSM* revisions.

How Useful Is Diagnosis?

The subject of diagnosis has engendered a good deal of controversy. The notion of diagnostic labels is not accepted universally. Many critics point out that psychiatric "symptoms" are actually interpretations based on the observations by the therapist and on reports from the patient. These symptoms are subjective in nature; there are few, if any, truly objective tests to verify the existence of a disease or the degree of dysfunction, as there are in physical medicine. Many different factors including cultural biases of the diagnostician can contribute to misclassification. The reality of practice and the frequent difficulties in accurate diagnosis have raised doubts in the minds of many clinicians about the validity of the list of neatly bounded categories, each encompassing a distinct disease.

Many critics, including some who accept the illness model, believe that diagnosis is irrelevant, and they prefer to use the broader term assessment, by which they mean the process of determining an individual patient's needs. Early theorists such as Abraham Maslow (1966), a founder of the humanistic movement, wrote: "I must approach a person as an individual unique and peculiar, the sole member of his class" (p. 10). The problem with ignoring the characteristics that the individual shares with others, respond the diagnosticians, is to recapitulate the errors of the past and to ignore the lessons of experience. "Would we not be totally ignorant of how to help each new patient," ask Shevrin and Schechtman (1973) "if all previous ones were also unique?" (p. 463).

The major function of diagnosis is to match a defined condition with an appropriate treatment. "Unless the diagnostic process facilitates treatment," wrote Modlin (1976), "it is of little worth" (p. 157).

On Being Sane in Insane Places

The debate over diagnosis in psychiatry flared dramatically in the early 1970s with the publication of a report by D. L. Rosenhan (1973) in the journal *Science,* entitled, "On Being Sane in Insane Places." Rosenhan, a professor of psychology and law at Stanford University, sent eight pseudopatients to 12 psychiatric hospitals, where they gained admission on the basis of a complaint that they had heard voices for a period of three weeks.

All the applicants were admitted. At this point, they immediately ceased simulating any symptoms of abnormality, and behaved as they normally did. When asked by attendants, they reported that they no longer experienced symptoms. What Rosenhan found remarkable is that, while other patients often recognized the normality of the pseudopatients, the staff never did. Rosenhan wrote:

> Failure to detect sanity during the course of hospitalization may be due to the fact that physicians operate with a strong bias toward what statisticians call the type 2 error. This is to say that physicians are more inclined to call a healthy person sick (a false positive, type 2) than a sick person healthy (a false negative, type 1). The reasons for this are not hard to find: it is clearly more dangerous to misdiagnose illness than health. (p. 252)

Beyond the tendency to call healthy people sick, wrote Rosenhan, "the data speak to the massive role of labeling" (p. 252). Labeling in psychiatry, he charged, carries a stigma that does not obtain in medicine; most medical illnesses are not pejorative. But psychiatric diagnoses carry personal, social and legal stigmas. "The tag colors others' perceptions of [the individual] and his behavior," Rosenhan wrote, "Once a person is designated abnormal, all of his other behaviors and characteristics are colored by that label" (p. 253).

Rosenhan was curious to see if misdiagnosis could occur the other way – that is, if the disordered would be diagnosed as normal. He informed the staff at a research and teaching hospital that at some time within the next three months, he would send one or more pseudopatients who would attempt to be admitted to the psychiatric hospital. Each staff member was asked to identify pseudopatients. The results: of 193 patients who were admitted for psychiatric treatment during the next three months, 41 were alleged, with high confidence, by at least one member of the staff, to be pseudopatients. Of these, 19 were suspected by at least one psychiatrist and one other staff member. Actually, not a single pseudopatient had been sent!

Rosenhan criticized the hospital personnel for not considering differential diagnoses, as would be done routinely in physical medicine, and he contended that the chances of misdiagnosis are great in psychiatry. Moreover, in reviewing the case summaries, he found that normal family histories were distorted and reinterpreted, probably unintentionally, to make them fit into a theoretical mold. In other words, the diagnostic labels not only became self-fulfilling prophecies of the way patients would behave but they colored the therapist's perception of what had happened in the past. Rosenhan concluded that such labels serve no useful purpose and do more harm than good. "We have known for a long time," he asserted, "that diagnoses are often not useful or reliable, but we have nevertheless continued to use them. We now know that we cannot distinguish sanity from insanity" (p. 257).

As was to be expected, Rosenhan's report was received with a combination of embarrassment and anger in the psychiatric community. However, it also stimulated a good deal of thoughtful self-examination among responsible psychiatrists. Robert L. Spitzer, later to head up the American Psychiatric Association's task force that revised the *DSM,* pointed out (1975) that admitting staff members are trained to assess symptoms, not to identify fraud. He identified a number of flaws in Rosenhan's study, and argued that "the clinical picture includes not only the symptom (auditory hallucinations) but also the desire to enter a psychiatric hospital, from which it is reasonable to conclude that the symptom is a source of significant distress" (p. 446). He argued that psychiatry is not the only branch of medicine plagued by inaccurate diagnosis and poor interpretations of diagnostic data. However, he did concede the prevalence of a major diagnostic distortion that Rosenhan had noted: the revision of historical facts to achieve consistency with psychodynamic theories. He wrote in the *Journal of Abnormal Psychology* (1975): "Here, for the first time, I believe Rosenhan has hit the mark. What he described happens all the time and often makes attendance at clinical case conferences extremely painful, especially for those with a logical mind and a research orientation" (p. 448).

Psychiatric Labels and Arts Therapists

There is a wide range of opinion among arts therapists on the utility of the psychiatric label. Yet, exactly because of the expanded range of settings in which arts therapists practice, mentioned earlier, the current culture of accountability in healthcare, and the plain fact that services delivered must be reimbursed – psychiatric, medical, and educational diagnoses and labels are now simply a fact of arts therapies practice based in many settings.

Moreover, arts therapists themselves may be involved in assigning the diagnostic or educational label. Their own assessments of the behavior of clients or patients sometimes contribute to the decision;

sometimes the arts therapist may even be employed in the position of assigning the diagnostic label. Increasingly over time, dance/movement therapists, art therapists, and music therapists interpret the ways patients behave in their sessions in terminology common in psychiatric and other settings; the body dysfunctions, the distortions in drawings, the regular and irregular rhythms that are observed by arts therapists are often viewed as specific manifestations of psychiatrically classified disorders or symptoms.

The application of psychiatric labels in arts therapies assessment has not met with universal approval. Many arts therapists continue to contend that such labels are of limited utility in guiding the treatment of patients in their disciplines. Some resist what they consider the subordination of the arts therapies to the verbal therapies, making the arts therapies "handmaidens of psychiatry." To some arts therapists, the dysfunctions they observe, even if they parallel psychiatrically defined symptoms, are expressions of problems that can be identified and treated without knowing the psychiatric label. Some object to the dichotomous nature of diagnostic labels; someone has a disorder or doesn't have it. Kanfer and Saslow (1969) suggested that the difference between "normal" and "abnormal" behavior is one of degree, not of kind. Someone who exhibits obsessive-compulsive behavior, for example, usually does what all of us do – but to excess. A painfully shy person has the fears and concerns that we all have – but exhibits insufficient assertiveness to overcome them. So Kanfer and Saslow's functional approach ignores the diagnostic label and identifies behavioral excesses and deficits. The treatment, then, is directed toward having the patient or client increase the behavior in which he or she is deficient, and decrease the behavior in which an excess is identified.

On a practical level, regardless of the setting, arts therapists must conduct their own assessment of a client or patient's needs in planning their own therapeutic interventions. For example, a music therapist who faces a new client or patient diagnosed with schizophrenia must decide which treatment alternatives are most appropriate: instrumental group improvisation for reality orientation to address delusional thinking; assignment to an instrumental performance ensemble as a mnemonic device to deal with impaired memory; guided music listening to evoke feeling responses as a way of addressing flattened affect; or the use of music techniques to provide themes for later verbal psychotherapy. In fact, sometimes the arts therapist may not even be informed of a label or diagnosis but only of the symptom, such as the need for increased socialization or inability to communicate coherently.

Many arts therapists consider themselves "arts psychotherapists," which provides a way to further delineate themselves to the public as trained professionals and to distance themselves from those who use arts as activity therapy, or those who use arts in a therapeutic or counseling format but who have not had the specific training required for one of the national arts therapies certifications. Other arts therapists seek an art-oriented "glimpse of the inner life of the patient-in-crisis" (Moon, 1992, p. 138), looking for clues in the patient's preference for and choice of media, procedures, tools, postures, and verbalizations as guides in determining the patient's needs; and indeed, many arts therapists are pragmatic and combine both clinically-based and arts-based approaches.

Many arts therapists deal with clients and patients whose problems have little to do with traditional "disease" categories of mental disorders as originally conceived. As noted previously, in recent decades, hospitals employ arts therapists to ameliorate trauma and expedite healing and help clients control psychological sequelae of illness and surgery such as, stress and anxiety. Increasing numbers of arts therapists work with medical patients recovering from injuries or disease, with those suffering from developmental disabilities, and with those who need assistance in working out their relationship problems.

Arts therapists working with individuals with developmental delays, perceptual problems, physical disabilities, or even drug and alcohol abuse, may see little value in psychiatric labels. However, in each of these areas, therapists must deal with the prevailing language and labeling that are endemic to all settings. All have a need to identify clients' needs, or strengths and weaknesses so that they may develop appropriate interventions or individualized plans.

Monitoring and Summative Evaluation

Once the assessment is made and treatment begins, the process of evaluation has not ended. In 1967, Michael Scriven, an authority on curriculum evaluation, distinguished between the kind of ongoing evaluation that he called formative and the kind that is conducted at the end of a program, which he called summative. These terms are still in use, and formative evaluation is a continuing process. It provides information on changes in a patient's condition, so that the clinician can make adjustments in the treatment program until the treatment is to be terminated.

In today's treatment settings, limits are placed on the length of interventions by insurers or funding agents – often regardless of the recommendations of the person delivering the intervention. However, when outside influences are not calling the shots, it may not be easy for a clinician to know when to stop treatment. The basic purpose of evaluation is to help us make decisions, and there are times to recognize that there is little or nothing more to be gained by further treatment. The decision to terminate treatment may be one of the most difficult for a therapist to make; sometimes, it is hard to know when he or she has done as much as is reasonable or even possible.

When the clinician considers whether the client or patient is ready to terminate the treatment, evaluation questions will probably include: Has the client or patient improved about as much as he or she is likely to improve? Have the objectives of the treatment program been achieved? Does the client or patient consider that he or she is ready to leave therapy?

In addition, a major function of summative evaluation is to help the clinician learn from the experience. The end of treatment should be an opportunity to review the experience and to ask appropriate questions: What methods and techniques were particularly useful for this client or patient, and which seemed to be ineffective? What should be done differently the next time? How useful were the diagnostic or assessment procedures in shaping treatment?

Many of the evaluation methods and techniques discussed in this book can be used either for formative or summative evaluation. What distinguishes them is the purpose for which they are employed.

QUANTITATIVE AND QUALITATIVE EVALUATION

We must be careful to avoid viewing quantitative and qualitative evaluation as antagonistic. Writing in the HIV/AIDS Newsletter of the Center for Disease Control, Assistant Surgeon General Gary R. Noble (1991) wrote:

> The best way to plan for evaluation is to establish programs that incorporate specific, measurable goals. Quantitative evaluation can then

> tell us what effect we are having (how much, where, who, when); qualitative evaluation can tell us why the program is effective or why there is a problem. Both are equally important. (p. 2)

This approach of using all available methods as they are appropriate to evaluation questions has expanded dramatically since the early 1990s with more and more acceptance (Patton, 2002).

Quantitative Evaluation

When we speak of quantitative evaluation, we are really referring to two distinct processes: measurement and evaluation. Measurement is a quantitative description of a behavior or thing. When we measure something, we compare it against a standard: an inch, a degree, a pound, or a meter. Or we measure the frequency with which something opens. The measurement, often gathered through tests and expressed in a number, is useful for describing something, but in itself, it tells us little about whether the thing being measured is big or small, cold or warm, heavy or light, healthy or unhealthy, or good or bad. Measurement is usually considered objective, in that the standards are fixed and there is little personal judgment involved in the process, although, of course, there is a good deal of personal judgment involved in deciding what to measure and how to measure it. The bias in measurement is far less obvious than it is in qualitative description.

Measurement involves a particular way of collecting data on which to base either research findings or value judgments. In itself, it is neither research nor evaluation.

Evaluation and assessment, by definition, involve value judgments. Again, we usually need standards for comparison, but these are usually clearly subjective and frequently they are fuzzy or elastic. Both *DSM-I* and *DSM-II* specified the symptoms that indicated the presence of a psychiatric disorder, but left it to the judgment of the psychiatrist to decide how many symptoms had to be present for a diagnosis. The task force preparing the revised *DSM-III* tried to reduce the ambiguity by specifying an arbitrary number in the criteria for diagnosis.

While assessment in the therapies often involves testing (measurement), there are clear distinctions between "testing" and "assessment," not only in terms of definition, but in terms of the therapist-client relationship. In his presidential address to the American Psychological Association, Joseph D. Matarazzo (1990) said:

> . . . objective psychological testing and clinically sanctioned and licensed psychological assessment are vastly different, even though assessment usually involves testing . . . psychological testing [is] an activity that has little or no continuing relationship or legally defined responsibility between examinee and examiner. Psychological assessment, however, is engaged in by a clinician and a patient in a one-to-one relationship and has statutorily defined or implied professional responsibilities. (p. 1000)

Qualitative Evaluation

Any evaluation that does not involve measurement could be called qualitative. Used in this sense, it would include intuitive, impressionistic, and clinical techniques. However, in education and in some of the therapies, the term is often used to refer to a specific group of approaches, sometimes called "descriptive," "naturalistic," or "goal-free."

In contrast with quantitative description, qualitative information gathering is highly personal, since the investigator is the primary instrument. The evaluator needs a considerable tolerance for ambiguity, because there are often no set procedures or protocols, nor is there any single "correct" way to proceed, and each next step flows from the evaluator's perception of what is unfolding and what needs to be clarified. Whereas those who quantify strive to be as objective as possible, the very concept of objectivity is suspect to many who use qualitative methods.

The evaluator, therefore, must be sensitive to the clues that reveal a subject's views and perceptions, or the function that is served by group behavior, or to the reasons why a program may not be operating as the clinician or the administrator had hoped. The evaluator must be sensitive, also, to the questions that arise as the procedure develops: What does the information tell you? Where is it suggesting you go? How can it direct you to the next question or observation?

Guba and Lincoln (1981) wrote that qualitative evaluators do not measure. They "do what anthropologists, social scientists, connoisseurs, critics, oral historians, novelists, essayists, and poets throughout the years have done. They emphasize, describe, judge, compare, portray, evoke images. . ." (p. 149).

Obviously, given the subjective nature of this approach, bias is inevitable. But, contend the proponents of qualitative evaluation, bias exists in every form of evaluation. It is simply more obvious in qualitative than in quantitative approaches, because it cannot be as easily concealed.

The fundamental protection against bias is recognition. "The best cure for biases," wrote Guba and Lincoln, is to be aware of "how they slant and shape what we hear, how they interface with our reproduction of the speaker's reality, and how they transfigure truth into falsity" (p. 148). Obviously, a key to this approach is the evaluator's effort to uncover his or her biases. As the theorists of this approach describe qualitative evaluation, a number of principles emerge.

Human behavior is always bound to the context in which it occurs – historical, social, genetic, or environmental. Any attempt to divorce behavior from context is "context-stripping" (Mischler, 1979). The search for meaning is constructed by the subject or inheres in the situation. It is not imposed by the evaluator. The purpose of the evaluation is to focus on what is actually happening, rather than to see if the intent of the educational or therapeutic program is being achieved. Purpose is not just in the what, but the why and how, so the evaluation is interpretive and explanatory.

The collection of data and their analysis occur simultaneously; meanings emerge and change as more data are gathered. Consequently, the evaluator must rely on hunches and working hypotheses that change as more data are gathered.

Important for all evaluators regardless of whether they use quantitative or qualitative methods, is that the perspective of the client or patient and what he or she considers a "good" outcome be included. More and more the perceptions and perspectives of clients and patients as individuals with less power or privilege must be considered (Patton, 2002; (Ponterotto, Casas, Suzuki, & Alexander, 2010). In some cases, it might be most valuable to also include families and even communities in defining "good" mental health outcomes (Cross et al., (2011). The influence of social justice and multicultural theorists in recent years has been helpful in awakening therapists to the power differential experienced by clients, but as yet is often forgotten in the assessment and evaluation of treatment.

THE DIFFERENCE BETWEEN EVALUATION AND RESEARCH

The word "evaluation" is ambiguous. The term is sometimes used to describe a process of finding answers to general questions: Which of two methods is most effective in treating alcohol abuse? Can we identify similar components in different forms of therapy? Which types of therapy lend themselves most effectively to group situations? Can comparable results be obtained through short-term therapy as are achieved in an extended course of treatment? To what degree does personal rapport between client and therapist affect the outcome of treatment? Are there significant outcome differences between therapies that combine nonverbal and verbal approaches and those that rely mainly on the nonverbal aspects?

The methods of investigation in research and in evaluation may overlap; in some cases, they may be identical. Both may use tests and measurements, interviews, self-reports, behavioral observations, or checklists. In fact, the process of standardizing a test must involve research. What distinguishes the two is purpose (Cruz, 2012).

Research involves a systematic inquiry that is designed to broaden our understanding of the subject under study. The approach is often based on an inductive logic, working from the particular to the general. From an examination of specific cases, we can develop generalizations that can be applied to large numbers of situations (in quantitative approaches, this process is referred to as inferential statistics). The validity of these generalizations is often established by applying deductive predictions that are verified by testing them in specific cases and under a variety of circumstances, particularly in the case of the exceptions that "prove" the rule (from the original meaning of proof as a test or trial).

Research findings in themselves are of limited value. Developing a broader understanding of the subject under study is useful beyond the specifics. Research findings, therefore, are almost always accompanied by conclusions or interpretations that attempt to explain or account for the findings. The explanation itself is subjective, and its accuracy is usually tested and validated through replication or additional research.

Perhaps the outstanding characteristic of research, as distinguished from evaluation, is its nomothetic quality or "generalizability." It involves the search for general statements that describe relationships between classes of phenomena. At the highest levels of abstraction, such statements will hold up over time and space, and will accurately describe large numbers of specific situations or cases. Such generalizations are often referred to as principles or, if they have held up over long periods of time and differentiated applications, as laws.

Examples of generalizations that develop from research may include the following: Art productions of patients with schizophrenia often use single images to describe elaborate and complex sequences of ideas. Listening to music produces changes in blood pressure, changes in posture, pulse rate, and general activity in people with schizophrenia, and measurable mood change in all listeners. Children with autism tend to exhibit little of the self-synchrony between their own body parts, or the interactional synchrony with others that characterizes communication between normal individuals.

While the results of research may be used in the development of policy decisions and program designs, the researcher's fundamental purpose is to advance knowledge and understanding in the field, and not to come up with practical applications in specific cases. He or she is not likely to address the question of whether a particular method or technique is likely to help a particular patient.

Evaluation and assessment, on the other hand, refer to the process of gathering information on the basis of which we make specific decisions about specific programs for a particular client or patient or an identifiable group of patients or clients in a specific setting. In contrast with research, evaluation deals with the ideographic, or the particular. Whereas research culminates in conclusions, evaluation is the basis for decisions.

The function of evaluation is to provide information on which to base decisions: What treatment is most likely to help a particular client or patient? What do we need to know to help us decide if one program is of more value for an institution than another? Should a method or a technique be continued, revised, or abandoned for a specific client or group of clients?

Not every therapist is interested in conducting research, or is qualified to do so. But if therapists want to know whether what they do makes a difference in their clients' or patients' lives, or if their treatment programs are doing what they are supposed to do, they must be concerned with evaluation.

SUMMARY

There are five basic functions of evaluation: to predict; to identify a problem or a need as a guide to treatment; to monitor change; to learn how to improve the therapy or the program; and to know when to stop. The initial determination of a client's needs is usually referred to as an assessment. In the medical, or illness, model, the process of identifying and labeling the patient's disorder is referred to as diagnosis. This process of differential diagnosis has become increasingly important from a clinical standpoint as well as a financial standpoint. With the growth in the use of psychopharmacology, psychiatric medications are increasingly disease specific; not only will they not work on a problem other than the designated one, but they may cause unnecessary side effects without helping the patient. In addition to the medically oriented differential diagnosis (and often in place of it), arts therapists will almost always need to conduct their own assessments in their own disciplines to determine the most appropriate therapeutic intervention for a particular patient or group, matching up treatment processes or activities with the patient's or client's needs, interests, attitudes, and deficiencies.

The process of evaluation is an ongoing one, from the original assessment to the determination that a purpose has been accomplished. There are two basic forms of assessment and evaluation in the psychotherapies: quantitative and qualitative. The first is based on measurement, often in the form of testing. The latter is based on the intuitive judgment of the clinician, and it often utilizes "naturalistic" or unstructured approaches. The two approaches should not be viewed as antagonistic but as complementary, providing different kinds of information, often for different purposes. Evaluation and research share many characteristics and use the same techniques and processes. What distinguishes them is the purpose for which they are undertaken. Research is designed to provide answers to broad questions; it results in generalizations and conclusions about the relationship between broad classes of phenomena. Evaluation, on the other hand, is undertaken to provide information about a specific patient or program.

REFERENCES

Andreasen, N., & Flaum, M. (1994). Characteristic symptoms of schizophrenia. In DSM-IV Sourcebook, Chapter 2, pp. 351–376. Washington, DC: American Psychiatric Association.

Ayd, F. J., Jr. (1976). Diagnosis in planning psychopharmacological therapy. In P. W. Pruyser (Ed.), *Diagnosis and the difference it makes.* New York: Jason Aronson, Inc.

Bernstein, C. A. (2011). Meta-structure in DSM-5 process. *Psychiatric News, 46*(5), 7–8.

Bleuler, E. (1911). Dementia praecox or the group of schizophrenics. Joseph Zinkin, trans. New York: International Universities Press, 1950.

Brandt, A. (1975). *Reality police: The experience of insanity in America.* New York: William Morrow.

Cross, T. L., Friesen, B. J., Jivanjee, P., Gowen, K., Bandurrage, A., Matthew, C., & Maher, N. (2011). Defining youth success using culturally appropriate community-based participatory research methods. *Best Practices in Mental Health, 7*(1), 94–114.

Cruz, R. F., & Berrol, C. (Eds.) (2012). *Dance/movement therapists in action: A working guide to research options* (2nd ed.). Springfield, IL: Charles C Thomas.

Cruz, R. F. (1995). An empirical investigation of the Movement Psychodiagnostic Inventory (Doctoral dissertation, The University of Arizona). Dissertation Abstracts International *(2B), (HMI No.AAM962042257).*

Cruz, R. F. (2012). What is evaluation research? In R. Cruz & C. Berrol (Eds.), *Dance/movement therapists in action: A working guide to research options* (2nd ed.). Springfield, IL: Charles C Thomas.

Guba, E. G., & Lincoln, Y. S. (1981). *Effective evaluation.* San Francisco: Jossey-Bass.

Ho, P., Tsao, J. C., Bloch, L., & Zeltzer, L. K. (2011). The impact of group drumming on social-emotional behavior in low-income children. *Evidenced Based Complementary and Alternative Medicine,* doi: 10.1093/ecam/ neq072.

Kanfer, F. H., & Saslow, G. (1969). Behavioral diagnosis. In C. M. Franks (Ed.), *Behavioral therapy: Appraisal and status,* pp. 417–444. New York: McGraw-Hill.

Kapitan, L. (2010). *Introduction to art therapy research.* New York: Routledge.

Maslow, A. (1966). *The psychology of science: A renaissance.* New York: Harper and Row.

Mischler, E. G. (1979). Meaning in context: Is there any other kind? *Harvard Education Review, 49,* 2–10.

Modlin, H. C. (1976). Psychiatric diagnosis and the law. In K. Pruyser (Ed.), *Diagnosis and the difference it makes.* New York: Jason Aronson.

Moon, B. L. (1992). *Essentials of art therapy training and practice.* Springfield, IL: Charles C Thomas.

Neugebauer, R. (1979). Medieval and early modern theories of mental illness. *Archives of General Psychiatry, 36,* 477–483.

Noble, G. R. (1991). Director's update. *CDC HIV/AIDS Newsletter,* Feb., 1991.

Patton, M. Q. (2002). *Qualitative research and evaluation methods* (3rd ed.). Thousand Oaks, CA: Sage.

Ponterotto, J. G., Casas, J. M., Suzuki, L. A., & Alexander, C. M. (2010). *Handbook of multicultural counseling* (3rd ed.). Thousand Oaks, CA: Sage.

Pruyser, P. W., & Menninger, K. (1976). Language pitfalls in diagnostic thought and work. In P. W. Pruyser (Ed.), *Diagnosis and the difference it makes.* New York: Jason Aronson.

Rosenhan, D. L. (1973). On being sane in insane places. *Science, 179,* 250–258.

Scriven, M. (1967). The methodology of education. In R. E. Stake (Ed.), *Curriculum evaluation.* American Educational Research Association Monograph Series on Evaluation, No. 1. Chicago: Rand McNally.

Shevrin, H., & Schectman, F. (1976). The diagnostic process in psychiatric evaluations. *Bulletin of the Menninger Clinic, 37*(5), 451–494.

Spitzer, R. L. (1975). On pseudoscience in science, logic in remission, and psychiatric diagnosis: A critique of Rosenhan's "On Being Sane in Insane Places." *Journal of Abnormal Psychology, 84,* 442–452.

Stuckey, H. L., & Nobel, J. (2010). The connection between art, healing, and public health: A review of current literature. *American Journal of Public Health, 100* (2), 254–261.

Wheeler, B. L. (2005). *Music therapy research* (2nd ed.). Gilsum, NH: Barce-lona.

Zilboorg, G. (1941). The diseases that deprive man of his reason, such as St. Vitus' dance, falling sickness, melancholy, and insanity and their correct treatment by Theophrastus von Hohenheim, called Paracelsus. In H. E. Sigerist (Ed.), *Four treatises of Theophrastus von Hohenheim, called Paracelsus.* Baltimore: Johns Hopkins Press.

Chapter 2

PSYCHOTHERAPEUTIC BIAS IN EVALUATION

It was six men from Indostan/ To learning most inclined,
Who went to see the elephant/ (Though each of them was blind),
That each by observation/ Might satisfy his mind.

The First approached the elephant,/ and happening to fall
Against his broad and sturdy side,/ At once began to bawl:
"God bless me, but the Elephant/ Is very like a wall!"

The Second, feeling of the tusk,/ Cried "Ho! What have we here,
So very round and smooth and sharp?/ To me 'tis very clear
This wonder of an Elephant/ Is very like a spear!"

The Third approached the animal,/ And happening to take
The squirming trunk within his hands,/ Thus boldly up he spake:
"I see," quoth he, "the Elephant/ Is very like a snake!"

The Fourth reached out an eager hand,/ And felt about the knee
"What most this wondrous beast is like/ Is mighty plain," quoth he;
"'Tis clear enough the Elephant/ Is very like a tree!"

The Fifth, who chanced to touch the ear,/ said: "E'en the blindest man
Can tell what this resembles most;/ Deny the fact who can,
This marvel of an Elephant/ Is very like a fan!"

The Sixth no sooner had begun/ About the beast to grope,
Than seizing on the swinging tail/ That fell within his scope,
"I see," quoth he, "the Elephant/ Is very like a rope!"

And so these men of Indostan/ Disputed loud and long,
Each in his own opinion/ Exceeding stiff and strong,
Though each was partly in the right,/ And all were in the wrong!

The Blind Men and the Elephant
John Godfrey Saxe (1816-1887)

There is no universally accepted definition of the term "mental health." As with the blind men of Indostan, the investigators who formulated their theories of intelligence or personality usually felt a different part of the beast. Sigmund Freud's view of childhood personality development was based on his analysis of the recollections of his adult patients in psychoanalytic therapy. Jean Piaget, whose investigation was based on direct observation of children, came to different conclusions about how infants and children developed.

In addition, someone who adheres to a particular approach to therapy "selects" the aspect of the client on which he or she focuses: changing an ineffective way of coping, for example, or helping the client develop greater insights into the reasons for his or her behavior, or helping the client enhance his or her self-esteem or develop more satisfying interpersonal relationships.

Moreover, many clinicians deal with specific kinds of clients whose needs may differ. Some practitioners work with individuals who need help in dealing with serious and persistent mental disorders; some endeavor to help essentially normal people cope with the problems and frustrations of daily living or attain a higher level of growth and self-achievement. While therapists usually accept as patients or clients those for whom their approach seems to be appropriate, there are wide overlaps: the same client may be treated quite differently by therapists with different views of the needs of the client or of the purpose of therapy, or with different systems of diagnosis.

In diagnosing patients, in monitoring change, and in evaluating the results of their efforts, therapists apply varying standards. Some, believing that therapy is a science, seek "objective" ways of ascertaining the patient's condition or the effectiveness of their work; others, who view therapy as an art, believe that an experienced therapist must be guided by experience in making an intuitive judgment; still others contend that only the client can decide whether the therapeutic experience has been helpful or effective. The ways in which clinicians define disorders, behaviors, and "diagnosis" itself will influence their approaches to assessment. The way the therapist perceives the nature of the work in which he or she is involved, and the nature and purpose of assessment will influence the way the therapist will know what the patient or client "needs" and will determine whether the therapy is "working."

The issue of evaluation is particularly thorny in the psychotherapies, because there are so many divergent, and even conflicting, views of the purpose of therapy and the nature of "success" or "failure" in therapy. The theoretical orientations of clinicians are shaped not only by the prevailing approach in the colleges and universities in which they had their professional training but by their experiences as therapists, their personal predispositions and their individual life experiences. There is nothing wrong with having a multiplicity of explanations for personality development and models of psychotherapy. To some degree, each may add something to an understanding of the subject. In contrast with Saxe's conclusion that all of the explanations are wrong, it's simply that none of the explanations in theoretical orientations provide a complete understanding of the beast.

Historically, the problem was the tendency of psychologists and therapists to create "schools" of orthodoxy and, like the blind men from Indostan, to argue loud and long over the exclusive truth of their particular views. When the field is structured into competing therapies, wrote Louis Breger (1974), "one feels compelled to take sides – to choose one or the other. . . . behavior is determined by both environmental influences and intrinsic factors" (p. 15). Not only does loyalty to a particular "school" or theory influence one to ignore other possibly useful ideas and strategies, but it often is a cause for the production of technical languages and jargons that are understandable only to the members of the particular school, cutting off communication between practitioners.

Because the arts therapies began to be professionalized in the 1940s, some such as art therapy and dance/movement therapy began with a fair amount of psychoanalytic influence in their theoretical and practice formulations (Wadeson, 2010; Cruz, 2006) while early music therapy was a mix of psychoanalytic, activity, and behavioral orientations by the 1950s (B. Davis, personal communication, January 30, 2012). However, as theoretical models proliferated, all arts therapists began to become more eclectic in their theoretical orientations, as did other psychotherapists. In fact, some counseling and psychology texts, for example, Kottler and Sheppard (2008), offer instruction on how to both identify and organize elements to include in an eclectic or more personalized theoretical approach for new therapists.

Yet, due to the impact orientation has on practitioners' approaches to evaluation it may be useful to survey a number of different ways in which some original psychotherapy practitioners saw and understood both treatment and evaluation.

IS ANYONE OUT THERE NORMAL?

A significant change in the practice of psychiatry was the abandonment of the distinction between the "sane" and the "insane" that underlay the nineteenth century practice of psychiatry. From this either-or dichotomy as the standard of mental health, the profession turned to the concept of a continuum of normality in mental health, along which each individual could be located.

The word "norm," however, has several definitions, depending on who is using it and the context in which it is used. Social norms, for example, are shared definitions of desirable or acceptable behavior; they may or may not describe the ways people actually behave. In contrast, metric norms are based on measurements of the ways people actually act; they are not concerned with value judgments about the behaviors. As a result, the terms normal, abnormal, and pathological can have different meanings and different connotations to different groups of people.

To statisticians, the words norm and normal are associated with an average: a mean, mode, or median. They are value-free descriptions of central tendency. This notion of norm as average is the basis for standardized tests. So, normality describes what is usual, regular, or typical, not necessarily what is desirable or good.

Abnormal behavior as psychopathology is a complex and much argued determination. While the two psychiatric approaches, *ICD* and *DSM,* mentioned in Chapter 1, prevail in most healthcare settings, perusal of a psychopathology text such as that by Adams and Sutker (2004) reveals in great detail the difficulties in arriving at acceptable definitions. It gives one a sense of the respect due to those who engage in the data collection and arguments necessary to update and revise systems such as the *DSM.*

For psychotherapists who are doing clinical work rather than contributing to formal classification systems, the terms norm and normal can have different meanings that can depend on the philosophical orientations of the therapists and on their training. Assessment for treatment purposes in psychotherapy often is based on a concept of normality that has more to do with social and cultural constructs and values than with statistical norms. Normality itself is largely a social construct; behavior that is "normal" in one social or cultural group or in one situation may be "abnormal" in another. It is important that practitioners not confuse cultural differences with abnormality (Sue, 1998). There is a wide range in behaviors that may not be typical in a given society but are certainly "natural." Moreover, behavior that is neither average nor typical may be a perfectly functional method of adaptation to a given situation. Abnormality doesn't necessarily indicate disorder in the sense used in psychopathology.

To a degree that many of us might find disturbing, both reality and normality are defined by the culture in which we live and by our perceptual or occupational biases, and they are shaped by our sources of information about the world around us, including the newspapers we read, the television programs we watch, and the public relations and educational information coming from various mental health organizations.

For some practitioners, the concept of normality is irrelevant in psychotherapy. Those who work within a behaviorist framework, for example, prefer to deal with behavior that is "maladjusted," as defined by a client who seeks help, or by authorities who seek to change behavior that is deemed to be inappropriate, disruptive, or harmful. Abraham Maslow, a pioneer in the development of existential psychology, derided the notion of normality as "a psychopathology of the average . . . [a] general phoniness . . . living by illusions and by fear" (Maslow, 1961, p. 60).

As we can see from this short section, the definitions of normality run the gamut from average to exceptional. Because the concept of normality is central to a good deal of assessment in the therapies, it is important to identify the express or implied meaning of the term as it is used in specific contexts.

ALTERNATIVE VIEWS OF PSYCHOTHERAPY

Three major branches of psychotherapeutic practice developed in the twentieth century, each based on a specific theory of personality. The latter part of the twentieth century saw a proliferation of further evolutions of the original three major branches, Psychoanalytic, Behaviorism, and Humanism. Notably, several of the more recently popularized evolutions, Cognitive Behavioral Therapy, Dialectical Behavior Therapy, and Motivational Interviewing grew out of Behaviorism, and their popularity can be directly related to how evaluation and empirical validation are approached in these therapies. For example, Cognitive Behavioral Therapy (CBT) was researched extensively in randomized controlled trials (Butler, Chapman, Forman, & Beck, 2006). As evidence mounted for this approach, it coincided with the movement for "Evidence-Based Treatments" (Spiegel, 2006). Supported by the Institute of Medicine (2001) and the American Psychological Association (2005), insurers and funding sources added monetary support as they began to reimburse only for services that were deemed "evidence-based." Of course, debates continue about what exactly counts as evidence and by whom.

Assumptions about the nature of personality and its determinants influenced the three major branches of psychotherapy by offering various approaches to diagnosis of problems, psychotherapeutic methods and techniques, and monitoring of change. The relatively brief descriptions of these major branches and some of their evolutions provide illustration of their potential influence and impact on evaluation.

Psychoanalysis and Psychodynamic Therapy

Today, various forms of psychodynamic practice deal with the interaction between the conscious and the unconscious parts of the mind, and were derived from the theories of Sigmund Freud or one of his disciples. In addition to psychoanalysts, a host of clinicians practice a variety of therapies that might be described as Freudian or neo-Freudian.

The bulk of personality theory was built on the basis of clinical observation rather than scientific experimentation. As a result, personality theory is clearly susceptible to the biases of the theorist and the environment in which the theory developed. It is not surprising therefore, that Freud's theory of personality was quickly challenged by many of his own disciples, including Carl G. Jung, Alfred Adler, Harry Stack Sullivan, and Karen Homey.

Traditional Freudian psychoanalysis was based on the assumption that innate aggressive and sexual drives are in constant conflict with the demands of society and other external realities. Urges and drives that have been repressed because of anxiety populate the "dynamic unconscious" from which they create neurotic anxieties or even psychotic problems. Neo-Freudian theorists, such as Sullivan, Karen Homey, and Erich Fromm, saw an interpersonal shaping of the child. The individual is driven less by instinctual demands than by the clash of basic needs in a social environment. The child's personality is shaped by the conflict between the child's drive towards growth, autonomy, and power, and his or her need for security. Where the child's growth is not encouraged, the need for growth is subordinated to the need for security, leading to later emotional problems.

Despite the disagreements among the various schools of Freudian-based psychotherapy, the theoretical basis for all the psychodynamic approaches rests on the principle that the determinants of human personality may be found in the dynamics of the unconscious, although there are widely divergent views on the nature of the unconscious. Whereas Freud saw the unconscious as a "seething cauldron" of repressed wishes and urges, others, like Carl Jung, saw it as a source of wisdom and creativity. Various groups of practitioners believe that the unconscious is shaped by structural, genetic, or cultural influences, or by combinations of these influences.

Because of Dr. Freud's prestige, and a frank lack of other models, for many years, the practice of psychiatry in the U.S. was tied to Freudian theories of personality and treatment. Psychoanalysis and related therapies were based squarely on a quasi-medical, or illness, model and rested on two major assumptions, both of which weigh heavily in the realm of assessment – both diagnostic and outcome evaluation.

The Problem as Symptom

The assumption is that problematic or "abnormal" behavior cannot be treated directly, because such behavior represents only the symptoms of an underlying problem. Only recognizing the nature of the problem and resolving it can lead to health. A change in behavior that does not resolve the underlying problem will only lead to symptom substitution or to a recurrence of the problem behavior when triggering events occur.

In this view, just alleviating or even getting rid of symptoms, through medication or behavior modification, for example, may not get to the root of a problem. In addition, confirmation of the therapist's hypothesis about the underlying cause of the problem must be inferred from the patient's betrayal of concerns and fears of which even he or she may not be aware. The sources of these fears and concerns must be traced by probing the unconscious through an examination of dreams, free associations, "Freudian slips," projections, and other devices for bringing the problem into the open, where it can be handled on a conscious level. The problem, then, is dealt with through recognition on a verbal level, the basis of Freud's "talking cure."

Problematic behavior is seen as abnormal. Normality is a highly subjective concept in the psychodynamic or psychoanalytic psychotherapies, and judging the outcome of treatment is likely to be based largely on professional judgment. Since the abatement of symptoms alone may not indicate a resolution of the problem the psychoanalyst or psychodynamic therapist must apply his or her clinical judgment in determining that the underlying problem has been resolved.

Unlike evaluation in either medicine or behavior therapy, which are based on the attainment of clearly specified goals, evaluation in psychoanalytic therapy tends to be more global and less clear-cut. The patient may have been cured of more conditions than he or she had initially complained about. On the other hand, external events may have complicated the patient's life even more. "In the face of objective reality, the claims of psychoanalysis must be modest. At best, Psychoanalysis tries to help the patient effect the best possible solution of difficulties that circumstances will allow" (Arlow, 1989, p. 43).

Behaviorism

John B. Watson, the father of American behaviorism, contended that psychology should be the science, not of consciousness, but of behavior. He believed that personality was shaped almost exclusively by the environment and that all behavior is learned. He wrote, in 1913, that the idea of consciousness, of a mental life independent of behavior, is a superstition. The unconscious – the heart of psychodynamic personality theory – like the concept of soul, is a notion for which there is no empirical evidence. Like the soul, it cannot be observed, measured, or even defined to everyone's satisfaction. Such concepts, he charged, are theological inventions to cover our ignorance about biological functions and to satisfy our need for explanations (Watson, 1913). To Watson and to the behavioral therapists who followed, the problematic behavior was the problem.

Behavioral theory was expanded significantly after Watson's day by such thinkers as B. F. Skinner, a Harvard psychologist who pioneered in the work of operant or "trial-and-error" conditioning. Skinner rejected the Pavlovian stimulus-response sequence on which Watson had built his classical conditioning approach, for two reasons. First, he was interested primarily in what reinforced behavior, not in what caused it. Second, he was interested in making specific change in specific areas and needed a method that could be employed by people in their everyday lives. Skinner also modified Watson's exclusive concern with overt behavior alone. Thinking, contended Skinner (1971), represents covert behavior and is a proper area for investigation and treatment.

The current uses of behaviorism represent dramatic growth since the 1960s. Behaviorists work in many areas such as the treatment of substance abuse, the modification of criminal and delinquent behavior, and the treatment of children with developmental or physical disabilities. As mentioned earlier, three adaptations, Cognitive Behavioral Therapy, Dialectical Behavior Therapy, and Motivational Interviewing, are somewhat widely used. In addition, behaviorism influenced the theory and practice of other forms of psychotherapy. Many psychodynamically-oriented therapists use behavior modification techniques for the treatment of specific problems in eclectic practice.

Three major tools of behavior therapy bear brief mention: systematic desensitization, aversion therapy, and operant conditioning. Specific uses of these are still practiced today. Systematic desensitization refers to the weakening of a patient's inappropriate or exaggerated response to a fear or anxiety-producing stimulus. Aversion therapy is designed to extinguish or suppress undesirable behavior. Operant, or trial-and-error, conditioning, on the other hand, is based on a free choice of behaviors.

In aversion therapy each instance of unwanted behavior is followed quickly by an aversive stimulus – electric shock or chemical stimulation, for example, or a psychological punishment, such as verbal censure – in an effort to evoke a clear and direct association between the behavior and pain or anxiety instead of pleasure. Aversion therapy is not widely practiced. In the other forms of behavior therapy, therapist and patient work together to overcome a problem that the patient recognizes as undesirable and that may cause him or her considerable pain or discomfort. Aversion techniques, on the other hand, are often in clear conflict with the patient's short-term gratification and sense of needs.

Operant conditioning evolved from classical, or Pavlovian, conditioning in which the subject acquires a conditioned, or learned, response to a stimulus. Pavlov's dogs learned to salivate when a bell was rung, because previously the bell had been rung whenever food was offered.

Desirable behavior is "rewarded" or reinforced; undesirable behavior is either "punished" with negative consequences or ignored. Because behaviorists are generally concerned with behavior rather than with diagnostic labels, a problem must first be broken down into whatever component behaviors are exhibited. Operant procedures are then designed to change the specific component behaviors.

The Behavior as the Target

Behaviorists assert that their approaches to the treatment of problem behavior are grounded in sound laboratory experimentation and are susceptible both to replication and to outcome studies. Evaluation in behavior therapy is simple and straightforward: the assessment is focused on identifying the problematic behavior, and monitoring is based on measuring and recording changes in the target behavior. When the offensive behavior has been changed or extinguished, the course of therapy has been successful. Careful measurement and recording, therefore, are the keys to behavioral assessment and evaluation. At least, so goes the theory. As we shall see later, the expansion of behavioral assessment into the areas of cognition and perception created problems for behaviorists that can parallel those of the other approaches.

Humanism

The humanistic and human-potential movements, sometimes billed as the "third force" in psychotherapy, encompass a wide array of therapies. Practitioners include existentialists, phenomenonologists, gestalt therapists, existentialists, and others. Humanism, according to the Articles of Association of the American Association for Humanistic Psychology, is concerned with topics that have little place in existing theories and systems: e.g., love, creativity, self, growth, basic need-gratification, self-actualization, higher values, being, becoming, spontaneity, play, humor, affection, naturalness, warmth, ego-transcendence . . . transcendental experience, peak experience, courage, and related concepts (Severin, 1965, pp. xv–xvi).

The stress in most humanist approaches is on the here and now. Because so many therapies are grouped under the humanist label, it is difficult to describe with any kind of precision the theory or practice of humanist therapies. A number of such therapies are based on the principles of phenomenological psychology, which is concerned with the ways in which the individual perceives the world rather than with "reality." It is argued, not only that there are multiple realities, but that individuals adjust to their perceptions of events, not to the events themselves. As a result, phenomenologists, existentialists, gestalt therapists, and other groups of humanistic therapists are more concerned with "awareness" – perceiving, feeling and acting – than with recognition or understanding of a problem, which they tend to see as rationalization and intellectualization.

A therapy that is more or less representative of a large group of humanist approaches is existential psychotherapy. Introduced in the United States in the 1950s, it is based largely on the philosophy that bears the same name. Existential therapists, in the words of Rollo May and Irvin Yalom (1989), see each individual as unique with his or her own way of experiencing, feeling, and behaving.

Whereas Freudians see the basic psychic conflict as one between instinctual drives and the demands of society, neo-Freudians see it as one of growth versus security, and behaviorists view it as a struggle to overcome problematic habits and responses, existentialists view the central struggle as the individual's confrontation with the "givens" or the "ultimate concerns" of existence: death, freedom, isolation, and meaninglessness. However, within the given limits, individuals have the capacity to transcend the constraints of the immediate situation and therefore to make change.

May's central thesis appeared in the book *Freedom and Destiny* (1981), an apparent response to Skinner's *Beyond Freedom and Dignity.* May's contention was that human freedom is always in juxtaposition with destiny, the things over which we have no control, like our genetic inheritance, our culture, and such biological inevitabilities as death. We are free to the extent that we confront and struggle with our destinies. Paradoxically, freedom is a major source of anxiety. In the words of Jean Paul Sartre, humans are "condemned to freedom" (Sartre, 1956, p. 631), because each must accept the responsibility for creating his or her own world by making decisions and choices and by confronting the limits of destiny. Anxiety, in itself, is not only a universal human trait, it is inevitable.

Existentialists define normality in terms of appropriate response to a problem. Normal anxiety was described by May and Yalom in terms of three characteristics. It is proportionate to the situation; it involves something with which we can come to terms, like the recognition of our mortality; and it can be the stimulus for creativity (May, 1977).

Abnormal anxiety, on the other hand, is not appropriate to the situation; it may lead to obsessions and compulsions. It is repressed; dark, unacknowledged fears or concerns color the victim's approach to the world. Third, it is destructive, not constructive; it tends to paralyze, rather than to foster creative responses to problems. Similarly, May and Yalom distinguished between normal and neurotic guilt. Whereas normal guilt sensitizes us to the ethical aspects of our behavior and can lead to salutary changes in behavior, neurotic guilt, like neurotic anxiety, can lead to dysfunctional behaviors like obsessions and compulsions. People can free themselves from neurotic anxiety and guilt simultaneously with the recognition of normal anxiety and guilt.

From this brief thumbnail sketch of existential therapy, it is apparent that it is concerned less with the issue of mental health than with self-improvement, growth, and willed change. Because each person functions in a perceived world that is individual and unique, existential therapists tend to reject both the concept of "normal personality" and any form of evaluation that rests on measurement. May and Yalom wrote:

> Symptomatic relief or behavioral change may be quantified with reasonable precision. But more ambitious therapies, which seek to affect deeper layers of the individual's mode of being in the world, defy quantification. (May & Yalom, 1989, p. 391)

ANOTHER LOOK AT THE ELEPHANT

If the proponents of the various schools of therapy like the blind men from Indostan, disputed loud and long, it would be a mistake to exaggerate the theoretical differences among them. The lineages and the relationships between psychoanalysis and humanism might emerge somewhat more clearly if we put aside the traditional labels and traced the evolution of some of the newer therapies. There is a continuous cross-fertilization of ideas and methods of some therapies that sometimes proclaim their irreconcilable differences. It might be helpful if we viewed various therapies other than through the traditional labels and saw them, instead, in terms of their basic goals: self-understanding, interpersonal communication, and personal growth.

Many psychodynamically oriented clinicians nowadays actually practice ego psychology, which de-emphasizes the aggression of the id – the seat of the instinctual drives and urges – that was so central to Freudian theory and focuses instead on the ego's search for identity and meaning. Both of the two major thrusts among the newer psychotherapies, the promotion of growth and self-realization, on the one hand, and the improvement of interpersonal relations, on the other, can therefore trace their theoretical lineages to Freud. In many cases the differences among the psychodynamic and humanistic therapies has less to do with theory than with social views of the role of therapy.

While Freud may be viewed as the theoretical ancestor of both psychodynamic therapists and humanists, many of the specific techniques used by many therapists of various persuasions have been adapted from the behaviorists. As noted earlier, many therapists borrow methods and techniques from various therapies, but some whole systems are built on combinations of treatment and assessment techniques taken from different philosophical orientations. One example is Albert Ellis's rational emotive therapy and Aaron Beck's cognitive behavioral therapy. They are designed to correct the patient's negative view of himself or herself, to adjust faulty inferences about the behaviors and thoughts of others, and to help the patient think more realistically and rationally. Treatment techniques are based on behavioral methods, using graded task assignments designed to provide patients with feedback that helps them adjust their views and thinking, and they often involve having patients rehearse specific encounters.

Finally, it is worth mentioning that systems approaches aim to create internally consistent "systems" that take into account the social environment in which the patient moves and acts. While there are many versions of systems approaches, most of the practitioners of systems approaches reject both the reductionist approach – the view that individuals are just collections of abilities and traits that can be identified and modified in isolation – and the holistic approach that claims that only a fundamental restructuring of the personality as a whole can be the basis for meaningful change. Generally, systems therapists believe that individual patterns can be identified and changed, but that each change will affect other parts of the entity – the individual or the family or the social unit (Compton, 2005). Most family therapists, for example, agree that changes can be made in the behavior of individual family members but point out that such changes inevitably affect the behaviors of other members of the family. They contend that therapy must take into account not only individual behaviors but the impact that a change in such behaviors will have on the way the whole family functions.

THEORY-DRIVEN APPROACHES TO EVALUATION

While there has been an exuberant cross-fertilization of theory and of therapeutic techniques, the divisions in the area of evaluation remain somewhat more clear-cut. The individual therapist's specific view of the structure of personality and the purpose of therapy will narrow the range of methods and techniques that are considered appropriate for evaluation.

Yet, there is a marked trend towards an expanded view of assessment. While we describe below the positions of a few various schools of therapy, we must note that increasing numbers of clinicians are willing to use a variety of assessment tools, instruments and procedures.

Psychoanalytic Approaches

To the psychoanalyst, evaluation is highly subjective and, understandably, is couched in terms of psychoanalytic theory. Central both to treatment and to evaluation are the concepts of transference and resistance. Transference refers to the patient-therapist relationship in which the therapist becomes the focus of the patient's feelings. When the patient recognizes the elements of transference and his or her resistances to the process abate, the goals of the treatment have been accomplished, and the time is ripe for ending the treatment.

In psychoanalysis, the final stages of therapy have some striking features. First, there is a very sudden and intense aggravation of the symptoms for which the patient first sought treatment. While this turn of events might suggest that treatment has been in vain, psychoanalysts interpret this as a last attempt to hold on to the comfort of the psychotherapeutic relationship. A series of hitherto repressed memories emerge that tend to confirm the revelations and interpretations that have emerged in previous sessions. And, finally, the patient will reveal his or her suppressed hopes of becoming omnipotent or omniscient as a result of the therapy.

To recognize the clues to the successful resolution of therapy, of course, the therapist must not only be cognizant of psychoanalytic theory but must be perceptive to the indications that the patient is, in fact, ready to terminate treatment. The evaluation depends largely on the perception of the therapist and the acceptance by the patient of the stages of successful termination (Arlow, 1989, pp. 39–40).

In general, few psychoanalysts use psychological tests although tests such as the Rorschach and the Thematic Apperception Test, based on Freudian principles and concepts, are sometimes used to assess patient condition and progress.

Evaluation in analytical psychotherapy, based on the theories of Jung, is similar to Freudian psychoanalysis in that the methods are highly subjective and are based squarely on theoretical considerations. In Jungian therapy, however, far less emphasis is put on either the therapeutic importance or the evaluative significance of transference. Instead, Jungian therapists rely on their understanding of the patient's relationship with the unconscious. In fact, transference itself (the patient's projection on the therapist) and countertransference (the therapist's projection on the patient) are seen as aspects of the archetype of polar opposites: guru-disciple; saint-sinner; master-slave (Kaufmann, 1989, p. 140).

To the Jungian, both diagnosis and evaluation rest on an analysis of the patient's relationship with his or her unconscious. But, because the unconscious communicates in symbols, the messages must be interpreted, usually by the therapist, who is trained to recognize the cryptic contents. For Jung the unconscious consisted of two elements. One was the collective unconscious, a storehouse of the accumulated memories of humankind, usually in the form of archetypes – universal concepts that are expressed in metaphors or symbols. The other was the personal unconscious, the myriad of experiences that have been pushed out of the conscious mind because they were unnoticed, forgotten, or repressed, but which remain to surface as anxieties and stresses.

The patient's relationship with the unconscious is ascertained by inferring how the patient or the therapist is dealing with the archetypal symbols that the unconscious presents in dreams, urges, free associations, and drawings. The analyst, using his or her knowledge of the archetypal patterns, will interpret the manifestation of the symbol to gauge the patient's progress. So, the processes of diagnosis and evaluation are highly inferential, based on the therapist's skill in relating dreams, images, and associations with what Freud called "archaic remnants" of ancient memories and what Jung called "psychic elements surviving in the human mind from ages long ago" (Jung, 1964, p. 47). These messages from the unconscious reveal the patient's status – but they must be interpreted.

Because the Jungian concept of therapy is based on the achievement of "wholeness," rather than "cure," Jungian analysis is often viewed as closer to Humanist than to Freudian views of the nature of therapy. And, like Humanists, Jungians often are troubled by the notion of curing or alleviating a specific problem.

Behavioral Approaches

Because behavior therapists define a problem in terms of the behavior that is to be changed, the basic evaluation of patient progress is the degree to which the behavior has changed. Similarly, the basic evaluation of a program or a schedule of reinforcement is the degree to which it has been successful in changing the target behavior. The major technical problem, then, is in identifying the specifics of the problem behavior.

In the diagnostic assessment, the therapist must first identify the problem, seeking detailed information: under what circumstances does the problem occur? How frequently? How severe are the manifestations? What has the client done to cope with it? The approaches that are used in assessment are also the ones that are frequently used in outcome evaluation, since the problem and the behavior are synonymous.

The most obvious approach is questioning the client. The therapist will not necessarily take the client's words at face value and may probe for inconsistencies, evasiveness, or apparent distortions. Nevertheless, behaviorists tend to rely more on clients' self-reports than on direct observation, especially in probing feelings, fantasies and thoughts.

Most people tend to describe themselves in terms of broad categories or traits (aggressive, shy, angry, calm, passive), and the therapist must find ways of finding the specific behaviors that are to be modified. Several techniques have been developed for this purpose, including self-monitoring, guided imagery, role playing, direct observation, and physiological arousal (Wilson, 1989, pp. 258–260). For the most part, behaviorists resist using standard psychodiagnostic tests. They tend to interpret problem behavior as maladjusted responses that have been learned under unfavorable circumstances. It is possible, therefore, to identify a specific behavior to be changed rather than try to ascertain the inferred personality traits that are the subject of traditional personality tests. Behaviorists use checklists, scales, and questionnaires that are descriptive self-reports.

Humanistic Approaches

It is difficult to attempt to describe a theory-driven approach to evaluation in humanism, which represents a broad movement rather than a specific theoretical framework. The range of views among humanists runs the gamut. Some see no problem with using quantitative methods; some reject measurement, preferring to rely on qualitative or intuitive methods; some humanist arts therapists evaluate their patients' progress through their creative productions rather than through verbal methods, while others let their patients make their own evaluations. And some humanist therapists resist the whole notion of evaluation on the assumption that it is impossible to get a fix on changes in the whole person; if the treatment is intrinsically worthwhile, then some good will inevitably flow from its use.

It might be illuminating to compare the views on evaluation of two humanist therapists who would appear to begin with similar assumptions and premises. Carl Rogers, a pioneer in the humanist movement, formulated the elements of a "client-centered" therapy in 1940. The base on which the therapy was built is the principle that the troubled individual knows more about himself than does anyone else and is in the best position to find the ways to resolve his or her problems. The role of the therapist, or facilitator, is to provide a "sympathetic climate" of trust, nonjudgmental caring, and empathy. Each client is deemed to be the architect of his or her own life and the judge of his or her own reality. Therefore, the client, not the facilitator, chooses the needs and problems to be explored, determines the length of therapy, achieves his or her own insights, and determines if and when the purposes of the therapy have been achieved (Raskin & Rogers, 1989).

It may appear surprising, in light of this orientation to self-direction and self-actualization, to note that Rogerian therapists have no aversion to the notion of quantitative evaluation. In fact a standard evaluation instrument is the Q-sort technique. Rogers chose the Q-sort as a device for defining the self as defined by the individual. One hundred cards, with such self-descriptions as "I feel inadequate," "I am assertive," "I am a responsible person" are sorted by the patient into nine piles, in a continuum from "most like me" to "least like me." This allows for a quantified description of self-concept and associations of self before and after therapy (Raskin & Rogers, 1989).

Existential art therapist Bruce L. Moon, wrote about the function and nature of psychotherapy in terms that are quite compatible with those of Rogers:

> The primary thrust of my work is to journey with the patients as they explore and discover the meanings of their lives, reflected in their creative work. In training interns, I stress that we should not be seduced into becoming merely interpreters, assessors or diagnosticians. . . . I believe that if the necessary work is done by the patient as we walk together, he or she will make all the interpretations, judgments and alterations that are important. (Moon, 1990, p. 55)

Yet, Moon advanced a very different view of evaluation. To Moon, not only the exploration and discovery of the meanings of patients' lives is reflected in what he calls "the canvas mirror," but the change in the patient's condition is manifested in the patient's creative work. He wrote:

> I have refrained from saying too much about how to do anything. I have tried to present a way of thinking and of looking at things. . . . I believe I have revisited the deep roots of our profession. It is my most sincere wish that these roots will stand out in sharp contrast to those who would steer us and future generations of art therapists toward scientific research, quantifiable data and measurable outcome surveys, and away from soul, spirit and image. . . . I am not opposed to research activities, but I do proclaim as loudly as possible, "WHAT WE ART THERAPISTS DO CANNOT BE MEASURED OR COUNTED!" (p. 164)

Interestingly, this sort of proclamation reverberated throughout the different arts therapies for some time and still has vestiges in all of them. However, most arts therapies practitioners have been influenced by the changes that have taken place since the 1990s in terms of the prevailing healthcare market in the U.S. and the focus on evidence-based treatments. They tend to place more and more value on research and evaluation as ways to promote the professions (see for example, Cruz & Hervey, 2001; Meekums, 2010).

SUMMARY

Not only the form of treatment that a therapist provides but his or her way of assessing the client's needs and evaluating the client's progress depend largely on the therapist's theoretical orientation.

In general, therapists see at the heart of the client's problem a conflict or struggle, which clinicians of various persuasions interpret differently. Freudians see the central conflict as one between instinctual drives and societal requirements that force the developing child to repress aggressive and sexual urges. Neo-Freudians, who adhere to the theories of some of Freud's disciples, see the conflict as one between the child's need for security and his or her drive for identity, growth, and mastery. Behaviorists and learning theorists in general see the conflict as the discomfort of the patient with the "maladjusted" behavior that he or she has learned as a response to a stimulus, or with the disapproval of such behavior by society. Existentialists see the struggle as the individual's confrontation with the ultimate problems of existence: death, freedom, isolation, and meaninglessness.

Each of the various theoretical frameworks carries a divergent view of personality, normality, the significance of symptoms, the role of the therapist, and the goals and objectives of treatment. As a result, the nature of evaluation is conceptualized differently in each approach.

REFERENCES

Adams, H. E., & Sutker, P. B. (2004). *Comprehensive handbook of psychopathology* (3rd ed.). New York: Springer Science.

American Psychological Association. (2005). Report of the 2005 presidential task-force on evidence-based practice. Retrieved from: http://www.apa.org/practice/resources/evidence/evidence-based-report.pdf.

Arlow, J. A. (1989). Psychoanalysis. In R. J. Corsini & D. Wedding (Eds.), *Current psychotherapies* (4th ed.). Itasca, IL: F. E. Peacock.

Breger, L. (1974). *From instinct to identity: The development of personality.* Englewood Cliffs, NJ: Prentice-Hall.

Butler, A. C., Chapman, J. E., Forman, E. M., & Beck, A. T. (2006). The empirical status of cognitive-behavioral therapy: A review of meta-analyses. *Clinical Psychology Review, 26*(1), 17–31.

Compton, W. C. (2005). *An introduction to positive psychology.* Belmont, CA: Thomson Wadsworth.

Cruz, R. F., & Hervey, L. W. (2001). The American Dance Therapy Association research survey. *American Journal of Dance Therapy, 22,* 89–118.

Cruz, R. F. (2006). Assessment in dance/movement therapy. In Stephanie Brooke (Ed.), *Creative arts therapies manual.* Springfield, IL: Charles C Thomas.

Institute of Medicine. (2001). Envisioning the national healthcare quality report. Retrieved from: http://www.iom.edu/Reports/2001/Envisioning-the-National-Health-Care-Quality-Report.aspx.

Jung, C. G. (1964). *Man and his symbols.* Garden City, NY: Doubleday.

Kaufman, Y. (1989). Analytic psychotherapy. In R. J. Corsini & D. Wedding (Eds.), *Current psychotherapies* (4th ed.) (pp. 119–152). Itasca, IL: F. E. Peacock.

Kottler, J. A., & Shepard, D. (2008). *Introduction to counseling: Voices from the field* (6th ed.). Belmont, CA: Wadsworth.

Maslow, A. (1961). Existential psychology – what's in it for us? In R. May (Ed.), *Existential psychology.* New York: Random House.

May, R., & Yalom, I. (1989). Existential psychotherapy. In R. J. Corsini & D. Wedding (Eds.), *Current psychotherapies* (4th ed.). Itasca, IL: F. E. Peacock.

May, R. (1981). *Freedom and destiny.* New York: Norton.

May, R. (1977). *The meaning of anxiety* (rev. ed.). New York: Norton.

Meekums, B. (2010). Moving towards evidence for dance movement therapy: Robin Hood in dialogue with the king. *The Arts in Psychotherapy, 37,* 35–41.

Moon, B. L. (1990). *Existential art therapy: The canvas mirror.* Springfield, IL: Charles C Thomas.

Raskin, N. J., & Rogers, C. (1989). Person-centered therapy. In R. J. Corsini (Ed.), *Current psychotherapies* (pp. 155–194). Itasca, IL: F. E. Peacock.

Sartre, J. P. (1956). *Being and nothingness.* New York: Philosophical Library.

Severin, F. T. (1965). *Humanistic viewpoints in psychology.* New York: McGraw-Hill.

Skinner, B. F. (1971). *Beyond freedom and dignity.* New York: Bantam Books/Vintage.

Spiegel, A. (2006, February 14). More and more favored psychotherapy lets bygones be bygones. *New York Times.*

Sue, D. W. (1998). *Multicultural counseling competencies: Individual and organizational development.* Thousand Oaks, CA: Sage.

Wadeson, H. (2010). *Art psychotherapy* (2nd ed.). New York: John Wiley & Sons.

Watson, J. B. (1913). Psychology as the behaviorist views it. *Psychological Review, 20,* 158–177.

Wilson, G. T. (1989). Behavior therapy. In R. J. Corsini & D. Wedding (Eds.), *Current psychotherapies* (4th ed.). Itasca, IL: F. E. Peacock.

Chapter 3

WHAT TO LOOK FOR IN EVALUATION PROCEDURES

The major problems in evaluation have little to do with number crunching or formulas or even theories. They have more to do with common sense, and they become most obvious when the whole issue is viewed with a healthy skepticism. The essential elements of responsible assessment and evaluation apply to all procedures, qualitative as well as quantitative, but for illustrative reasons and to clarify the issues involved, this discussion will deal largely with tests and testing in which the problems are most apparent.

Douglas Shelley and David Cohen began their irreverent review of psychological testing, *Testing Psychological Tests* (1986), with a familiar optician's wall chart. "It may not look like a psychological test," they write, "but it is one. It assesses perceptual and mental ability" (p. 1).

Even this simple and straightforward test suffers from many of the problems that afflict far more complex tests. Among the questions Shelley and Cohen raised: How well would someone whose first language was Arabic do on this test? How would a subject's score be affected if his or her perception was based on the habit of reading from right to left? To what degree would anxiety affect the score? What about the sensitivity (or insensitivity) of the optician administering the test? How accurate would the score be if the person being tested believed that he or she needed glasses? Or hated the idea of wearing glasses?

All too often, psychological assessment procedures – tests, scales, profiles, interviews, checklists, questionnaires, and the like – and the results derived from them are distorted by the assumptions, biases, and expectations of the examiner. A brief survey of the history of intelligence tests, the oldest of formal psychological tests, provides lessons for all test-givers and test-takers.

WHAT'S INTELLIGENCE AND WHO'S GOT IT?

The notion of a formal intelligence test is generally attributed to a Frenchman, Alfred Binet, whose book, *L'Etude Experimentale de L'Intelligence,* published in 1903, laid the groundwork for standardized intelligence testing. In 1905, with Theodore Simon, he produced a test to identify schoolchildren who needed remedial work. The test was revised and expanded several times, and, in 1916, Lewis Terman of Stanford University adapted it for use with American adults.

The major popularizer of the Americanized Binet scale was Henry H. Goddard, director of the Vineland Training School for Feeble Minded Girls and Boys in New Jersey and the originator of the word moron, from the Greek word meaning foolish. To Goddard, intelligence levels were genetically determined and were an attribute of national origin.

The work for which he is best remembered today was his examination of immigrants on Ellis Island "to observe conditions and offer any suggestions as to what might be done to secure a more thorough examination for the purpose of detecting mental defectives" (Goddard, 1917, p. 253). On a foggy day in 1912, he began his investigation:

> We picked out one young man whom we suspected was defective, and through the interpreter, proceeded to give him the test. The boy tested 8 by the Binet scale. The interpreter said, "I could not have done that when I came to this country," and seemed to think the test unfair. We convinced him that the boy was defective." (Goddard, 1913, p. 105)

The next year, Goddard sent two women to Ellis Island for two-and-a half months. They were given the task of picking out the feeble-minded by sight and then having these subjects take the Binet test. Because government officials had already culled out "defectives," Goddard and his associates "passed by the obviously normal," and tested only "average immigrants" (1917, p. 244). This procedure was based on the interesting assumption that the "average" immigrant was obviously not "normal," the very notion that Goddard claimed to be investigating. Goddard's conclusions: 83 percent of the Jews, 80 percent of the

Hungarians, 79 percent of the Italians, and 87 percent of the Russians were feebleminded (1917, p. 247). "The intelligence of the average 'third class' immigrant," he wrote, "is low, perhaps of moron grade" (1917, p. 243). Nevertheless, Goddard himself was taken aback by his conclusion that the vast majority of immigrants from southern and eastern Europe were morons, and he toyed with his figures to get the percentages down to about half, a more believable figure.

Robert Yerkes, a Harvard professor, was able, as Colonel Yerkes, to preside over the administration of mental tests to recruits during World War I, a task to which he attributed a major part in the winning of the war. Before being shipped overseas, 1.7 million American soldiers were crowded into unheated wooden sheds, where they sat on the floor and took the world's first mass IQ test. Try a few of the more oddball questions.

- The Pierce-Arrow is made in:
  [ ] Flint [ ] Buffalo [ ] Detroit [ ] Toledo
- The Brooklyn Nationals are called the:
  [ ] Giants [ ] Orioles [ ] Superbas [ ] Indians
- The number of Zulu legs is:
  [ ] Two [ ] Four [ ] Six [ ] Eight

Among the results of Yerkes' labors: the determination that the average American adult stood just above the level of a moron, at a mental age of 13, that 89 percent of African-Americans were morons, and that the darker people of southern Europe and the Slavs of eastern Europe were less intelligent than the fairer people of western and northern Europe (Yerkes, 1921).

One of Yerkes' disciples, Princeton professor Carl Brigham, later to become the father of the Scholastic Aptitude Test (SAT), warned that continued immigration would result in a new American who "will be less intelligent than the present native-born American" (Brigham, 1923, p. 205).

This kind of thinking, based on the "scientific" evidence of the IQ tests compiled by the leading experts of the day, contributed to the national quota system, which discriminated against immigrants from eastern and southern Europe and those of Asian and African descent, and underlay U.S. immigration policies for almost a half century. The interest in mental testing that crested after World War I was based largely on the expectation that it would support commonly held assumptions about the inferiority of African-Americans and immigrants at a time, in the words of historian Kenneth Stampp.

> When xenophobia had become almost a national disease, when the immigration restriction movement was getting into high gear, when numerous Northern cities (among them Philadelphia and Chicago) were seriously considering the establishment of racially segregated schools, and when Negroes and immigrants were being lumped together in the category of unassimilable aliens. (1965, p. 49)

At this juncture, statisticians presented what they regarded as convincing evidence of innate racial traits. The social scientists, writes Stampp, "supplied the racists of the late 19th century and early 20th centuries with something that ante-bellum pro-slavery writers had always lacked: a respectable scientific argument" (pp. 49–50). As in so much of psychological testing, the expectation was father to the "fact."

In the light of hindsight and in the context of a more sophisticated view of testing, one would imagine that we are not likely to repeat the more egregious errors of the experts of the early decades of the twentieth century. However, In 1994 and 1995, a number of books (Herrenstein & Murray, 1994; Itzkoff, 1994; Rushton, 1995) raised the same spectre of IQ scores as destiny and of a society adulterated by low intelligence groups, again correlated with race and social class. Far more sophisticated than the work of the earlier psychometricians, the arguments were more seductive, even for those whose knowledge of the excesses of the earlier statisticians had put them on guard. The Bell Curve, by Herrenstein and Murray, pointed to demographic data, declining test scores, and the 15-point gap in the average IQ scores of whites and African-Americans, concluded gloomily that the lowest intellectual levels of the population, particularly African-Americans and poor whites, were outbreeding the brightest, with grim consequences for the nation. (One interesting difference between the authors' findings and those of the earlier statisticians is that Jews apparently had made a quantum leap from congenital mental deficiency in the 1920s to become the intellectual champs of the 1990s.)

The Bell Curve acknowledged that IQ tests had been used in the past to support "outrageous racial policies" (DeParle, 1995, p. 78). But the authors, undaunted, contended that their own work was firmly grounded in solid research. However, the conclusions were also grounded in the same questionable assumption that was made by the early eugenicists: that intelligence is a single, unitary, biological entity – a "g" (for general) factor, rather than a collection of different and distinct abilities (factors), or the result of environmental factors. This idea is a hypothetical construct that is vigorously disputed by many psychologists. A *New York Times* editorial at the time pointed to the problem of interpreting statistical data without sufficient regard to environmental variables.

It is probably this intimidation that helps to account for the remarkable proportion of questionable psychological tests on the market today. One has only to recall Oscar Buros's exasperation with the quality of so many of the tests reviewed in his *Mental Measurements Yearbooks* to recognize that this aura of statistical certitude can often cloak the questionable nature of many tests. And one has only to read the reviews of psychological tests in the most recent *Mental Measurements Yearbook,* in *Test Critiques,* or in professional journals, to find how little the situation has changed.

This chapter is based on the assumption that more knowledge and a healthy dose of skepticism will help arts therapists to choose, use, and create evaluation instruments that more clearly match their purposes and to guard against the biases that lurk in the shadow behind every evaluator. From the publication of the first *Mental Measurements Yearbook* in 1938 until the last one that he personally edited, in 1972, one of Buros's six major objectives was "to impress test users with the desirability of suspecting all standardized tests – even though prepared by well-known authorities – unaccompanied by detailed data on their construction, validity, use, and limitations" (Buros, 1970, p. xviii).

The key to dealing intelligently with scores, numbers, and observations is to recognize that these things rarely, if ever, provide answers to our fundamental questions. What they do provide is the basic raw materials; the data that must be interpreted. Our interpretations are often colored by our expectations, our fears, our hopes, and our biases.

Two questions, in particular, must be asked of any evaluation procedure. Does it assess, in some relevant way, what it purports to assess? And how close is our approximation of a subject's behavior during the assessment to his or her "true" behavior?

When we take our temperature, we are taking a test that involves both measurement (the reading) and evaluation (the interpretation). While 98.6° may represent a "normal" reading, the actual reading will vary depending on the time of day, the time of the month for menstruating women, our general level of function and efficiency, and our own idiosyncratic temperature patterns.

While readings may vary, we expect the thermometer to do two things. First, we expect the reading to indicate only temperature, not metabolism or blood pressure or cardiovascular function. Second, we expect it to be stable in its measurements. We expect that if we take our temperature several times within a short time, the consecutive readings will be more or less consistent, unless we've done something to affect the measurement. And we expect that if we hand the thermometer to another person, he or she will read the same number.

These are the same expectations with which we approach psychodiagnostic programs. In this chapter, we offer suggestions on choosing, using, and creating reasonable assessment instruments and procedures.

VALIDITY

Validity is the degree to which a test measures what it is supposed to measure. However, we can't simply say that a test or a procedure is valid; we can say only that it is valid for a particular purpose and for a specific group of people. And even this assertion must be made with caution, because establishing the validity of a procedure can be tricky.

For one thing, most psychological tests deal with "constructs" – abstract concepts, such as anxiety, compulsion, fear, anger, stability, and personality. These are not real things that can be seen, smelled, tasted or felt. They are hypothetical and must be inferred from real things or from observable behavior. One problem is that various schools of therapy have drawn from the same observations very different maps to describe and to differentiate behavior, with very different constructs, each with its distinct boundaries. Moreover, constructs change over time, as theories change.

Some terms, like "insanity," have disappeared from the taxonomy of mental disorders, only to resurface somewhere else. Insanity has become a legal term and it represents a very different construct than it did when it was a medical one. Others have been rethought and redefined. Often, when the old names survive, the constructs they represent have changed over the years as theorists and clinicians reconceptualize them.

Even if there is a clear connection between the behaviors and the construct that a procedure is designed to assess, the assessment may not be focused on what it is supposed to evaluate. For example, there is a clear connection between scores on IQ tests, designed to measure intelligence and school achievement. However, this correlation doesn't tell us whether the tests measure an innate ability or are simply achievement tests that measure previous learning. Does the IQ score predict school achievement, or does prior achievement at home and in school predict IQ score? So the definition of the construct is vital to its accurate measurement. "We do not say, 'If you can't measure it, it doesn't exist,'' said psychometrician Robert Ebel, "We do say, 'If you can't define it clearly, you cannot. . . measure it validly'' (Ebel, 1975, p. 84).

Basically, there are only two ways to validate a procedure. One is by opinion and the other is by comparing the results with something else. There are several variations of these methods, each designed to establish a different aspect of validity and each for a specific purpose.

Content Validity

Content validity refers to the relationship between the items on a test or an interview and the purpose or subject of the test or procedure, and the only method of validation is by subjective examination, or validation by opinion. The central question is: How representative is the assessment procedure of the universe of relevant tasks and situations that could have been employed? Do the items represent a true sample of the possible choices? For example, if an interview designed to assess feelings of sexual inadequacy includes questions that deal only with heterosexual dating, it could not be said to have high content validity for the stated purpose.

Remember that the validity of an assessment procedure depends on the purpose for which it is used. The Myers-Briggs Type Indicator, Form G (1992) measures 16 personality traits to identify a subject's preferences or customary approach to situations in four areas: introversion/extroversion; sensing/intuition; thinking/feeling; and judgment/perception. The terms are based on Jungian definitions and, as in so many psychological constructs, the meanings are quite different from the common everyday meanings of the words. The housing directors of several universities used to use the 94-item indicator to match up roommates with compatible personalities. As a result of numbers of student complaints, some universities stopped using the screening instrument. The problem: the Myers-Briggs doesn't deal with some of the personal habits that seem to be major triggers of disharmony, such as eating habits and smoking (Bixler, 1993). While the Myers-Briggs might be useful for some purposes, charge the critics, for the purpose for which the instrument was used in these cases, it's too low in content validity to be useful.

Most psychological disorders involve numbers of attributes or symptoms. A test that is designed to identify mania, for example, should consider all of the criteria by which a manic episode may be diagnosed. A test that probes only for distractibility or mood, and that ignores the other possible signs and symptoms spelled out in the *DSM* (such as diminished need for sleep, flight of ideas, increase in psychomotor activity, and inflated self-esteem), would be considered to be low in content validity.

Content validity is sometimes referred to as face validity, but the two, while closely related, are not the same. While content validity refers to the degree to which a test is a representative sample of the universe of relevant possibilities, face validity refers to the appearance of a test, and it has more to do with persuading test users that a test does what it's supposed to do, and with persuading test takers that it is a legitimate test, than with the question of whether it provides a representative sampling of the content to be considered. Some tests are widely accepted and used, despite the fact that they don't seem to possess very high face validity. Why, on the "face of it," should a series of inkblots be useful in examining neurotic tendencies? Only by accepting the rationale of the Rorschach does the relevance of the technique make sense. On the other hand, some self-reports, which appear to demonstrate a good deal of face validity, are viewed by clients or patients as attempts to trick them, sometimes with good reason, as we shall see later.

Nevertheless, face validity is important, despite the fact that it has more to do with appearance than with content. Lee Cronbach pointed out that a good deal of the power of treatment has to do with the patient's faith in the tools and instruments that the clinician uses (1970, p. 182). One must consider how worthwhile a test or procedure will appear to the subject who takes it.

Construct Validity

Construct validity has to do with the ability of a procedure to assess a client's status in terms of an abstract quality or hypothetical construct, such as "self-esteem," "motivation," or "anxiety." Validation is established by a combination of opinion and comparison, and it is frequently difficult to determine what is actually being assessed. Is a clinical judgment that a client is suffering from "incest survivor's syndrome" a judgment about repressed memory or suggestibility? Is a children's drawing test a test of personality, or of maturity, or of previous training? Or of the ways the children perceived things that particular day? Leona Tyler recommended that in evaluating the validity of a test or procedure, the first knack that a clinician must acquire is the habit of disregarding the title or name, and asking, "What are scores on this test related to?" (Tyler, 1963, p. 28).

If a test is designed to measure a trait like intelligence, or fear, or anxiety, or dominance, then the items should bear some relationship to the behaviors by which we judge intelligence, fear, anxiety or dominance and not some other variable that we may not have considered, like unfamiliarity with the language, or test anxiety, or health. The test should discriminate only on the basis of the quality being tested.

Ronald Jay Cohen and his colleagues (1992) described types of evidence that help to establish the construct validity of a test:

Homogeneity. The test measures a single construct. Homogeneity can be established statistically, by establishing a significant positive correlation between scores on each subtest or each item of a test and the total score on the test. A rough estimate of homogeneity would be based on the finding that high scorers on the test tend to pass each item more frequently than low scorers.

Conformity with Theory. Changes in test scores conform with theoretical expectations. It can be expected that "reading ability" will improve dramatically between the ages of six and the early teens, and a test of reading ability should show that scores increase significantly in increasingly higher age groups. For constructs that are not expected to show major change over time, such as "intelligence" or "self-esteem," test scores should not show significant differences between different age groups.

Evidence of Expected Change. Pretest/posttest changes reflect intervention and experience in line with general expectations. By the same token, if the intervention (such as therapy) was terminated after the posttest, scores on a subsequent posttest should show little, if any, change.

Evidence from Contrasted Groups. There are significant statistical differences between the scores of criterion groups and those of others. For example, Item 40 of the MMPI ("Much of the time my head seems to hurt all over") was answered true by 12 percent of a sample of previously diagnosed hypochondriacs but only 4 percent of the "normal controls," so it was included in the clinical scale for hypochondria. The item was cross-validated by trying it out on another sample of clinical patients to see if there were still significant differences.

Convergent and discriminate validity. The relationship between the items in a test or procedure and the behaviors by which we judge the qualities or concepts involved is referred to as convergent validity or convergent evidence. The results of the test or procedure should converge, or correlate highly, with other variables that are theoretically associated with it. Someone who scores high in a test of "introversion" should be expected to spend more time alone than someone who scores high in "extroversion."

The construct validity of the test or procedure is also measured by its ability to discriminate between the quality or trait that we want to identify and variables that may be similar but are not the ones we want to consider. So a procedure designed to identify schizophrenia should have the capacity to distinguish between individuals with schizophrenia and those who have bipolar disorder. This test quality is usually referred to as the specific accuracy of the instrument. A complex statistical method for determining the degree to which a test has convergent and discriminate validity is to calculate the test's factorial validity. Using a procedure known as factor analysis, statisticians derive groups of variables that measure distinguishable aspects of the problem to estimate the degree to which they correlate. A high correlation suggests convergent validity, while a low one indicates discriminant validity.

Criterion Validity

Criterion validity means that the results of a test or evaluation procedure are compared with something else: current behavior that can be compared with the test's description, the results of another test, or behavior at a future time that can be matched against the test's prediction. Of note here is that criterion validity can be concerned with predictive validity which is addressed below, but not all criterion validity is predictive validity. It simply means comparing test scores to some other direct measure of the construct of interest.

Concurrent Validity

Concurrent validity refers to the consistency between the set of information derived from one test or interview and the information from another source, such as another test or a psychiatrist's diagnosis. It would be disconcerting and confusing to find that one procedure assessed an individual as high in assertiveness when another found the same individual as low in the same quality.

The problem with concurrent validity is that some testers invest their faith in a test simply because the test manual showed that it correlates well with another test or set of data. Two tests can have concurrent validity, scale by scale, and category by category, and yet neither may be rooted in behavior in real life. On the other hand, both scores can reflect nothing more than a subject's ability to see through a test and to fake responses, or the inability of the test to discriminate well among the pool of subjects. Consider this long ago comment by a reviewer of the Medical College Admission Test in *The Seventh Mental Measurements Yearbook* (1972):

> Overall, the validity data suggest that the MCAT measures adequately what similar tests measure but what is being measured has little utility in the selection of medical students. Restriction of range is the explanation for such findings usually suggested by proponents of the MCAT. (Richards, 1972, p. 1101)

"Restriction of range" means that the test takers are too similar for the test to discriminate meaningfully among them; differences in scores may reflect test error as much as true differences between applicants. In other words, the test will not have much predictive validity, making it of limited value for the purpose for which it was intended.

Predictive Validity

Some procedures are designed specifically to predict future behavior. A scholastic aptitude test should predict, with some reasonable degree of accuracy, how well subjects can be expected to perform in school. A job interview should help the interviewer to predict how well someone will be able to perform on the job. And a psychodiagnostic test or interview should not only diagnose but predict a patient's behavior, including his or her response to drugs or to a specific therapeutic program. The MCAT mentioned above was supposed to discriminate between those students who could be expected to succeed in medical school and those who would not.

According to critics a high IQ may lead to school success (and frequently to career success) because it is a "credential" that opens doors to better schooling and more opportunities (Zoelner, 1976, p. 18). As a result, the scores often become self-fulfilling prophecies: children with low IQ scores are put in "slow" track, low-expectation classes where they will perform as little as is expected of them, and children with high IQ scores are put in "fast" track classes, where most of them will perform as expected. So, the critics charge, while such tests may have reasonable predictive validity, they have low construct validity. That is, they purport to measure one thing when they may be measuring something else. As a result of such criticisms, many of the group tests that used to be called "intelligence tests" are now referred to as "scholastic aptitude tests" or "tests of scholastic performance intelligence."

It must be emphasized that while a test's predictive validity is calculated on the basis of its general accuracy for large groups, they aren't nearly as accurate in predicting what a given individual will do. The closer an individual is to the norm, in fact, the more difficult it is to predict how he or she will behave. In the MCAT example we cited above, the standard deviation from the norm is numerically low (another way of saying that the applicants are all close to the norm for their group), so the test scores were of limited value in predicting how well a given applicant would do. Predicting for an individual is a task that must be approached with a good deal of caution, no matter how high the reported predictive validity of a test or procedure may be.

Similar criticisms have been made of psychodiagnostic procedures. You may remember Rosenhan's charge that the family histories of his pseudopatients were distorted to make them fit the diagnostic labels, and Spitzer's admission that such diagnoses often became self-fulfilling prophecies (see Chapter 1).

Incremental Validity

Incremental validity (Sechrest, 1963) has to do with the degree to which an additional procedure or test adds to the accuracy of a description or prediction. In many cases, a complex battery of tests or procedures creates the illusion of accuracy but adds little to a simple assessment procedure.

In the case of the MCAT that we mentioned above, a reviewer, referring to the restricted range of validity raised the issue of incremental validity. By the time they apply to medical school, students have already been stringently selected on academic aptitude through the procedures for selecting college students, admitting students to premedical programs, and evaluating the performance of students in premedical courses. Considerable self-selection on academic aptitude probably also takes place. As a consequence, medical colleges may be working with an applicant pool sufficiently restricted that it simply does not make sense to use yet another test of academic aptitude in selecting students.

We would suggest that any clinician considering using an assessment procedure ask: What will the results add to the information that I already have or can get easily?

Test Validation

To find correlations between tests and other data, test designers usually norm or standardize their products on a representative sample of the kind of populations on which the test is to be used. If the sample on which the test was standardized is not representative, then the test will be biased, and the results will be inaccurate and undependable. Norming and validating a test can be tricky.

First of all, validity in the world of evaluation doesn't mean what it means in conversational English. A birth certificate, a passport, or a driver's license is either valid or it is not. Such a document cannot be a little bit valid. But an assessment procedure can. A procedure can be valid on a continuum; that is, it may be valid to a degree. The degree of validity (sometimes, as in the case of standardized tests, expressed as a "correlation coefficient") may be so small that it may be of limited use for the purpose for which it is used.

A second reason has to do with the fact, to which we've already alluded, that most tests used in psychology attempt to probe theoretical concepts, such as anxiety, fear, stability and personality. Not only do psychologists and therapists disagree on the definitions of such concepts, but some deny the existence of such constructs altogether. Such constructs are derived from basic assumptions (which sometimes may not be warranted) and from specific theoretical considerations. Let's consider some problems that may arise in each case.

In 1929, Robert C. Tryon set out, at the University of California at Berkeley, to breed a highly intelligent race of laboratory rats. To measure the trait of rat intelligence, he developed a large automatic maze that kept a record of the corridors through which each rat passed. Tryon bred the "brighter" rats, which went directly to the food at the end of the tunnel, without blind side excursions (Garcia, 1972).

After seven generations, Tryon had two clearly differentiated lines of thoroughbred rats: "bright" and "dull." The problem was that the only criterion of a rat's intelligence seemed to be its ability to get to the food fast. The "bright" rats seemed to be no better than their "dull" counterparts in other tasks. It began to occur to Tryon that his bright rats might have scored high on his test because they might be insensitive, undisturbed by clanking doors and clicking switches. Other evidence suggested that they were more food-oriented than were their slower counterparts who, in turn, might have been more cautious and curious than the fast rats and prone to explore side corridors. In fact, one might make a case that caution and curiosity are aspects of intelligence that may be more adaptive than the desire to bolt down food. One writer suggested that "To get a rat with a full spectrum of adaptive talents one should probably go to the city dump and trap one – the one that is hardest to catch" (Garcia, 1972, p. 232).

In dealing with construct validity, a good standard precaution is to consider differential explanations for a behavior or a score: What factors other than the assumed ones might explain the behavior or score? Constructs that are based on specific theoretical postulates pose a different problem; a therapist must accept the theoretical framework on which a test is built for the test to have meaning. A test or structured interview that has high validity for one examiner may have little or no validity for another.

A third reason has to do with the technical problems of standardizing, or "norming," the test or procedure. If a procedure is to have "generalizability" for a large population, then the validation sample must be chosen on a random basis. The word "random," does not mean haphazard, as it does in everyday conversation. A random sample is one that gives every member of the target population an equal chance to be included; it is designed to avoid bias or "selection" in the choice of sample members. A classic error in sampling was committed by pollsters who predicted the election of Alf Landon as president of the United States in 1936 on the basis of a telephone poll. However, in 1936, only affluent people owned telephones, so the sample was not representative of the population at large, which swept Franklin D. Roosevelt into his second term of office. Random sampling is a procedure that uses precise methods to insure a random result.

On the other hand, if the procedure is to be used to identify a specific segment of the population, such as depressed persons, then the sample must be drawn only from those who are depressed. But even such a stratified sample must be random for the population of depressed persons. It must be designed so that any segment of that population has a chance to be considered in the same proportion to its presence in the population, including depressed people of all ages, races, socioeconomic and educational levels, and geographical distribution. Many norming and validation procedures fall short of these standards.

The norming of the Minnesota Multiphasic Personality Inventory (MMPI) is often cited as a product of solid empirical construction. The authors of the original test assembled over 1000 statements relating to morale, attitudes, and health, to which respondents were to answer true, false, or cannot say. These items were reviewed to eliminate duplications and ambiguities, and the test was administered to patients of a state hospital (the criterion group) who had been diagnosed as suffering from specific disorders. The test was also given to people who were considered normal (the control group).

When the results were tabulated, it was found that there were marked differences in the responses of "normal" subjects and patients. Subsequent test administrations also demonstrated that patients with one group of symptoms responded to particular clusters of items quite differently from those with other sets of symptoms. By matching up responses to the 550 statements that were finally selected with the norms for each group, the test's developers demonstrated that they could differentiate between people who were normal and those who were behaviorally abnormal, and between various categories of disorders among patients. Some scales of the MMPI that were developed subsequently went beyond the original scope of the test and aimed for more ambitious types of personality discrimination.

There are those who defend the validity of the test on an empirical basis. After all, if a test can discriminate between a criterion group and a control group, the items don't have to show much face validity. A study of college students some years ago indicated that the behavioral correlates are quite similar to those that prevailed a generation earlier

– that is, the students' interpretations of these concepts were much the same as their parents' interpretations, presumably when they, too, were students (Todd & Gynther, 1988). It would be interesting to have more updated data on this.

This brings us to a central issue. It is interesting how many tests are standardized or validated on the population of college students. Interesting, but not surprising. It isn't easy to find participants for the myriad of psychological tests and studies that help professors move forward in academia. College students represent a large and easily tapped pool of subjects, who may participate in such studies in order to fulfill course requirements. The word "sophomoric" takes on an interesting dimension when it is considered how many tests designed for use on a general population are validated on college sophomores; this phenomenon is so widely recognized that academic psychologists often jokingly define psychology as "the science of the college sophomore."

Some construct measurements will change with age or experience, motor coordination, or tolerance, for example. Others may not. Some will vary with race, ethnicity, sex, or nationality. Unless the sample is stratified and correlations made between scores and other variables, we can't be sure that the test has validity for subjects who are different from those in the standardization sample. This issue of base rate is one that we shall explore in greater detail in a later chapter.

Subjects may change in other ways. Many, if not most, mental disorders tend to be cyclical. A person with bipolar disorder, for example, may be in a manic phase, or in a depressed stage, or may be in remission, exhibiting no symptoms at all. His or her responses to a particular test item or an interview question may depend on the particular phase of the cycle. Both the validation and the evaluation procedure, therefore, must take into account the cyclical nature of the disorder, considering the subjects' previous idiosyncratic histories and the types of responses or behaviors that could be expected in each stage of the disorder. Unless the procedure is validated and stratified at each stage, it will be of limited use in the evaluation of a particular patient.

Up to this point, we have discussed problems of validation for tests that attempt to assess permanent trait characteristics or recurrent pathologies. Behavioral therapists sometimes contend that validation in their work avoids many of the problems that plague other tests; for one thing, they have no need for construct validation, because they deal with observable behavior, not with hypothetical constructs, such as personality traits. However, in the past few decades, the concept of behavioral assessment has expanded well beyond the realm of observable overt behavior. Some of the current scales and inventories deal with clusters of behaviors that are assigned labels, such as fear, assertiveness, and social skills. In terms of psychometrics, such tests walk and quack very much like personality tests that attempt to identify traits, and they are not free of problems of validation.

For example, the Rathus Assertiveness Schedule (RAS) was developed to test whether clients benefitted from assertiveness training. It was developed on the usual population of college students and validated in a rather peculiar way. Instead of relying on real behaviors, either observed or self-reported, the 30 items on the test were derived from the diaries kept by the author's students, in which they described behaviors they would like to have exhibited, but from which they refrained out of discretion. The responses require subjects to rate, on a six-point scale, how descriptive each statement is of their own attitudes or behaviors.

Examination of the items themselves provoked concerns about validity, with the first item raising a red flag. "Most people seem to be more aggressive and assertive than I am." How are subjects to answer this item if they see themselves as quietly assertive – as firm and polite in maintaining a position – rather than as aggressive?

While construct validity is not supposed to be an issue in behavioral assessment, consider the item, "I am open and frank about my feelings," designed to assess assertiveness. The response may reveal the degree to which the subject is assertive. Or it may be evidence of emotionality, or just social immaturity.

Before we leave the subject of validation, we would like to touch upon the difficulty of finding a representative sample of subjects on which to standardize a test or procedure. When Kinsey was planning his investigation of the sexual habits of Americans, he wrote to a friend:

> We have suggestions from a number of psychologists of Terman's generation that we should confine ourselves to a good normal, middle-class group, such as college professors. In actuality, the histories of this group represent one of the widest departures from anything that is typical of the mass of the population. (Pomeroy, 1982)

No therapist should ever choose an evaluation procedure without examining with a skeptical eye the validation data in the test manual or the literature on the procedure, as well as the reviews in the professional literature. In particular, the therapist should be satisfied that both content validation and construct validation make sense in light of his or her own theoretical approach, and that the population on which the test was validated is representative of his or her own clientele.

Most test manuals specify the uses for which the test is recommended, and the author's validation is focused on these uses and on specified situations. Any therapist who is choosing an evaluation procedure or designing an evaluation program should conduct his or her own validation research to be sure that the evaluation procedure or program is appropriate for the specific situation and for the particular patients or clients on which the procedure is to be used, referring not only to the manual but to reviews in current and past editions of the *Mental Measurements Yearbook, Test Critiques,* or *Tests: A Comprehensive Reference for Assessment in Psychology, Education, and Business.* Many of the resources are now available online, for example, Buros Institute (http://buros.unl.edu/buros/jsp/search.jsp), and through the American Psychological Association (http://www.apa.org/science/programs/testing/find-tests.aspx). In addition, an excellent volume *Handbook of Psychiatric Measures* (Rush, First, & Blacker, 2007) assesses 275 different measures, and the *Handbook of Psychological Assessment* (Groth-Marnat, 2009) reviews many brief instruments.

Questions to Ask About a Procedure's Validity

Validation Data

Does the manual, description, or review provide enough information on which to base my own estimate of the procedure's validity?

Content Validity

Are the content and scope of the procedure appropriate for the purpose for which I intend to use it?

Are they appropriate for the patients or clients with whom I intend to use it?

Construct Validity

Do I accept the theoretical base on which the procedure rests?

Do the items on the test or procedure correspond to the theoretical description of the constructs?

What evidence is presented (or can I determine) to support the construct validity, such as homogeneity, conformity with expectations, or evidence from distinct groups?

To what extent does it identify the qualities that I want to measure or assess? To what extent does it distinguish between those qualities and others that are similar?

Criterion Validity

To what criteria or criterion groups do results relate?

If the instrument has been standardized or normed, is the standardization sample identified? And is this sample representative of my patients or clients?

RELIABILITY

Every test, interview, or observation is a sample of behavior. Actually, as Henry Dyer, former vice-president of the Educational Testing Service, pointed out long ago (1965), the behavior or situation simultaneously constitutes four different kinds of samples.

It is a sample of all the situations or procedures that could have been chosen to assess the subject's behavior, such as the situation to be observed, the time of day chosen for the procedure, the kinds of questions asked, or the task required to get the information needed. It is a sample of all the ways the subject could have responded. It is a sample of all the possible psychological and physiological factors that could have influenced the subject's response, such as stress, fatigue, euphoria, or concern. It is a sample of all the perceptions and judgments that might have been made about the subject's response by a universe of judges or observers, with differences in personality, training, observational patterns and skills, and interviewing style. It is even a sample of the various observations and judgments that could have been made by the same observer at different times of day or under different circumstances.

Observers can only approximate the "true" response of any subject. The estimate of how close this approximation is to the true response is referred to as the reliability of a test. "The reliability of [a] . . . test is thus an estimate of the degree to which it approximates the universe of the four kinds of events of which it is a sample" (Dyer, 1965, p. 33).

A procedure that produces reasonably consistent scores or judgments is likely to approximate the true score better than one in which there is a good deal of variability in scores or judgments. There are several techniques for estimating the reliability or consistency of a procedure, but "probably none of them accounts adequately for all four categories of sampling" (Dyer, 1965, p. 33).

Some techniques deal with the internal consistency of the test itself, some with the consistency of the test in measuring the same quality in the same person at different times, and some deal with the degree to which different interpreters agree on the results of the test for an individual or group. Each technique is useful for certain purposes.

In a later chapter, we'll deal with some of the mechanics of correlation, but for our purposes here, an understanding of the principles involved is far more important than skill in manipulating numbers. In fact, most experienced therapists can come to a rough determination of a procedure's reliability by relatively simple examinations and comparisons of results, scores, or interpretations. However, for complex tests or procedures, the published coefficients of reliability are more accurate indicators of the consistency of a test. While a reliability coefficient of .70 is acceptable for research purposes, a test used as the basis for a clinical decision should be around .90 or higher. If it is lower than .90, the scores should be treated as suggestive hypotheses about the patient or client. Information on reliability should appear in the test manual or in the reviews of a test.

Reliability of the Test

If a procedure is designed to assess a specific quality or trait, then it should agree with itself. This principle applies to both tests and qualitative assessments.

Test-Retest Reliability

Let's assume that a test score indicates that you tend to be introverted. If you take the same test after a short interval, the score should be close to the original one. A significant difference raises questions about the test-retest reliability of the procedure. The longer the time between the test and the retest, the less consistent the scores are likely to be, because people do change over time.

There are major limitations to test-retest reliability. For one thing, the experience of taking the test itself is a factor. If the test is an educational test, you will improve with practice alone. If the test is one of personality, you will have had the opportunity to rethink some of your answers and to engage in what has been called "impression management." The Greek philosopher Heraclitus suggested that someone never steps into the same river twice.

For this reason, there have been modifications in the analysis of test-retest reliability. Originally, the words "same test" meant precisely that. However, test-retest has come to describe different forms of the same test, although such correlations are more frequently called alternate form reliability or parallel form reliability. While the terms are often used interchangeably, there are technical differences between them. Parallel forms are designed to correlate with each other in terms of psychometric qualities, while alternate forms are different versions of a test that are deemed to be equivalent in scope and content.

In any event, test-retest reliability, in any of its forms, is not considered as important as it once was. First, there are almost always variations in the administration of the two testing periods and in the psychological status of the subject. Second, the experience of taking the first test usually does have an influence on the score of the second test. Third, in the case of alternate forms of the test, the two forms may not, in fact, be identical in content or construct validity; in such a case, no matter how reliable the tests may be, their basic validity is suspect. Fourth, and perhaps the most important, people themselves change over time; if test-retest reliability is low, this may be the result of change in the person taking the test and not a deficiency in the test, and there is often no reasonable way of ascertaining which factor is responsible, if we don't have statistical evidence of the test's reliability.

The area in which test-retest reliability might be considered extremely important is in monitoring the progress of a patient or client. If the test-retest reliability of a test has been established, then we can assume that changes in test results are more likely to reflect changes in the patient than testing error. However, the examiner must always consider the influence of such extraneous variables as health, mood, family difficulties – even a bad hair day.

Internal Consistency

The comparison of test scores in recent years usually focuses on the administration of a single test, so that there is no variation because of time or experience. The focus is on the internal consistency of a single procedure.

The degree to which the items on a test are consistent with each other (homogeneity of test items) is sometimes cited as evidence of the construct validity of the test (Cohen et al., 1992, pp. 176–177). Obviously, if a test is designed to measure anxiety, then each item on the test should deal with anxiety and not with aggression or introspection. However, the internal consistency of a procedure is also considered evidence of the procedure's reliability.

There are several methods for calculating a test's internal consistency, each with a different purpose and each with specific applications. For example, some formulas measure a test's inter-item consistency, the degree to which all the items on a test agree. A homogeneous test is one in which all the items focus on a narrow trait or a single factor, such as test anxiety. Such a test would have a higher inter-item consistency than would a heterogeneous test, such as a test of anxiety in general. Most statistical software packages easily compute coefficients of inter-item consistency.

For most therapists, the most useful measure of a test's internal consistency is the split-half reliability coefficient. It is also the easiest to use for clinicians with a limited background in (or a profound distaste for) statistics.

As the name suggests, split-half reliability is designed to estimate how closely the scores on two halves of a test correlate. The easiest way to see this correlation is simply to divide a test in half, score each half and compare the scores. The problem is that this method would yield distorted results, because it would not take into account such factors as the fatigue that would be more likely during the second half, the differences in test anxiety, the varying difficulty of items on the two halves, and the decrease in reliability as a result of a smaller number of items on each half than on the whole test.

There are several acceptable ways to split a test. One is to assign items randomly to one half or the other. Another, and one that is more commonly used, is to split the test into even-numbered items and odd-numbered items. While there are formulas for calculating split-half correlation, for practical purposes most clinicians can simply compare the scores on the two halves to ascertain if they are close enough to make the test acceptable for their purposes. There is one major weakness in all methods for estimating internal consistency. While such techniques limit the variability of samples in the test situation, they do not take into account two of the other sources of variability:

> the range of all the possible responses the subject could have offered and the range of the psychological conditions under which the subject might have taken the test. As a result, an estimate based on internal consistency alone "is probably in most cases an overestimate." (Dyer, 1965, p. 34)

Paradoxically, in the split-half approach, there is a likelihood that we might underestimate consistency. Reliability is influenced by the total number of items on a test (the more items, the greater the reliability). Because the split-half method cuts the number of items by half, reliability suffers in each half. In the literature about a test, you may find references to the Spearman-Brown formula, which is used to correct for this underestimation.

Which Measure of Test Reliability to Use?

Test-retest reliability and measures of internal consistency are both useful indicators of a test's reliability. However, there are certain circumstances that may make one much more useful than the other in specific situations.

Homogeneity. If the items on a test are all focused on a specific trait or behavior, we should expect a high degree of internal consistency. On the other hand, if the items on the test are heterogeneous, dealing with a spread of related factors, the level of internal consistency would probably be much lower. In this situation, a test-retest reliability study might make more sense.

Stability of the Trait or Quality. Some characteristics, like intelligence or test-wiseness or assertiveness, are assumed to be relatively stable over periods of time. For tests measuring such traits or behaviors, test-retest reliability would be a reasonable way to ascertain the consistency of the test. On the other hand, some traits or qualities, like anxiety or fear, may be erratic, changing from situation to situation. Some mental disorders are highly cyclical; we can't always be sure when a patient is nearing the end of a period of depression or approaching the beginning of a manic one. For tests designed to measure such dynamic or erratic qualities, we could not be sure of the value of a test-retest correlation. For such tests, a measure of internal consistency would make more sense.

Norm-referenced and Criterion-referenced Procedures. Norm-referenced tests compare people's performances against those of others. Criterion-referenced tests, on the other hand, are those that indicate how well a subject has achieved a predetermined behavioral objective without reference to how others have done. While most psychological tests are norm-referenced, some assessment procedures are criterion-referenced. For example, a therapist may be interested in knowing how well a child has mastered a specific skill. Traditional measures of test reliability are more appropriate for norm-referenced than for criterion-referenced procedures. There are statistical techniques that can be used for criterion-referenced procedures (Hambeton & Jurgensen, 1990), but most therapists who deal with such behavioral objectives are more likely to be concerned with inter-rater reliability (see below) than with test reliability.

The Standard Error of Measurement

In its broadest sense, test reliability indicates the degree to which individual differences in scores are attributable to chance errors of measurement and the degree to which they are attributable to true differences in whatever is being measured (Anastasi, 1961, p. 108). In addition to the methods that we have discussed, one way of estimating the reliability of a test is by measuring directly the amount of error in the instrument. This is known as the standard error of measurement (SEM) and is actually an estimate of the standard deviation of error (more on this is presented in Chapter 5, which deals with basic psychometric statistics).

For the clinician, the SEM provides an indication of the reliability of a test that is less easily influenced by differences in the samples from which reliability is estimated. For example, if a test's SEM is reported as five, then the clinician knows that changes in scores from one administration to the next of less than five points are likely to be due to error in the test itself and that only differences of five or more are likely to represent real change. In general, the smaller the SEM the greater the reliability of the test.

Inter-Observer Reliability

An assessment is based not only on the stability of the instrument or procedure but on the person doing the assessment. In 1912, Daniel Starch and Edward Elliot questioned the growing use of grades to indicate student proficiency. In a classic study (Starch & Elliot, 1912), they found that an English examination paper graded by 142 experienced teachers received grades that ranged from 50 to 98. A geometry paper graded by 138 geometry teachers received grades from 28 to 95. Some teachers deducted points for wrong answers, some for sloppiness, or spelling errors, or form, or procedure.

What was particularly noteworthy about the study was the fact that "probable error," or chance alone, would account for only a seven-point difference among the grades given one paper, based on the mean grade of 85. The math paper, given 80 percent by the test-taker's own teacher, was given failing grades by 15 percent of the teachers and grades of over 90 by 12 percent. The Starch and Elliot studies spurred the drive to create "objective" testing techniques and to measure the variability in the scoring and rating of evaluation procedures, including the calculation of variations in the ways different observers measure or evaluate behaviors.

Inter-rater reliability, also referred to as inter-scorer reliability, refers to the degree to which two or more examiners agree in their measurement of a subject's performance. Inter-judge reliability refers to the degree to which they agree on the evaluation or interpretation of the performance. The term inter-observer is more neutral and is used to describe either kind of agreement.

Published figures in test manuals provide an indication of how carefully the author prepared the instructions for administering and scoring the test in a uniform manner; low correlations usually indicate problems in one or both of these areas. For example, the scoring instructions may be so ambiguous that they are open to varying scores. Expressions such as "uses rhythm appropriately," or "higher level of sophistication" are stated in vague terms, but can be adequate if precise and specific directions are included for judging such terms as "appropriately." For example, "hands must show five fingers," is clear and clear examples can be offered as guides.

Even if the reported inter-rater reliability is high, a group of clinicians may not achieve the same degree of consistency in assessment. In most cases, observers or users must be carefully trained in scoring techniques that can include group discussions, practice sessions, exercises and feedback. Consequently, it is important that clinicians working in groups estimate their own consistency in scoring a particular test or procedure.

In later chapters, we discuss methods for calculating inter-observer reliability, but, for most practical purposes, this can be estimated informally by comparing scores or conclusions. Clinicians who work in institutions or in teams can improve the inter-observer reliability of their assessment procedures by doing what the test authors do to improve their published figures: confer, practice, get feedback, and discuss.

Questions to Ask About Reliability

Test Reliability

Are the reported reliability coefficients sufficiently high (generally around .90 for clinical decision-making)?

Have I considered alternative explanations for changes in the scores of patients or clients, such as the cyclical nature of a problem or the relative stability of a trait (or state)?

Have I taken into account intervening events, such as changes in health, in family relationships, in emotional states? Have I invited my client to help interpret variations?

Have I considered the implications of the method of estimating reliability on variations in scores?

Inter-Observer Reliability

Does the manual or the description provide enough detailed information to provide for relative uniformity in the administration of the test or procedure?

Have my colleagues and I taken precautions to develop a uniform and consistent method for administering, scoring, and interpreting the test or procedure? Do I (or they) need additional training?

PRACTICAL CONSIDERATIONS IN CHOOSING A PROCEDURE

In choosing a test or procedure, therapists certainly have to consider its validity and reliability. However, there are numbers of practical issues involved in the choice. The therapist first has to ask: "What is the purpose of this assessment?" In far too many instances, a "diagnosis," whether it involves assigning a label or assuming the causes for the problem, offers little guidance in planning or providing therapy. Unless the results of an assessment help you plan or improve upon the treatment, or an evaluation tool provides feedback on whether therapy is working, there is little purpose in the process.

Directness

The degree to which a score or an assessment finding reflects the actual behavior, thought processes or feelings of a client is referred to as directness. Instruments that rest on inferences about hidden and underlying causes are considered indirect. Direct measures, such as behavioral observations, demonstrations of rhythm, movement dysfunctions that are pinpointed for treatment, and client self-reports that are taken at face value provide samples of behavior, while indirect ones that require interpretation are considered symbols of the problem (Fischer & Corcoran, 1994, p. 25). The more directly the instrument measures manifest and observable behavior, the less likely the therapist is to have problems with reliability and validity.

Reactivity

Assessment is highly susceptible to the working out of the Heisenberg Principle that relates to the way observing something changes it. Reactivity refers to the degree that the observation or measurement influences behavior. Some methods of measurement and assessment invite reaction (self-monitoring of behavior, for example). Others, particularly unobtrusive or "naturalistic" approaches, are less likely to provoke reaction. To the degree that a procedure itself distorts the client's behavior, it suffers a loss of validity. At first glance, a reactive procedure may seem to promote beneficial change. If a client's self-monitoring cuts down on maladjusted behaviors, such as smoking, why not encourage it? The problem is that changes resulting from reactive assessment procedures seldom last (Fischer & Corcoran, 1994, p. 25). Therapists should try to use instruments that don't artificially affect the result or, at least, to try to minimize the distortions provoked by reactive approaches, perhaps by making them less obtrusive.

Questions to Ask

Utility

Will the results of the assessment procedure make a difference in the way I plan or conduct the treatment program? If not, why am I conducting this assessment?

Directness

How directly does the score or assessment result reflect the actual behavior or feeling or thought processes of my client?

Reactivity

To what degree does the assessment procedure I am considering artificially distort the results?

Are there relatively nonreactive methods that will provide the needed information? If not, how can I minimize the distortion caused by the use of the reactive procedure?

SUMMARY

In the 2,400 years since Socrates exhorted his students to strive to know themselves, we have come increasingly to recognize how difficult it is to know ourselves, to understand our own motives, and our own behaviors. How much more difficult, then, to understand another human being?

Yet, those who deal with people with disorders and disabilities must attempt to get a fix on the workings of the minds of those they try to help, as a guide to determining how best to help them. All assessments are hypotheses about the ways subjects have organized their personal realities. They are guesses, based on samples of behavior that must be corroborated and verified by observing still other samples. However, no single sample or collection of samples encapsulates the "true" behavior of the subject. All assessment procedures involve a complex interaction between the patient or client and the observer. Whatever behavior the observer notes, even in a "naturalistic" setting, is only a sample of the total behavior of the patient, and it is influenced by factors that may never again coexist in precisely the same way. The four major sources of distortion are the situation, the patient's behavior, the examiner's observations, and the examiner's interpretation.

The degree to which an approximation of a subject's behavior or inner reality comes close to his or her "true" behavior or reality is referred to as reliability, which has several dimensions, each based on the concept of consistency. Among them are: internal consistency (how well does the procedure agree with itself?); test-retest, or temporal, reliability (how consistent are the results over time?); and inter-observer reliability (how well do different judges or observers agree on their observations and/or their conclusions?).

No matter how consistent a procedure may be, it is of little or no value for decision-making unless it assesses what it purports to assess. This quality is referred to as validity and, like reliability, it has several dimensions. A good procedure has content validity, meaning that it provides a reasonable sampling of the entire universe of relevant behaviors. It has construct validity, meaning that it discriminates only on the basis of the particular construct or concept that it is designed to identify. It has one or more aspects of criterion validity, meaning that the results are consistent with external data.

Validation of a procedure is based on opinion or on comparison with something else or with a combination of the two. Any clinician who considers using a test or assessment procedure should research the validity and reliability data reported by the authors or developers of the procedure and should conduct his or her own research to be relatively sure that the procedure is suitable for the patients to be assessed.

In addition, the therapist should refer to a number of practical considerations in choosing an instrument or in planning an assessment procedure. Among these are utility (the degree to which the procedure will help in planning or conducting the therapy), directness (the degree to which the assessment results reflect the actual behavior or patterns of the client, and need no interpretation), and reactivity (the degree to which the instrument or procedure itself affects the result).

REFERENCES

Anastasi, A. (1961). *Psychological testing* (2nd ed.). New York: Macmillan.

Bixler, M. (1993, November 7). Matching roomies for harmony. *New York Times Education Life*, Section 4A, pp. 7–8.

Brigham, C. C. (1923). *A study of American intelligence.* Princeton, NJ: Princeton University Press.

Buros, O. K. (1970). *Personality tests and reviews, 1970.* Highland Park, NJ: Gryphon Press.

Buros, O. K. (1972). *Seventh mental measurements yearbook. Vol. I.* Highland Park, NJ: Gryphon Press.

Cohen, R. J., Swerdlick, M. E., & Smith, D. K. (1992). *Psychological testing and assessment.* Mountain View, CA: Mayfield.

Cronbach, L. J. (1970). *Essentials of psychological testing* (3rd ed.). New York: Harper and Row.

DeParle, J. (1994, October 9). Daring research or 'social science pornography'?: Charles Murray, *New York Times.*

Dyer, H. S. (1965). Educational measurement – its nature and its promise. In H. D. Berg (Ed.), *Evaluation in social studies.* The 35th Yearbook of the National Council for the Social Studies. Washington, DC: NCSS.

Ebel, R. L. (1975, October). Educational tests: Valid? biased? useful? *Phi Delta Kappan,* 83–89.

Fischer, J., & Corcoran, K. (1994). *Measures for clinical practice* (2nd ed.). Vol. 1. New York: Free Press.

Garcia, J. (1972). IQ: The conspiracy. *Psychology Today, 64,* 232–236.

Goddard, H. H. (1913). The Binet tests in relation to immigration. *Journal of Psycho Asthenics, 18,* 105–107.

Goddard, H. H. (1917). Mental tests on the immigrant. *Journal of Delinquency, 2,* 243–277.

Groth-Marnat, F. (2009). *Handbook of psychological assessment* (5th ed.). Hoboken, NJ: Wiley & Sons.

Hambeton, R. K., & Jourgensen, C. (1990). Criterion-referenced assessment of school achievement. In C. R. Reynolds & R. W. Kamphaus (Eds.), *Handbook of psychological and educational assessment of children: Intelligence and achievement* (pp. 456–476). New York: Guilford Press.

Hernstein, R. J., & Murray, C. (1994). *The bell curve.* New York: Free Press.

Itzkoff, S. W. (1994). *The decline of intelligence in America.* Westport, CT: Greenwood.

Pomeroy, W. B. (1982). *Dr. Kinsey and the institute for sex research.* New Haven, CT: Yale University Press.

Richards, J. M. (1972). Review of the medical college admissions test. In O. K. Buros (Ed.), *Seventh mental measurements yearbook.* Highland Park, NJ: Gryphon Press.

Rush, A. J., First, M. B., & Blacker, D. (2007). *Handbook of psychiatric measures.* Washington, DC: American Psychiatric Association.

Rushton, J. P. (1995). *Race, evolution, and behavior: A life history perspective.* New Brunswick, NJ: Transaction.

Sechrest, L. (1963). Incremental validity: A recommendation. *Educational and Psychological Measurement, 23,* 153–158.

Shelley, D., & Cohen, D. (1986). *Testing psychological tests.* New York: St. Martins Press.

Stampp, K. M. (1965). *The era of reconstruction.* New York: Knopf.

Starch, D., & Elliot, E. C. (1912). Reliability of grading of high school work in English. *School Review, 20,* 442–457.

Todd, A. L., & Gynther, M. D. (1988). Have MMPI Mf scale correlates changed in the past 30 years? *Journal of Clinical Psychology, 44,* 505–510.

Tyler, L. E. (1963). *Tests and measurements.* Englewood Cliffs, NJ: Prentice-Hall.

Yerkes, R. M. (1921). Psychological examining in the United States Army. Washington, DC: Memoirs of the National Academy of Sciences, Vol. 15.

Zoelner, R. (1976, September 27). Review of reverence for numbers. *The Chronicle of Higher Education.*

Chapter 4

TRAPS, QUIRKS, AND FALLACIES IN EVALUATION

In his later years, after observing his system of psychoanalysis in operation for several decades, Freud commented, in his essay, *Analysis, Terminable and Interminable* (1937), on the propensity of many psychoanalysts to use defense mechanisms and to project onto their patients their own emotional problems.

Therapists are generally aware, at least in the abstract, that their own emotional problems may distort the decision-making process. They tend to be less aware of the peculiar quirks that lead fallible humans, including therapists, into distorted perceptions, irrational decisions, and damaging behaviors.

There are two major sources for irrational or mistaken decisions. The first has to do with heuristics, the ways we gather and organize our information. The second, less obvious and therefore more serious, has to do with the ways we perceive the information. We often have enough data on which to base a judgment or decision, but we misinterpret or distort them through errors in our thought processes.

In their landmark book, *Judgment Under Uncertainty: Heuristics and Biases* (1982), Daniel Kahneman, Paul Slovic, and Amos Tversky presented the work of researchers who had investigated decision-making patterns of people in a number of diverse fields, including medicine and psychotherapy. Their work made it clear that when people must make decisions, their perceptions and judgments are flawed by some predictable traps, fallacies, and peculiarities in the ways they gather and process information. Because they are predictable, we can guard against them.

PROBLEMS OF INSUFFICIENT OR BIASED DATA

Therapists tend to overestimate the accuracy of the assessment procedures on which they rely. Many clinicians tend to be impressed, and often overwhelmed, by numbers and complicated formulations that produce the illusion of precision. This is perhaps the major reason why so many therapists accept test results so uncritically. And those who rely on clinical judgment often have a confidence in their judgments that is not always warranted. Moreover, there appears to be no relationship between a therapist's confidence and his or her accuracy, and this information is not new (Kelly & Fiske, 1951; Oskamp, 1965). If therapists approached all assessment procedures and instruments with a clearer understanding of how the rules of probability work and how our thought processes sometimes operate to fool us, they might use both tests and clinical assessment procedures more realistically.

Accuracy Is Affected by the Base Rate

Let's start with a problem based on one presented many years ago to a group of physicians by Dr. David Eddy (1982, pp. 252–254). Susan, a young woman in her early thirties, came to her doctor with a complaint about a lump she had just found in her breast. The physician, after a physical examination, after checking her personal and family medical history, and after reviewing the literature on the prevalence of breast cancer, estimated that her chances of having the disease were less than 1 percent. However, he ordered a mammogram as a precaution, assuring Susan that the test had an 80 to 90 percent accuracy (sensitivity) rate in detecting cancer. On her return visit, the physician somberly informed Susan that the radiologist's report had come back positive, and that he would have to remove the suspected tissue surgically for an examination by the pathologist. What are the odds that the patient has cancer?

(a) 1 percent
(b) 80 to 90 percent
(c) between 1 and 90 percent, but closer to 1 percent
(d) between 1 and 90 percent, but closer to 90 percent

If you chose (d), you agreed with most of the physicians to whom Eddy presented the problem; the overwhelming majority of them estimated the odds that the patient had cancer at about 75 percent, an overestimate by about tenfold. Just as an underestimate could lead to a neglect of the disease, an overestimate might result in unnecessary procedures, each of which carries some risk.

The mistake that the physicians made is a common one. They neglected to consider the impact of the base rate, or the prevalence of the disease in the population under discussion.

To obtain the statistical likelihood that Susan has cancer, a formula known as Bayes' Theorem is used. Using this formula, it can be estimated that with an overall test accuracy rate of 80 to 90 percent, the odds that Susan actually has cancer would be between 6 and 10 percent.

Let's illustrate the paradox by simplifying the calculation. If the test has an 85 percent accuracy rate in terms of sensitivity (the ability to detect a true positive), the odds that the results were wrong would be 15 percent. But the probability that Susan, given her age, physical condition and family medical history, has breast cancer is only about 1 percent. Let's assume that 100 women in Susan's risk category were tested. Given the reported accuracy rate of the test (85%), 16 reports would come back positive. Of these 16, 15 would be false positives, and only one would be a true positive. In essence, it is 15 times more likely that the test result is wrong than that the patient has cancer. In any given population in which the base rate or odds that the subject has a disease is less than the rate of error in the test, a positive test result is likely to be in error.

If the figures are so far off, where did that impressive 80-90 percent true positive rate come from? It was calculated on a population of all women for whom the test had been used in differential diagnosis, regardless of their age or backgrounds. If it had been calculated only for women in Susan's risk category, this stratified base rate would produce an accuracy rate that was far lower.

Conditional Probability

If you chose a man's name at random from a telephone directory, the odds that he weighs 250 pounds are fairly remote. On the other hand, if you picked his name at random from a list of men who were all 6½ feet tall, the odds would be better. The principle of conditional probability refers to the likelihood that the base rate is affected when certain conditions are present. This principle masks the general unreliability of diagnosis in psychiatric hospitals and clinics.

The principle of conditional probability means that each additional symptom that is noted or reported improves the odds and increases the accuracy of a diagnosis. Moreover, the principle of base rate means that a clinician in the intake section of a psychiatric hospital in which half the admissions are people with schizophrenia could haphazardly diagnose patients as having or not having schizophrenia, or could even diagnose every patient as having schizophrenia and still be right 50 percent of the time. That conditional probability means that the admitting psychiatrist who relies on even one or two symptoms is likely to be right more than half the time. The accuracy of diagnosis often depends more on the base rate than on the diagnostic skill of the clinician.

Prediction Versus Hindsight

In Eddy's (1982) example, when Susan's doctor told her of the test's 80 to 90 percent accuracy rate, he was talking about retrospective accuracy, not predictive accuracy. For women whose biopsies later confirmed the presence of cancer, the test procedure had been accurate in identifying the cancer about 85 percent of the time. However, that retrospective figure does not take into account those women whose test results were positive, but who turned out not to have cancer, the cases of false-positive findings. Retrospective accuracy is always much higher than is predictive accuracy, so a test like a mammogram used for screening on a general population is not likely to show the same kind of accuracy as in the case of women who have been found to have cancer.

This confusion of retrospective accuracy and predictive accuracy appears frequently in medical literature; Eddy (1982) cited examples from major medical publications in which research studies confused the two (pp. 254–255) and presented very misleading statistics. It appears even more frequently in the reports of validation and reliability studies by designers of new tests that are used in psychotherapy. Some assessment instruments are "validated" by citing correlations with earlier psychiatric diagnoses. While this is an acceptable procedure in developing an assessment, it is misleading when it is used to diagnose individual patients. Because errors in test accuracy in the psychotherapies are not as easy to identify as in medicine, the issue is often unrecognized or simply ignored.

Base Rate and Psychodiagnosis

Medical diagnoses can be confirmed much more easily than can psychiatric diagnoses, so base rates for medical problems can be established far more readily. Base rates for various disorders or problems have been estimated by numbers of practitioners, groups, and commissions, often with divergent figures.

The importance of including, where possible, ranges of figures for various disorders based on available data were recognized in the *DSM-III-R* (1987). These figures appeared under the heading of "prevalence," which *DSM-III-R* defined as:

> . . . the proportion of adults who at some time in their lives will have a disturbance that meets the criteria for the disorder. This method of presentation has the advantage of being readily understandable, but it is highly dependent on the age at onset and the relative proportion of people in the population who have reached that age. The data are often presented as a range, based on more than a single study. (p. 22)

When data from epidemiologic studies are not available, the prevalence is stated in general terms preceded by "apparently" to indicate that the judgment is based on clinical experience (p. 22).

The 1994 revision of the *DSM* included differential rates for different settings, such as community, primary care, outpatient mental health clinics, and inpatient psychiatric settings "when this information is known" (*DSM-IV,* 1994, p. 9).

DSM-5 will continue to include estimates, and some research on changes in *DSM-5* criteria for diagnoses. such as posttraumatic stress disorder predicts increases in prevalence estimates (see for example, Elhai et al., 2012). Increases or decreases in prevalence estimates should affect all diagnoses where changes in criteria are planned.

However, even when figures are imprecise, they provide some guidance to therapists in determining how much confidence can be placed in a particular test or procedure. In light of the uncertain validity and reliability of many assessment procedures in the psychotherapies, a good deal of caution is urged in using tests or other procedures to assess a condition whose prevalence in a population is likely to be smaller than the possible error in the test.

The Unreliability of Small Samples

The issue of sample size is a major consideration both in research and in the standardization of tests. Most of us "know" the basic rules of probability as they relate to sample size. Yet, it appears that most of us ignore them in practical applications. If you are challenged to a game of table tennis by a better player, your chances of winning are far greater in a 15-point game, in which a few lucky fluke shots may help you win, than in a 21-point game in which the laws of probability will favor your opponent. Your opponent's skill is likely to be relatively stable, whereas any lucky shots you may have (or mistakes that your opponent makes) will soon be overwhelmed by your inferior performance. Yet, while most people recognize the principle that small samples are not really representative, they apparently do not infer from experience the relationship between sample size and sampling variability. "This fundamental notion of statistics is evidently not part of people's repertoire of intuitions" (Tversky & Kahnemann, 1982, p. 6).

The Gambler's Fallacy

In tossing a coin, we all know that the number of heads and the number of tails will be the same over a large number of tosses. Will you get the same odds in 100 tosses as in 1000? What about four tosses?

Most of us know that you'll approach the theoretical 50-50 split more closely in 1000 tosses than in four. But many think that you'll get the same odds in 100 tosses or in 50, because they fall victim to the so-called gambler's fallacy. Let's illustrate this trap with another problem. If the first four tosses have come up heads, what are the odds that the next one will be tails: one-to-one? two-to-one? four-to-one? sixteen-to-one?

The principle is that the odds will still be one-to-one, or 50-50. Coins have no memory. The gambler's fallacy is the assumption that the odds are self-correcting and self-adjusting, that a run of heads will be "corrected" by a tail. Another illustration of this misconception is the popular belief that "lightning doesn't strike twice in the same place."

The gambler's fallacy is based on a misinterpretation of the principles of probability. Large sample estimates are more reliable than small sample estimates, not because the odds are self-correcting, but because aberrations, which are likely to occur in both directions, are diluted in the sheer mass of the data and are less likely to distort the working out of the laws of probability.

Classroom teachers often give short quizzes on the assumption that students' scores are as representative of their achievement as are those of longer tests. But consider how dramatically the odds change with each change in the sample size in a true-false test.

Number of True-False Items	Chances of Attaining 70 percent *by Guess Alone*
10	1 out of 6
25	1 out of 50
50	1 out of 350
100	1 out of 10,000

Remember the point made in Chapter 3 that increasing the number of items on a test increases its reliability. Short quizzes will actually be more valid indicators than long tests, such as midterms or finals, if the quizzes are given frequently. In such a case, both the number of test items and the number of test situations are increased. It is noteworthy that misconceptions of the rules of probability are not limited to unsophisticated subjects. Indeed, a study of the statistical intuitions of experienced psychologists (Tversky & Kahneman, 1982) revealed that, while they acknowledged the basic principle that small samples are biased, their behavior betrayed a belief that their limited personal experiences are as representative as data drawn from studies of large samples.

The implications for standardized tests are clear. The therapist who intends to use a test should consider not only the composition of the standardization sample but the numbers of subjects involved in the process of standardization. Norms built on too small a sample may not be truly representative of the population the sample purports to represent or of the population on whom it is to be used.

Anecdotal Evidence

Back in January, 1993, *The New York Times* Book Review published an essay by Carol Tavris, entitled "Beware the Incest-Survivor Machine," suggesting that many of the stories of repressed memories of childhood incest might be the result of suggestion by the therapist rather than of authentic recovered memory. The article touched off a wave of letters to the editor, and researchers soon took to this issue questioning the "recovered memory" phenomenon. This research continues to be controversial (Mendez & Fras, 2010).

Individually reported experiences certainly grab our attention and remain in our memories. However, anecdotal evidence based on isolated data or a small number of cases is the best known example of small sample error. Anecdotal "proof" of the efficacy of a particular psychotherapeutic treatment is common.

Again, as an abstraction, most of us recognize the problems involved: unsupported testimonials, whether by patients or therapists, tell us nothing about how these patients would have fared without therapy or how those who did not offer testimonials managed. Unfortunately, the "evidence" may contradict the statistical odds; the anecdote bypasses the scientific safeguards of repeated and balanced clinical observation or of experimental method involving control groups. While it may be an oversimplification to suggest that the fundamental difference on which the validity of anecdotal evidence and that of meaningful statistical information rest is numbers, there is a kernel of truth in the aphorism attributed to political analyst Ben Wattenberg: "The plural of anecdote is data" (Leo, 1996, p. 34). Statistical data are accumulated "specific human experiences." Yet, despite the fact that most of us are aware of the limitations of anecdotal data, many therapists themselves often demonstrate an unfounded faith in the evidence of small numbers.

The Two Faces of Accuracy: Sensitivity and Specificity

Despite reports that a test is "90 percent accurate," the "accuracy" of any particular test cannot be expressed as a single number. There are two reasons for this. As with validity, the accuracy of a test varies with the population and with the purpose for which it is given. Thus validity is for a specific use of a test. In addition, for any test or procedure, there are two types of accuracy. Sensitivity refers to the test's accuracy in identifying true positives; it may identify every person who has a specific disorder; unfortunately, it may also include a large number of false positives. Specificity refers to the test's ability to distinguish or to identify true negatives.

PROBLEMS IN INTERPRETING DATA

Therapists are more likely to make errors based on bias, misconception and errors in thinking than on insufficient data. In fact, there is a rapidly diminishing level of accuracy when too much data are presented; it seems that when the data base is too broad, we have trouble distinguishing relevant from irrelevant information, and some peculiar errors in thinking seem to distort our judgments. In addition, we are often misled by our expectations.

Information Overload

There seems to be a common tendency among practitioners in various disciplines to assume that the more tests or procedures one uses, the more accurate and precise will be the resulting description or prediction. The problem is that people tend to make decisions based on a process researchers sometimes call "satisficing." What this means is that, when faced with too much information, they tend to jump to conclusions based on minimal initial data and stop considering additional evidence. Some experts who have examined the phenomenon among jurors report that the kind of thinking that leads to premature conclusions frequently goes along with unwarranted certainty (Goleman, 1994, p. 88).

Over the years, cognitive psychologists researching decision making have described some interesting findings. For example, the fact that the decision-making process itself changes when people are faced with too much data to handle comfortably. Tversky and Kahneman (1982) found that people respond very differently when they are given no evidence or scanty evidence and when they are given worthless evidence. When they are overloaded with information or given irrelevant information, they tend to abandon the complex task of assessing probabilities and to predict on the basis of "a limited number of heuristic principles" (p. 3), such as remembering situations that seem similar. In general, these common sense strategies may be quite useful, but sometimes "they lead to severe and systematic errors" (p. 3).

In addition, as the sheer volume of information increases, there is an apparent increase in the phenomenon of "illusory correlation," or the tendency for therapists to see in the material confirmations of stereotypes and common sense expectations, rather than the actual data

(Lueger & Petzel, 1979).

Over the years, observers have noted the tendency of physicians to order more tests than they need or use (Stutz & Feder, 1990, pp. 134–136). An editorial in the *Journal of the American Medical Association* (Reynolds et al., 1987) pointed out that failure to diagnose was a classic basis for negligence suits against physicians, and that the result was the defensive use of additional tests. However, reviews of closed malpractice suits showed that the original problem wasn't based on an insufficiency of tests; it was a failure to refer to or follow up test results that were already available. From this perspective, increasing the number of tests is more likely to exacerbate the problem than to relieve it (Stutz & Feder, 1990, pp. 135–136). Interestingly, since insurance companies began increasingly inserting themselves into the U.S. healthcare system via requiring preauthorization for most nonroutine and even routine medical tests information overload from medical tests, has transformed into an issue of sufficiency according to the American Medical Association (http://www.ama-assn.org/amednews/2010/04/12/bise0415. htm).

The issue of incremental validity is of particular relevance in light of the replacement in mental health of long-term treatment with short-term programs that took place during the 1980s and 1990s in the U.S. In short-term treatment, the results of a lengthy and cumbersome assessment procedure might not even be available until after the patient has been discharged. Thus, brief screening tools have developed to assist in assessing mental health issues, for example mood disorders (Meyer et al., 2011), but have been slow to enter many practice settings.

Before any clinician considers adding additional tests or assessment procedures, it might be appropriate to ask three questions:

1. Will the additional procedure or refinement add to the relevant information about the patient or client?
2. Are the additional data likely to change or influence the treatment decision?
3. If the additional procedure is particularly useful, should it be used to replace, rather than augment, existing procedures?

The Bias Toward Overinterpretation

Errors in human judgment, called type I and type II errors, may occur in either quantitative or qualitative evaluation. Type I error occurs when we accept a false hypothesis, and a type II error occurs when we reject a true hypothesis. Another way of putting this is that we commit a type I error when we accept a false negative (calling a sick person healthy), and a type II error when we accept a false positive (calling a healthy person sick).

To a large degree, such errors result clinically more from an attempt to resolve a value conflict than to apply scientific principles. They often reflect bias in value judgments. Is it more important for the Food and Drug Administration to approve a drug that is still in the experimental stage and that has not been adequately tested, although some patients may benefit from its use (a type II error), or to hold it back from the market until side effects have been determined even though some patients may suffer because it is not available (a type I error)?

Virtually every decision made in a climate of uncertainty involves the likelihood of one of these errors. Should you drop money in a panhandler's box and risk having it spent on drugs, or should you walk by and risk the possibility that you denied help to a desperately hungry human being? Should you sell a rising stock and risk losing out if it should continue to rise, or keep it and risk its possible decline?

Reasons for the prevalence of type II errors may be the result of a systematic occupational bias. Mental health practitioners are trained to find pathology. And where they look, they are likely to find what they are looking for. As one aphorism puts it, you don't ask a barber if you need a haircut.

Screening Versus Differential Diagnosis

This tendency towards bias can mislead us badly when a test that may be useful in differential diagnosis is used to screen a general population, like school children or the public at large.

A wonderful illustration of this problem that many may have forgotten today was the massive Midtown Manhattan Project, conducted in the 1950s by an interdisciplinary team of psychiatrists, psychiatric social workers, clinical psychologists, and social case workers, to learn how many people were suffering from psychiatric disorders. After having interviewed 1,600 New Yorkers, the group released its figures, which made headlines and confirmed the general impression in the rest of the country that New Yorkers were all nuts. Only 18 percent of those examined were considered "well," or free of psychiatric symptoms. The report's authors estimated "with 95 percent confidence" that between 21.9 and 25.9 percent of those they had interviewed could be considered "impaired," meaning that they were hampered by their symptoms. Moreover, the study concluded, "it seems likely that the true rate stands closer to the high point in this range" (Srolo et al., 1962, p. 138).

Are we to conclude, with the authors, that only 18.5 percent of the New Yorkers surveyed could be considered "well?" Or is it more reasonable to believe that mental health professionals, predisposed to finding symptoms, were likely to interpret as "symptoms" behavior that most of us would consider "normal?"

We must keep in mind that there are many more tests to find negative personality traits, like anxiety and paranoid thinking, than positive ones like loyalty or dependability or honesty.

The tendency of clinicians to look for and find evidence of disturbance has long been noted. For example, McMahon (1967) found that Ph.D. clinical psychologists within a semester of graduating tended to interpret the Rorschach responses of more intelligent test-takers as being disturbed, by overinterpreting the symbolic content given by the brighter persons (pp. 56–57). The prevailing attitude, apparently, was that different equaled disturbed.

Believing Is Seeing

There are two major ways in which our expectations distort our perceptions.

Autistic Reconstruction

The story is told of a man who thought he was dead. He lay in a luxurious silk-lined oak coffin in his living room, and turned away visitors with the words, "Let me rest in peace." His distraught friends brought a psychotherapist, who asked him if dead men bleed. "Of course not," snapped the dead man. At this point, the therapist drew a pin from his lapel and stabbed the man's thumb. When a drop of blood swelled, the man stared in surprise. "What do you know," he exclaimed. "Dead men do bleed!"

Faced with a conflict between what we believe and the evidence, there is a tendency for us to reconstruct reality to conform to our existing mental models or our beliefs than to modify our belief systems. This is a danger that is inherent in an uncritical allegiance to any theory of personality. It has been remarked that in human affairs, theory is the mother of certainty.

The best defense against this error is recognition of the fallibility of our perceptions and the tentative nature of the theories to which we owe allegiance.

Illusory Correlation

Back in 1967, Chapman and Chapman conducted a study (1967, 1971) of the way professionals interpreted two widely used psychological tests, the Rorschach Inkblot and the Draw-A-Person (DAP) Test. The Chapmans' research verified a long-held suspicion about these tests. "In interpreting the results of these tests," they wrote, "the average clinician may project his own preconceptions and assumptions into his description of the patient" (1971, p. 18).

The original Draw-A-Person Test, developed in 1949 by Karen Machover, was accompanied by a test manual that provided general correlations between an individual's personality and the way he or she drew a person. Suspicious or paranoid individuals, for example, drew large, elaborate or piercing eyes. Small heads indicated feelings of intellectual inadequacy. Such correlations were confirmed clinically by practitioners and carried into other tests, such as the Human Figure Drawing Test (HFDT), designed by Elizabeth M. Koppitz.

The trouble is that despite enthusiastic testimonials by practitioners, these correlations were not successfully validated by experimental researchers. Most clinicians are aware of the research, but some continue to use the tests and apply the associations, because they claim these associations stand up in their own clinical practice. The Chapmans quoted one psychologist who said, "I'll trust my own senses before I trust some journal article," and another who insisted, "I know that paranoids [sic] don't seem to draw big eyes in the research labs, but they sure do in my office" (1971, p. 20).

The Chapmans tested an alternate explanation: that the clinicians may have been victims of what they labeled an "illusory correlation." People have a predisposition to see what they expect to see. The Chapmans tested this hypothesis by using as subjects both clinicians who were familiar with the tests and "naive" subjects – college students who had never heard of the DAP test. They carefully screened a series of drawings and deliberately created sets of drawings and personality descriptions that contradicted the traditional correlations. Nevertheless, both the clinical psychologists and the college students reported that the drawings by those who had been described as "suspicious" had large eyes. "We know the signs were illusions," said the Chapmans, "because they were not in the data" (p. 106).

Interpretations of the Rorschach, they found, were similarly biased by what the interpreters expected to find. Again they tested both experienced psychologists and students who systematically paired inkblots and descriptions. Again, both groups reported seeing associations that had been carefully screened out. Why did the "naive" students, who had not known what the literature said, report that they, too, had seen the associations? The professional interpretations, apparently, were little more than expectations based on stereotypes.

The Chapmans wrote: "Clinicians must be made aware of illusory associations if they are to compensate for them" (p. 107). Retraining and compensation may not be easy: the trap of illusory correlation was found to persist even when subjects were cautioned to guard against it (Waller & Keeley, 1978).

Causes and Effects

A major difference between assessment and research is that the two involve very different kinds of logic. Inductive cause-effect logic lies at the heart of experimental research. Researchers manipulate or isolate possible factors to ascertain whether one or more may cause specific results; their working hypotheses are predictions about the outcomes of their manipulations.

Assessment, on the other hand, involves effect-to-cause logic. We must hypothesize about possible causes in situations in which we cannot usually experiment. The danger in effect-to-cause logic is that it invites conclusions that are based on assumptions rather than evidence or probabilities, and that are usually not possible to nullify.

Postfactum Explanations

There are several types of what logicians call postfactum explanations. One is called, in formal logic, post hoc, ergo propter hoc (Latin for "after this, therefore because of this") or, sometimes, the postmortem fallacy. People can always find reasons in their conduct to explain all the things that happen to them, good or bad. More common in psychiatric and psychotherapeutic assessments is the assignment of cause on the basis of theoretical principles.

Self-Limiting Symptoms

Postfactum explanations are often offered as evidence of the effectiveness of treatment. Unfortunately, all forms of therapy are fertile fields for exaggerated claims, for one major reason: most symptoms are self-limiting. The disease or disorder that produced the symptoms may simply go away, like a simple cold, or depression when a love affair or a friendship is shattered. Even the symptoms of a major disorder are likely to abate; few disorders, even if they are incurable, follow a straight-downward pattern. Many mental disorders show themselves in a clearly cyclical pattern; virtually all exhibit periods of remission.

Nevertheless, it is not uncommon for individual therapists to view any patient improvement as a tribute to the efficacy of therapy, and any failure as the result of outside influences or as evidence, in medical cop-out parlance, that the patient is "unresponsive." To "enthusiastic clinicians," it is self-evident that any improvement was the result of their efforts; to "the skeptical researcher," it is equally evident that therapists often take credit for changes that would have occurred anyway.

However, the rate of symptom remission seems to vary across types of disorders; we can't escape the pervasive influence of the base rate in making judgments. Symptom remission is thought to be less common for schizophrenia than depression. But some depressed individuals have only one or two bouts of clinical depression in their lives. Others have recurring episodes, sometimes on a periodic basis, and some researchers point to the fact that depression remission is multidimensional and requires assessment of additional information to be more specific (Nease, Aikens, Kinkman, Kroenke, & Sen, 2011).

Until we have a baseline to ascertain the odds of symptom remission in specific disorders, we can never be sure of the likelihood that a patient's recovery or remission is attributable to the intervention. To date, this is an open question. We must wait for more complete research findings on base rates.

The distortions in evaluation that result from symptom remission are the result mainly of one factor. Because most patients or clients seek help only after they have been suffering for a time, it is natural for the patient to show an upturn during treatment. It is equally natural for both therapist and patient to attribute the improvement to the treatment or the competence of the therapist.

That therapists themselves fall victim to the postmortem fallacy is evidenced by the anecdotal data that often fill the pages of professional journals and books. Case histories are a legitimate way of illustrating the application of a principle, or of offering a hypothesis to be tested. All too often, however, the case histories that appear in the pages of the journals are little more than testimonials by therapists who attribute improvement to their treatment.

Regression to the Mean

Changes in patients frequently are the result of the operation of a statistical principle known as regression to the mean. Unfortunately, the operation of this principle often goes unrecognized and is frequently misinterpreted, leading to the likelihood of errors in assessment and evaluation.

In the mid-1960s, Kahneman, then a junior professor at Hebrew University, was teaching a course in the psychology of training to a group of air force flight instructors. He cited some studies to make the point that reward was a more effective teaching tool than punishment. One of the flight instructors impatiently disagreed: "I've praised people warmly for beautifully executed maneuvers, and the next time they almost always do worse. And I've screamed at people for badly executed maneuvers, and by and large the next time they improve. Don't tell me that reward works and punishment doesn't. My experience contradicts it," (McKean, 1985, p. 24). The other flight instructors agreed.

Kahneman suddenly realized that this was an example of regression to the mean and that "nobody else had . . . seen this before. I think that this was one of the most exciting moments of my career" (McKean, 1985, p. 24). Regression to the mean is the principle first enunciated by Sir Francis Galton: in any series of random events clustered around a mean, any extraordinary or unusual event is likely to be followed, in the working out of the law of probabilities, by a more ordinary event – one that is closer to the mean. In fact, the study of the principle of regression (then called "reversion") led Galton to develop formulas for calculating correlation coefficients between different variables. He called this "coefficient of regression" *r*. (The formula that is now commonly used to calculate correlation was developed by Galton's contemporary, Karl Pearson; correlation is still symbolized by Galton's *r*.)

While regression to the mean is usually expressed as a theoretical statistical principle, it affects every series of events that is random to some degree. Since virtually every activity in our lives is governed, at least in part, by chance, regression will affect the outcome in some of the situations in which we would not look for causes that are unrelated to our purposeful behavior; consequently, it is often explained as the result of other factors.

Regression to the mean is why very tall parents tend to have children who are not quite as tall, and very short parents usually have children who are taller than they. It's why athletes rarely repeat particularly spectacular performances, and improve after particularly poor showings. It's a major reason for "the sophomore slump," the tendency of outstanding rookie college athletes to turn in disappointing performances the second year, and it's why schoolchildren seldom repeat exceptionally good or exceptionally bad schoolwork, and why patients who show marked improvement one day are often likely to show deterioration the next.

Because the principle of regression seems to be counterintuitive, the results of regression are generally attributed to other – and usually extraneous – causes. Since teachers tend to criticize or punish students for unusually poor work or behavior, they tend to explain the predictable improvement by their criticism. And therapists often assume that short-term patient change is the result of their intervention. Significant changes in learning or behavior are usually so slow that short-term changes are more likely to be a matter of chance – actually of regression to the mean – than of the results of therapy. This is why monitoring of patient change on a day-to-day basis is likely to be misleading.

Questions About Questions

When Werner Heisenberg formulated his now-famous uncertainty principle that the act of observing something changes what you're observing, he was talking about the behavior of subatomic particles and the emission of energy. But it is remarkable how frequently the principle applies to virtually any observation or measurement.

The Influence of the Instrument

A simple illustration of the way the measuring instrument itself can influence the result is the effect of the thermometer with which you measure the temperature of a glass of water. Unless the thermometer is exactly the temperature of the water before the measurement (a very unlikely possibility), its immersion is likely either to raise or to lower the temperature slightly. Virtually every instrument used to measure or to assess personality, ability, thought processes, or feelings is likely to change the response of the subject.

The Influence of the Situation

The primary way verbal psychotherapists elicit information from a client or patient is to ask questions (either in a test or an interview) or to ask the client to perform some task. In most assessments, the question or task is imposed by the therapist, who usually assumes that the client will respond to it as he or she would respond in a normal interaction with the environment.

The problem is that therapist's questions or imposed tasks are not normal in the patient's usual environment. Interrogative conversation is not a simulation of everyday conversation. Certainly creative arts therapists also understand that most adults do not draw pictures or dance, or make music as part of their day-to-day interaction with others.

When the examiner interprets the subject's responses, the usual assumption is that they represent the typical behavior of the patient, and that the question or task included the necessary requirements to elicit what the examiner wants to know. But any imposed question or task alters the context of the patient's behavior.

From the client's point of view, the situation is fraught with hazards and thicketed with concerns: Is there a response that the examiner expects? Are there clues in the question or task demands? Is every part of the task relevant? Is the question or task rigged to get me to reveal what I don't want to reveal?

The Bias of Presentation

As an illustration of the power of presentation to influence behavior, consider the decision a number of years ago by some stores to charge customers extra for using credit cards. The credit card industry bowed to the pressure, but insisted that the price difference be labeled a discount for cash rather than a surcharge for credit. People find it easier to give up a discount than to pay extra for a service; as Tversky and Kahneman pointed out, losses loom larger than gains (McKean, 1985, p. 30). Most readers should be able to think of many recent examples of this principle that has become part and parcel of modern advertising.

To avoid slanting or biasing the presentation, evaluators strive to be as objective as possible. However, investigators of decision making have been frustrated by the difficulty of screening bias out of the presentation, or "framing" of information. What makes the process even more aggravating is that much of the bias is so subtle that it is difficult to recognize. This difficulty poses an ethical dilemma for therapists once they become aware of the role of framing.

Tversky and McNeil (McKean, 1985) were interested in finding out whether the way a physician presents a problem might inadvertently influence a patient's choice of treatment. They posed a problem to doctors, chronic disease patients, and graduate students. Compare your response with theirs.

Imagine you have operable lung cancer and must choose between two treatments – surgery and radiation therapy. Of 100 people having surgery, 10 die during the operation, 32 (including the original 10) are dead after one year, and 66 after five years. Of 100 people having radiation therapy, none die during treatment, 23 are dead after one year and 78 after five years (McKean, p. 30). Which treatment would you prefer?

They found that when the question was presented in this form, more than 40 percent of their subjects chose radiation. But when the same information was presented in terms of the odds of survival, the number choosing radiation was cut in half.

Anchoring: Beginnings and Ends

Apparently, where people begin when they consider a question or a problem influences where they'll end up. Here is a problem that Tversky and Kahneman presented to two groups of undergraduates (1982, pp. 14–15). The students were asked to estimate, within five seconds, the answer to a multiplication problem. One group estimated the product of:

1 x 2 x 3 x 4 x 5 x 6 x 7 x 8

The other group estimated the product of:

8 x 7 x 6 x 5 x 4 x 3 x 2 x 1

To arrive at an estimate rapidly, people will usually perform a few steps of computation and estimate the product by extrapolation or adjustment. Tversky and Kahneman (1982) found that most adjustments were typically insufficient, and they predicted that both groups would underestimate the answer. Moreover, because each group started from a different "anchor" or starting point, the first few steps of computation would lead the first group to underestimate far more than the second group. Both predictions were confirmed. The median estimate for the group that started with one was 512, and the median estimate for the group that started with eight was 2,250. The correct answer: 40,320.

Tversky and Kahneman (1982) found that the anchor often predetermines the final judgment. In other words, people get stuck in their original positions or in the information given them, and typically make insufficient adjustments as later information unfolds. The principles that Tversky and Kahneman called "anchoring" and "adjustment" (and that psychologists now refer to as the "primacy" effect) apply in decisions about assessment and treatment in therapy in a number of ways.

First, questions that are asked in assessment often include a built-in anchor that skews the question. Such anchors may appear both in tests and in clinical interview procedures. Anchors tend to operate as subtle suggestions.

Even a change of a single word in a question can change the response dramatically. Two researchers, Loftus and Palmer, found that eyewitnesses give a higher estimate of a car's speed when they were asked, "How fast was the car going when it smashed the other car?" than when the question was, "How fast was the car going when it hit the other car?" (cited in Kahneman & Tversky, 1982, p. 502).

Second, anchors in the information that is conveyed to therapists will bias decisions about treatment. Especially in the nonverbal aspects of the arts therapies, it is often difficult for therapists to translate from one expressive language, like movement, to another, like words. Since diagnostic labels are always verbal, the arts therapist in a hospital or a clinic tends to rely on the diagnostic label that may already have been assigned by the admitting staff. Gestalt therapist Walter Kempler contended that labels can "astigmatize the vision of the next therapist who sees the chart before he sees the patient" (Kempler, 1973, p. 275).

Particularly in a hospital, clinic, or other group setting, a therapist who questions the accuracy of a psychiatric label may doubt his or her judgment in the face of a group consensus. And the psychiatric label likely influences the individual treatment program. This alteration of the normal environment for assessment purposes and the difficulty in screening the bias out of a presentation are major problems in evaluation.

Whose Reality Is More Real? The Fallacy of Reification

"Like the seven deadly sins," wrote Joyce Carol Oates, "despair is a mythical state. It has no quantifiable existence; it is merely part of an allegorical world view" (1993, p. 3). Scientists describe mythical states with the more prosaic term "hypothetical constructs." As long as we all accept the same myths and constructs, we can communicate intelligibly. But when we disagree on the nature of these myths and constructs and when we reify them, or treat them as though they were real things, we have problems in our perceptions and in our communication. Perhaps the best example of this problem is the field of mathematics. The distinguished mathematician Morris Kline described this view, "because mathematics and the happening of the physical world jibed so wonderfully, nobody had any doubts about the truth of it all. The truth about mathematics was affirmed as strongly and as unquestioningly as in the days of the ancient Greeks. Mathematics was the truth about nature" (1967, p. 7).

Into this neatly constructed mathematical reality came the jarring introduction of a variety of non-Euclidian geometries, each of which described the physical world as accurately as did Euclidean geometry. But, asked Kline (1967), if you have several geometries, each of which fits the real world, which one is the truth?

Of course, none of them is "true." Each is a structure that mathematicians have constructed to represent and describe the physical world and to make predictions about it. So Newton invented the laws of gravity and motion to describe phenomena he observed; the laws don't inhere in nature. It has been said that the Newtonian physicists proved that the world is an orderly place because they hypothesized orderly rules to describe and explain the things they observed.

In the same way, psychologists and psychiatrists have created structures and constructs to represent and describe the world of the psyche. These structures may hypothesize contradictory assumptions and perceptions as, for example, in the conflicting theories of personality and the etiology of disorders. Not only do many of these structures contradict each other, they may be specific to the disciplines or contexts in which they have been created. For example, revelations and hallucinations are both hypothetical constructs that may explain the identical experience.

Much of psychotherapy deals with abstractions and hypothetical constructs: anxiety, aggressiveness, self-esteem, fear, repression, anger, and love and, of course, disorder and disease. The fallacy of reification – treating these abstractions as though they were real things – leads us into a number of errors, not the least of which is the notion of treating a disease, rather than treating a person who has a problem that we have labeled a disease. Sometimes, we go even further, thinking of the patient as the disease: we may have had a session with a borderline this morning and have one later today with a depressive.

It is easy to lose sight of the fact that the words we frequently use in therapy – traits, symptoms, disorders, fixations, projections, sublimation, introjection – are abstractions that purport to describe reality, and that the meanings will vary from observer to observer, depending on their personal preferences, education, and theoretical orientations. The terms will also have different connotations at different periods of time.

Our belief systems are based on our assumptions about human nature, which derive from the "facts" that we have chosen to see as relevant, and we choose the ways we perceive and describe them. When we define, describe, analyze, and test, we do so in terms of mental and emotional constructs that we have invented, just as Newton invented the laws of motion to describe what he chose to perceive and study.

Just what impels us to accept the "facts" and the "reality" that are presented to us by theoreticians? Biologist Ruth Hubbard (1990) suggested that fact-making is a social enterprise undertaken by those with the proper credentials who have followed prescribed procedures. If they are reviewed and accepted by the appropriate community (scientific, therapeutic, medical, educational), they come to be

> accepted on faith by a great many people, who are in no position to say why what we put out are facts, not fictions. After all, a lot of scientific facts are counterintuitive [that is, they contradict our everyday

> expectations], such as that the earth moves around the sun or that if you drop a pound of feathers and a pound of rocks, they will fall at the same rate. (pp. 22–23)

The process of reification rests on intuition, but it often relies heavily on statistical evidence. Factor analysis, a useful method for establishing the construct validity of a procedure, is too often used to provide evidence for the reality of the construct. In a reversal of the idea that if something exists, it can be measured, some statisticians contend that if something can be measured, it must exist.

In *The Mismeasure of Man* (1981), Stephen Jay Gould wrote, "The history of factor analysis is strewn with the wreckage of misguided attempts at reification" (p. 268). Spearman himself, after a lifetime of attempting to prove the reality of a genetically transmitted "g" factor, recognized in his last work (Spearman & Jones, 1950, p. 25) that a mathematical abstraction does not necessarily reflect a physical reality. A reified construct in the therapies is far more elastic than it is in mathematics and far more difficult to refute. If geometry does not describe reality accurately, the geometry must be adjusted or modified, or abandoned. If a psychological theory does not describe reality, we can simply adjust reality.

How should we deal with psychological constructs? Perhaps the best approach is to accept that they are metaphors and similes that may be useful for describing and predicting reality – but that they are not themselves real.

SUMMARY

There are two major sources of error involved when we make decisions.

The first has to do with the ways we gather and organize the information on which the decision is based. Obviously, if the data are not complete and accurate, our conclusions must be suspect.

The second source of error, more serious than the first because it is less apparent, has to do with the ways we process information. Even when there may be enough data, we tend to commit errors in perception that distort the accuracy of our conclusions. Especially under conditions of uncertainty, people perceive odds and risks that are very different from those that can be calculated from statistical data. Major errors in perception arise from the following tendencies:

- Individuals tend to ignore base rates when confronted with too much information, erroneous information, or irrelevant information.
- Therapists tend to overestimate the accuracy of assessment procedures for a variety of reasons, including a faulty base rate and overconfidence in the accuracy of their own clinical judgments.
- When one phenomenon is followed by another, or even if they coincide, we tend to assume that one caused the other.
- We tend to look for "causes" for phenomena that can be explained better on the basis of probability theory or "chance."
- We believe what we remember, and we see what we expect to see, often ignoring or changing the information that contradicts our beliefs or our expectations.
- Our perceptions are colored by the situation in which data are presented, the ways they are presented, and the order in which they are presented. No assessment can be considered completely objective.

Our perceptions are bounded and limited by the theoretical concepts and constructs that we have accepted to describe and explain what we observe. When these constructs (such as personality, diseases, and traits) are reified – treated as though they had an objective existence – we can fall into a number of errors in assessing and treating emotional and perceptual problems.

REFERENCES

American Psychiatric Association. (1987). *Diagnostic and statistical manual of mental disorders–III-R.* Washington, DC: APA.

American Psychiatric Association. (1994). *Diagnostic and statistical manual of mental disorders–IV.* Washington, DC: APA.

Chapman, L. J., & Chapman, J. P. (1967). Genesis of popular but erroneous psychodiagnostic observations. *Journal of Abnormal Psychology, 72,* 193– 204.

Chapman, L. J., & Chapman, J. P. (1971). Test results are what you think they are. *Psychology Today, 5*(6), 18–22, 106–110. Also reprinted in D. Kahneman, P. Slovic, & A. Tversky (Eds.), *Judgment under uncertainty: Heuristics and biases.* Cambridge: Cambridge University Press, 1982.

Eddy, D. M. (1982). Probabilistic reasoning in clinical medicine: Problems and opportunities. In D. Kahneman, P. Slovic, & A. Tversky (Eds.), *Judgment under uncertainty: Heuristics and biases* (pp. 249–267). Cambridge: Cambridge University Press.

Elhai, J. D., Miller, M. E., Ford, J. D., Biehn, T. L., Palmien, P. A., & Frueh, B. C. (2012). Posttraumatic stress disorder in DSM–5: Estimates of prevalence and symptom structure in a nonclinical sample of college students. *Journal of Anxiety Disorders, 26*(1), 58–64.

Freud, S. (1937). Analysis terminable and interminable. In J. Strachey (Ed.), *Collected papers*. London: Hogarth, 1950. Vol. 5, 316–357.

Goleman, D. (1994, Nov. 29). Study finds jurors often hear evidence with closed minds. *New York Times*, p. B4.

Gould, S. J. (1981). *The mismeasure of man*. New York: W. W. Norton.

Hubbard, R. (1990). *The politics of women's biology*. New Brunswick, NJ: Rutgers University Press.

Kahneman, D., & Tversky, A. (1982). On the study of statistical intuition. *Cognition, 11*, 123–144. Reprinted in D. Kahneman, P. Slovic, & A. Tversky (Eds.), *Judgment under uncertainty: Heuristics and biases*. Cambridge: Cambridge University Press, 1982.

Kahneman, D., Slovic, P., & Tversky, A. (1982). *Judgment under uncertainty: Heuristics and biases*. Cambridge: Cambridge University Press.

Kelly, E. L., & Fiske, D. W. (1951). *The prediction of performance in clinical psychology*. Ann Arbor, MI: University of Michigan Press.

Kempler, W. (1973). Gestalt therapy. In R. Corsini (Ed.), *Current psychotherapies*. Itasca, IL: F. E. Peacock.

Kline, M. (1967). Some truths about truth and logic in mathematics. *The Hofstra Review, 2*(1), 4–9.

Leo, R. A. (1996). Inside the interrogation room. *The Journal of Criminal Law and Criminology, 86*, 266–303. DOI:10.2307/1144028.

Lueger, R. L., & Petzel, T. P. (1979). Illusory correlation in clinical judgment: Effects of amount of information to be processed. *Journal of Consulting and Clinical Psychology, 47*, 1120–21.

McKean, K. (1985). Decisions, decisions. *Discover, June*, 1985, 22–31.

McMahon, F. B. (1969). Personality testing – a smoke screen against logic. *Psychology Today, 2*(8), 54–59.

Mendez, M. F., & Fras, I. A. (2010). The false memory syndrome: Experimental studies and comparison to confabulations. *Medical Hypotheses, 76*(4), 492–496.

Meyer, T. D., Bernhard, B., Bom, C., Fuhr, K., Gerber, S., . . . Bauer, M. (2011). The hypomania checklist-32 and the mood disorder questionnaire as screening tools – going beyond samples of purely mood-disordered patients. *Journal of Affective Disorders, 128*(3), 291–298.

Nease, D. E., Aikens, J. E., Kinkman, M. S., Kroenke, K., & Sen, A. (2011). Toward a more comprehensive assessment of depression remission: The remission evaluation and mood inventory tool. *General Hospital Psychiatry, 33*(3), 279–286.

Oates, J. C. (1993, July 25). The one unforgivable sin. *New York Times Book Review*, Sec. 7.

Oskamp, S. (1965). Overconfidence in case-study judgments. *Journal of Consulting Psychology, 29,* 261–265.

Reynolds, R. A., Rizzo, J. A., & Gonzales, M. L. (1987). The cost of medical professional liability. *JAMA, 257,* 2776–2782.

Spearman, C., & Jones, L. W. (1950). *Human ability, a continuation of "The Abilities of Man."* London: Macmillan.

Srolo, L., Langner, E. S., Michael, M. K., & Rennie, T. A. (1962). *Mental health in the metropolis: The midtown Manhattan study.* New York: McGraw-Hill.

Stutz, D. R., & Feder, B. (1990). *The savvy patient: How to be an active participant in your medical care.* New York: Consumers Union.

Tversky, A., & Kahneman, D. (1982). Judgment under uncertainty: Heuristics and biases. Introduction to D. Kahneman, P. Slovic, & A. Tversky (Eds.), *Judgment under uncertainty: Heuristics and biases* (pp. 3–22). Cambridge: University of Cambridge Press.

Waller, R. W., & Keeley, S. M. (1978). Effects of explanation and information feedback on the illusory correlation phenomenon. *Journal of Consulting and Clinical Psychology, 46,* 342–343.

Chapter 5

THE MAGIC OF NUMBERS: BASIC STATISTICAL CONCEPTS

Throughout history, numbers have been endowed with magical properties. They have been used as powerful symbols, as incantations, as charms, and as tools for uncovering the secrets of the universe. Jewish, Christian, and Moslem mystics used numbers in soothsaying, in the interpretation of dreams, and in divination. The notion of numbers as magic persists into our own time. Some numbers like seven are "lucky." Others, like 13 are "unlucky." One of Sigmund Freud's closest associates, Wilhelm Fliess, created a system of "biorhythms" to predict an individual's life from the numbers in his or her birth date.

However, throughout much of history, the reverence for numbers has shown another face, that of "the scholar turned magician," in the words of mathematician-poet Jacob Bronowski. The Greek philosopher Pythagoras, wrote Bronowski, "was a kind of magician to his followers because he taught them that nature is commanded by numbers. There is a harmony in nature, he said, a unity in her variety, and it has a language: numbers are the language of nature" (1973, p. 156). The Greek heritage survived even through the darkest periods of Western history, kept alive by Moslem and Jewish scholars in the Islamic world, from which it sent out roots that emerged in the early European universities. Pythagoras' discovery that there is a basic relationship between musical harmony and mathematics was the basis for the study of music in the medieval universities as one of the seven liberal arts.

It was on this base that the scientific thinkers of the scientific revolution of the seventeenth and eighteenth centuries which followed hard on the heels of the Renaissance, built their models. Like the Greek philosophers and mathematicians, they were convinced that the world is not a completely chaotic place, subject to magical forces that could be placated and sometimes even controlled, but never completely understood. These investigators found that most recurring phenomena in the universe occur in some kind of order and that this order could best be expressed in the language of mathematics. One astronomer proclaimed that God must be a mathematician.

The discipline of statistics is an attempt to organize large amounts of data in such a way that relationships between facts can be seen in some kind of order. While we may never arrive at the truth, we can estimate probabilities; we can get a fix on what Bronowski called "the limits of tolerance" (1973, p. 365).

As with any other tool, statistics can be misused. Statistical methods have been employed to support questionable, or even false and outrageous, conclusions. As we noted earlier, statistics have been used to justify discriminatory practices, often by the very giants in the field of statistics who had provided the tools of analysis, but whose own zealous attempts to rationalize their prejudices blinded them. Casting a heavy shadow over the developing discipline was the gradual revelation of the duplicity of Cyril Burt, who inherited the mantle of Francis Galton and Karl Pearson at University College in London and who was the foremost psychometrician of his day. Burt was found, after his death, to have deliberately falsified many of his data to support hereditarian and racist explanations of intelligence (Kamin, 1974; Gruber, 1979).

As a result of the misuse and questionable use of quantification, statistics have been defined as a group of numbers looking for an argument, and a statistician as someone who draws a mathematically precise line from an unwarranted assumption to a foregone conclusion. A quip variously attributed to Benjamin Disraeli and to Mark Twain defines the three levels of untruthfulness as "lies, damned lies, and statistics."

We prefer the adage that while statistics don't lie, statisticians sometimes do. More frequently, they may reach unwarranted conclusions on the basis of their numbers, calculations, and findings. Blaming statistics for misuse and abuse of statistical methods is like blaming writing, because words, too, can be used to mislead, to confuse, and to lie. Like words, statistics are tools. Statisticians are certainly not the only investigators of the universe who may be mistaken or who may make unwarranted assumptions or arrive at foregone conclusions. Statistical methods are tools that can be used as a basis for seeing relationships among vast amounts of data that we could not otherwise see or comprehend. They can also be abused to distort truths. The basic principle in dealing with statistics is to understand that even if the statistics are gathered intelligently and reported truthfully, they rarely, if ever, speak for themselves; they must be interpreted.

So, in dealing with statistics, we must be on guard for two categories of error or bias: first, we must be aware of the possibility of flaws in the process of gathering data, and second, we must consider the possibility of bias or error in the ways the measurements are interpreted. Various observers may legitimately come to different conclusions on the basis of same data, depending on their philosophical orientations and their personal values and experiences.

Before any clinician relies on test scores for making decisions about patients or clients, he or she should have available all the relevant data on the purposes, the reliability, and the validity of the test, its applications and its limitations. For most tests, this information is provided in the test manual and in reviews in such sources as *The Mental Measurements Yearbooks* and *Test Critiques* and others mentioned previously.

However, much of the information is couched in the language of statistics. Unless you have a grasp of basic statistical concepts and knowledge of basic technical terms, much of this valuable information is inaccessible.

In this chapter, we will survey these concepts and define the terms that you are likely to encounter in the manuals and reviews. Because we want to stress fundamental principles rather than mathematical calculations, we have avoided including most of the formulas that statisticians use in their computations. However, we have attempted to explain the principles behind these calculations, so that test users can make sense of the psychometric data that are available. For those interested in formulas, these are readily available in statistics books and on statistics websites.

THE ORDERING OF NUMBERS

Statistics deal with numbers. The way numbers are generated by measurement has a good deal to do with the ways we can use them in calculations. No one type of generating data makes sense for all purposes. Data are broken down into four basic types or scales referred to as nominal ordinal, interval, and ratio.

Nominal Scales

Nominal scales use numbers to name, to identify, or to classify; they have nothing to do with quantities. Examples include telephone numbers, house addresses, and license tag numbers. Most of the *DSM* classification system is based on a nominal scale. Each number refers to a specific disorder and is used for identification purposes only. The categories are discrete; any relationship between them may have to do with organizational logic, but there is no mathematical or natural relationship between them; because 315.1 identifies Mathematics Disorder, and 315.2 signifies Disorder of Written Expression (in *DSM-IV*) doesn't mean that one is deemed more serious than the other. Nominal data are sometimes referred to as qualitative or categorical data.

Ordinal Scales

Ordinal scales are used to rank data in order from lowest to highest. There may or may not be an underlying unit of measurement. The ranking may be completely subjective, as in the rating of the relative taste of wines, or the quality of various works of art, or the ten best movies of the year. There is no indication of how much better one is than another. On the other hand, data can be ordered on the basis of measurable data, such as family income, years of education, percentile scores, or the ten best-selling novels. Sometimes, numerical and non-numerical data can be combined in the ordering, as in the ranking of candidates for a scholarship, or in the ranking of severity of disorders for triage, or priority of treatment. Some parts of the *DSM* are based on ordinal scales. For example, the Global Assessment of Functioning (GAF, Axis IV) scale is an ordinal scale.

Interval Scales

Like ordinal scales, interval scales show rank, but in the case of interval data, we can identify how far apart the rankings are. Temperatures, for example, are arranged on an interval scale. Most test scores are considered to be on an interval scale.

The major problem with interval scales is that there is no zero or starting point or, if there is, it has no meaning. Just because someone scores zero on an arithmetic test doesn't mean that he or she knows nothing about arithmetic; there always exists the possibility that somewhere in the school is a student who knows less. Someone who scores 60 on a hypothetical scale of anxiety isn't twice as anxious as someone who scores 30. Some arithmetic and statistical functions are legitimate with interval scales.

Ratio Scales

Ratio scales are amenable to all arithmetic computations for one simple reason: they start with a meaningful zero base. Our fundamental physical measurements – height, weight, length, width, and depth – all start from a true zero. We know that a can of olives weighing two pounds is twice as heavy as one that weighs one pound.

Cautions in the Use of Scales

Understanding the limitations of each scale category helps us to avoid major problems in working with psychometrics. For example, a therapist who is not aware of the limitations of ordinal scales may not consider that a 20-point difference in percentile scores will have a different meaning if we are comparing John, in the 40th percentile, and Sam, in the 60th percentile, than if we are comparing Sarah, in the 60th percentile, and Jane, in the 80th percentile. John and Sam are fairly similar to each other, both close to the mean or average; but Sarah and Jane are very different. While the numerical intervals may appear constant, the significance of the intervals is not. Numerical differences loom far larger as we move from the mean.

THE FREQUENCY DISTRIBUTION

All statistical calculations in psychometrics start with frequency distributions. Measurements of large groups of people are arranged in order from lowest to highest, together with the frequency with which they occur. When measurements are arranged in this way, certain or-

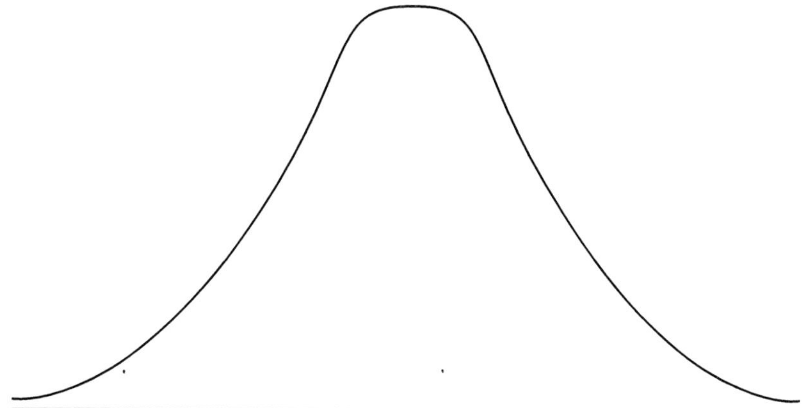

Figure 5.1. A normal distribution illustrated by a bell-shaped curve.

derly patterns emerge. Whether we are arranging measurements of height, or weight, or length of fingernails, the majority of the measurements will cluster around some central value or norm. This score or value is known as the measure of central tendency. A distribution can be "normal," or symmetrical, with the bulk of the cases in the middle, declining as we go further from the center in each direction.

Or it can be "skewed," with the bulk of the cases piled up on one side or the other, as in the case of per capita income in the world. There are far more people who earn very little than who earn very much, so such a distribution is positively skewed, with more of the incomes in the lower measurements.

The normal curve, also called the bell-shaped curve (because of its shape), or the Gaussian curve (in honor of the mathematician who formulated the equation for it), describes the distribution of most phenomena that occur randomly and in large numbers in nature. If a distribution is skewed, meaning that there are too many high or too many low scores to produce the symmetrical bell curve, special equations are required for statistical calculations with the data.

Central Tendency

Generally, the first question we ask about a frequency distribution is its average. Actually, there are three major forms of average, or central tendency. Each is useful for certain purposes and each has some limitations for other purposes.

The Arithmetic Mean

The arithmetic mean is the average with which most of us are familiar. We simply add the sum of the scores and then divide by the number of scores. This is probably the most commonly used form of average, and it is the most appropriate one for interval or ratio data, when the distribution is believed to be approximately normal. The arithmetic mean is most often symbolized by a capital X, with a bar on top, and it is referred to, appropriately, as "X-bar." However, for certain purposes, we may prefer another measure of central tendency. For one thing, if the distribution is not normal, one or two extreme scores can distort the mean. For another, the mean can be a number that has no counterpart in reality, like the two-and-a-half child average for families in Utopia, Wisconsin.

The Median

If all the subjects are arranged in order of the scores they received, the median score is the one that equally divides the subjects who scored higher than that score and those who scored lower. The median is not the mid-score, the score that is between the highest and lowest, but the mid-population point. The median is the most appropriate average for ordinal data and is useful for interval and ratio data, when the distribution is highly skewed. So, in estimating the average duration of a major depressive episode, it makes more sense to use the median than the mean. This way we minimize the impact of the atypical case that would distort the mean, like an individual for whom such an episode might have lasted 10 years.

The Mode

The mode is the most frequently occurring score in a distribution. If two scores compete for the designation "most frequently occurring score," then the distribution is said to be "bimodal," and the depiction would look something like a two-humped camel. Actually, a distribution can have even more than two modes. The mode is identified by examination, not by calculation, so it must be considered a nominal calculation, and not usually useful for any further arithmetic purpose.

In a completely normal distribution, the mean, the median, and the mode are identical. Since many distributions are not perfectly normal, we must often decide which is the most useful for our purposes. By and large, the mean is the preferred measure of central tendency in generally symmetrical distributions, and the median is preferred for severely skewed distributions. Because we shall be dealing mainly with normal (or "normalized") distributions, we will use the mean as our basic term for average.

Reification of the Central Tendency

Averages are constructs. Like theoretical concepts such as the unconscious or disease entities, they are abstractions that too often are reified, a source of bias and distortion in our thinking. To illustrate the need for caution in interpreting averages, we provide the case history of Stephen Jay Gould, an evolutionary biologist and science historian at Harvard. In 1982, Gould learned that he was suffering from a form of cancer known as abdominal mesothelioma. He learned, also, that mesothelioma is incurable, with a median mortality of eight months after discovery. "I suspect that most people, without training in statistics, would read such a statement as 'I will probably be dead in eight months'," Gould wrote three years later. "My technical training enjoined a different perspective on 'eight months mortality.' The point is a subtle one, but profound – for it embodies the distinctive way of thinking . . . in natural history" (Gould, 1985, p. 41).

Western Platonic heritage seeks sharp distinctions and separate immutable entities, Gould (1985) pointed out, leading us to view statistical measures of central tendency as "realities," and the variations that are the basis for calculation as "a set of transient and imperfect measurements of this hidden essence . . . but all evolutionary biologists know that variation is the hard reality, not a set of imperfect measures for a central tendency. Means and medians are the abstractions" (p. 41).

Gould wanted to know, first, what his chances were for being on the longer-lived side of the median. He concluded that he possessed every one of the characteristics offering a probability of longer life: he was young, had been diagnosed in an early stage of the disease, would receive the world's best medical treatment, and had an optimistic personality. Next, he recognized that the distribution of the variation around the central tendency must be right-skewed.

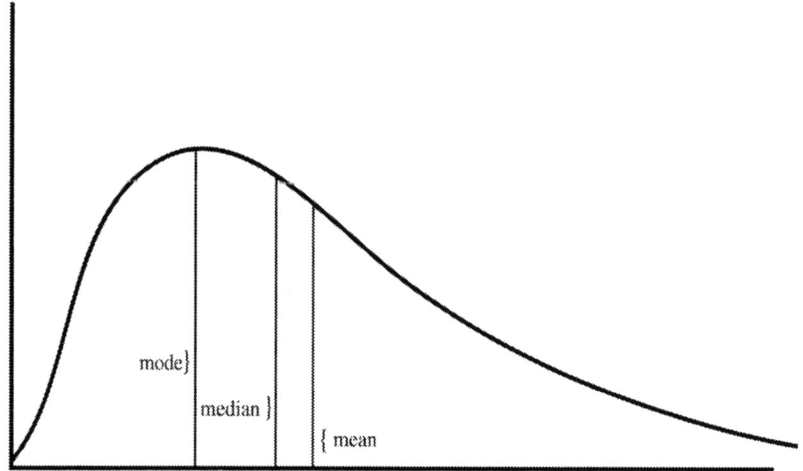

Figure 5.2. A right-skewed or positively skewed curve. This curve illustrates the mortality distribution for an incurable disease like mesothelioma. The measures of central tendency shown are from left to right, the mode, the median, and the mean.

Half of the people died between the time of diagnosis and eight months, but the longevity of those on the right tail of the distribution could stretch out for years and years (which is why the right tail is left open in the figure above). Gould's prospects for being in that tail were good.

Means and medians are powerful constructs but, like all potent tools, they must be handled with care.

Variability

The mean provides us with a rough representation of the scores for the population under study, but it doesn't describe other essential information. We need to know something about the variability of the scores – how they are distributed or dispersed around the mean.

Suppose a dance/movement therapist is planning a treatment program for children with physical disabilities, and administers a hypothetical standardized test of movement range and flexibility to two groups. The mean score for each group is the same, and the distributions are both normal. Can we assume, then, that the therapist can develop a single plan that can be used for both groups?

The Range

The therapist, in this case, might be as interested in the range of the scores as in the average. The range is the spread from the lowest score to the highest. In one group, the scores are clustered around the mean, suggesting that the therapist can plan activities in which all the members can participate, since their movement abilities are similar. In the second group, however, the scores show a far greater range. The children with the lowest scores would probably not be able to participate in the same activities as those with the highest scores. The therapist, in this case, would have to modify the program to provide for a greater range of activities within the group, start a separate group for those with the most severe restrictions, or plan individual activities for them.

There are several limitations in relying on the range alone to describe the distribution. The most obvious is that a single high or low score can seriously distort the description of how variable the group's composition may be. As a result, the range provides, at best, a rough approximation of variability.

The Standard Deviation

A more meaningful description of variability than the range is the standard deviation, which minimizes the influence of extreme scores. The standard deviation provides a measure of how far a given score is located from the mean. Any score's raw deviation from the mean is a simple matter of subtraction. Since the mean score is 75, if Rachel's score on the reading test is 95, the deviation from the mean for her score is 20. Jack's score of 55 has a deviation of minus 20.

The standard deviation is the square root of the mean of the squared deviations from the mean of a distribution. This is not quite as complicated as it sounds. Symbolized by the letters *SD*, or by σ, the lowercase Greek letter sigma – the standard deviation is calculated in the following manner.

1. Subtract the arithmetic mean from each score, giving us x, the deviation from the mean.
2. Square these differences, or deviations (x^2).
3. Add all the squared differences.
4. Divide the sum of the square differences by the number of scores.

This gives us a figure that is called the variance of the distribution.

5. Find the square root of this number.

In a distribution where the scores are clustered around the mean, the standard deviation will be small. In distributions where the scores are spread out on both sides of the mean, the distribution will be large. So, we can visualize the distribution, even in the absence of a plotted curve, if we know the mean and the standard deviation.

THE NORMAL CURVE

The concept of the normal curve can be traced to the middle of the eighteenth century; it was expanded by Karl Friedrich Gauss, who developed the formula for calculating it. The term normal curve to describe this bell-shaped symmetrical distribution was coined by Karl Pearson. While few samples of populations yield precisely normal distributions, the approximation of normality increases as populations increase, so it is used as a description of large random distributions.

Proportions Under the Normal Curve

Because there is no true zero base for normal distributions, the mean itself serves as the starting point, and is often designated as zero. From this mean, the area under the curve is often divided into the standard deviations that we described above, with data below the mean called minus and those above referred to as plus.

One function of the normal curve is to interpret and clarify the meaning of the standard deviation. The area enclosed within one standard deviation from the mean in each direction is 34.13 percent. This means that 68.26 percent, or about two-thirds, of all the measurements fall within one standard deviation above and one standard deviation below the mean, 95.44 percent within two standard deviations, and 99.74 percent within three standard deviations. On a practical level, we can tell from the standard deviation how similar or how diverse the scores are. If we examine two distributions and find that one has a large standard deviation and one a small one, we can tell that the latter represents scores that are closely clustered, and the former represents scores that are more spread out.

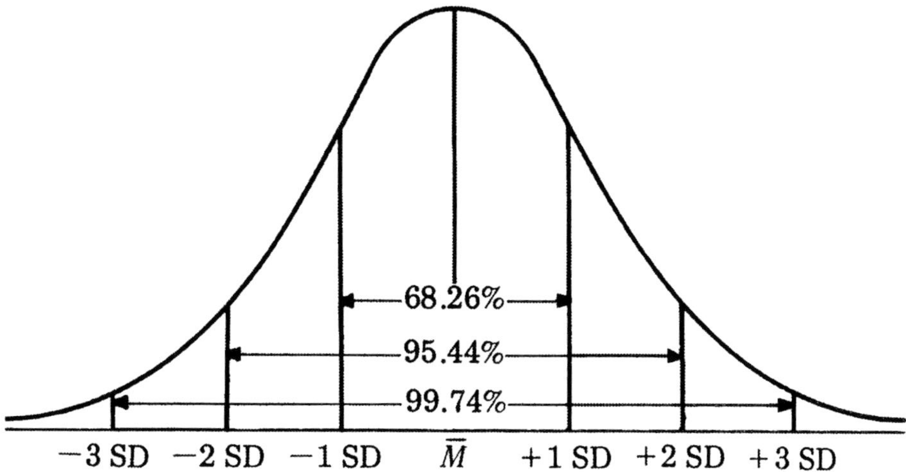

Figure 5.3. Percentages of the area under the normal curve in terms of standard deviations from the mean.

A therapist may want a rough estimate of the standard deviation in order to visualize the normal curve or to know where a client's or a patient's score fits in the distribution. There is a fast method for approximating the standard deviation without performing the calculations we described a little earlier.

As you saw, the vast bulk (95%) of all the cases under the normal curve will fall within two standard deviations below the mean and two above the mean. Because 95 percent of the cases come very close to constituting the total range of the distribution, we can simply divide the range by four to get a reasonable idea of the standard deviation of a distribution.

Derived Scores

If you have a routine blood test as part of a physical examination, you may be handed a computerized printout with all kinds of numbers: blood cell count, for example, and levels of glucose, calcium, phosphorus, triglycerides, and a long list of other things. For most of us, these numbers are meaningless, unless the printout also contains a "reference range," or a "criterion range," of what is considered either "normal" or desirable.

Similarly, a raw score of 30 on a test for anxiety tells us nothing unless we can compare it with what is considered a "normal" level of anxiety. Such raw scores don't have any meaning unless they let us know where those scores stand in relationship to the scores that were made by others.

For this reason, most standardized test scores are converted into some sort of "derived," "transformed," or "converted" score. Derived scores inform us quickly where the test-taker's performance is with regard to the mean.

Percentile Scores

Leonard's score of 70 on a spelling test was better than the scores of 60 percent of his classmates (plus one-half of those who received the same score of 70), his percentile score would be 60. You will have noticed that no reference is made to the mean; percentile scores are cumulative, starting at a zero base at the lowest score. They are ordinal scores; they tell us nothing about the intervals between raw scores. However, because most raw scores are clustered around the mean, we can expect the intervals between such scores to be shorter around the median, or the 50th percentile level, increasing as they move further from this median in both directions. Percentile scores are useful for research or for educational evaluation, but they are of limited value in therapy, because they have meaning largely in terms of competition.

Standard Scores

Standard scores, or standard deviation scores, provide information on scores in terms both of mean and of standard deviation. There are several standard score systems.

z Scores. The standard score is sometimes described as a mean of zero plus or minus one, meaning one standard deviation. The *z* score is calculated from the standard deviation. So someone whose *z* score is 1.33 scored one and-one-third standard deviations above the mean. The calculation is relatively simple. The *z* score equals the raw score minus the mean, divided by the standard deviation. So if a client obtained a raw score of 60 on a test in which the mean score was 55 and the standard deviation is 5, you would find the difference between the scores and divide by five. The *z* score would be one.

From standard scores, we can derive the same kind of information that is offered by percentiles. Your client's score, for example, was better than the scores of 84 percent of others who were tested (50% of whom scored below the mean and 34% of whom scored above the mean, but below +1 *SD*). Like percentiles and other derived scores, standard scores provide a common system for comparing scores across a series of tests with different raw scoring systems.

T Scores. There is one major problem with *z* scores. All scores below the mean are reported in negative numbers. Not only does this make further calculations cumbersome, it has unpleasant connotations when such numbers describe the scores of those who performed below average.

The solution is simple: add a number to the zero. So *T* scores (named in honor of psychologist E. L. Thorndike) were designed to have a mean of 50 and a standard deviation of 10. The system is composed of a scale with five deviations below the mean and five deviations above the mean. *T* scores are used for a number of well-known standardized tests, including the Minnesota Multiphasic Personality Inventory.

Other Standard Scoring Systems. There are numerous other scoring systems based on the concept of standard deviations. Stanines ("standard nines") are scores based on a mean of 5 and a standard deviation of 2, yielding nine units. Raw scores on the Scholastic Aptitude Test (SAT) and the Graduate Record Examination (GRE) are converted to a standard score system with a mean set at 500 and a standard deviation of 100. Intelligence tests were once based on a concept of "mental age." An intelligence quotient, or IQ was obtained by dividing someone's "mental age" by that person's chronological age and multiplying by one hundred to eliminate decimals. While the term IQ persists, it no longer is a literal description of a score. David Wechsler developed a system of "deviation IQs" – standard scores based on a mean of 100 and a standard deviation of 15. On Wechsler's system, therefore, IQs ranging from 85 to 115 are considered to be in the normal range.

Normalizing Standard Scores. While the normal curve represents the theoretical distribution for very large populations, few samples on which tests are standardized are truly normal. You will remember that standard scoring systems are predicated upon normal distributions. How, then, does one deal with a skewed distribution? There are two basic approaches to converting skewed samples into normal ones.

The first uses complex statistical calculations to transform scores and yield a normalized standard score scale. This conversion is rarely done for a variety of statistical and logical reasons. Most test developers simply play around with the difficulty levels of tests until they get the scores to yield approximately normal distributions.

STANDARDIZED TESTS

The term "standardized test" is often misunderstood. First of all, the words "standardized" and "objective" don't mean the same thing. Standardized tests are objective, meaning that the scoring is uniform, and follows predetermined criteria. However, objective tests are not necessarily standardized; just think of all of the teacher-made multiple choice and true-false tests you took in high school and college.

A standardized test must meet three criteria:

1. It must be based on a standard task or a standard group of tasks that are identical for all subjects.
2. It must be administered with standard directions under uniform conditions and be scored objectively.
3. It must have been standardized, or "normed" on a sample of subjects representative of the population for whom the test was intended. The norms that are established for this sample group are assumed to be the norms for the population from which the group was drawn and the norms for the groups that will be tested afterwards.

PREDICTING FROM STATISTICS

The field of statistics is often separated into descriptive statistics and inferential statistics. Descriptive statistics present data in a summary form. If we keep records of the percentages of patients diagnosed with mood disorders in a particular mental hospital, we may discover that out of every 100 patients diagnosed, 67 are women and 33 are men.

If we think that the proportion is typical of the patients who come to this hospital, we may extrapolate from this figure to estimate the proportion for new admits. This type of statistics is known as inferential statistics. It is the basis for sampling, working from a small sample to infer the nature of the whole population.

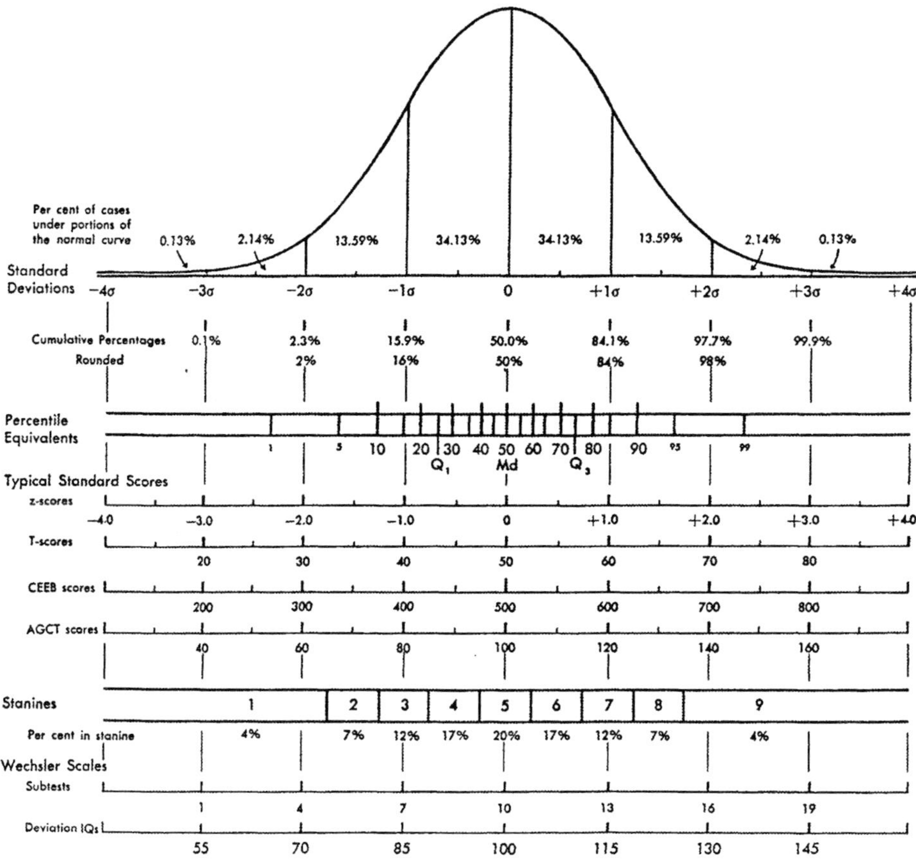

Figure 5.4. Relationships between standard deviations and various scoring systems. Reproduced by permission. Psychological Corporation *Test Service Bulletin* No. 48, 1955.

In inferential statistics, then, the choice of the sample on which we base our inference will determine the accuracy of our inference. For example, a procedure that has been normed on a haphazardly selected sample of hospitalized patients may not be representative of the referral patient, or of the self-referred client in a private office or clinic. A therapist should be aware of the characteristics of the sample on which a procedure was normed.

The concept of inferential statistics is based on inductive logic; it works from a part to a whole, from a sample to a generalization. In contrast, probability is based on deductive logic; it works from the whole to a part. Probability deals with the likelihood that the generalization is applicable to a particular subject or group of subjects. So, in our example, the probability that a patient with depression about whom we know nothing is male is about one in three.

The Standard Task

Because standardized tests are based on norms, the tasks must be as close as possible to identical for all the subjects in the standardization group and for all subjects who take the same test afterwards. If there are any differences in the tasks themselves, or in the time that is provided for the completion of the tasks, or in the scoring procedures, then the test results are not comparable for all the subjects or even for the same subject at different times.

This requirement presents a major difficulty in designing standardized tests in the arts therapies. Whereas intelligence tests or achievement tests focus on more or less clearly delineated tasks, it is difficult to standardize tasks in the arts. Even when the instructions are identical, the way someone moves, or creates or responds to a drawing or music depends a good deal on affect – on a fleeting mood, on the subject's relationship with the therapist, on preceding events, on the subject's inhibitions in moving or performing before others, or the subject's concerns about what he or she may reveal.

As a result of the variations in the ways subjects respond to the task, it is unlikely that any single test in the arts therapies is likely to capture the quality of a subject's "true" response. However, each individual does have characteristic ways of moving, styles of drawing, and ways of responding to or producing music. Several administrations of a standard task will produce a scattering of scores. Organized in a Gaussian curve, "The scatter marks an area of uncertainty. We are not sure that the true position is the center. All we can say is that it lies in the area of uncertainty, and the area is calculable from the observed scatter of the individual observations" (Bronowski, 1973, p. 358). The scatter can be analyzed in terms of standard error of measurement, a concept with which we will deal later in this chapter.

The Normative or Standardization Sample

In the process of developing a test, the test developer must target a clearly defined group as the population for whom the test is designed. This population is often called the "universe" of persons who share a common characteristic – anxiety or rigidity, for example.

For large target populations, it is clearly impractical, prohibitively expensive, or even physically impossible to administer the test to every member of the whole population in order to obtain base rates. As a result, the test developer is likely to administer the test to a sample of the population or populations involved that is assumed to be representative of the whole population. For a test designed for differential diagnosis, then, one sample will consist of a "criterion group" of individuals who are believed to share the characteristic or disorder; the other will consist of individuals who are believed not to share the characteristic or disorder, sometimes referred to as the "normal" group. In this way, norms can be established for the target group and for the control group. These norms become the basis for diagnosis or assessment of individuals later to ascertain whether they share the characteristic or the disorder.

The fundamental question in sampling is: "How can we select a sample that is representative of the target population?" This is not always easy to do. In addition, even if it is done carefully, the target population itself may change. For example, the College Entrance Examination Board's SAT was originally normed on a group of 10,000 college applicants in 1941. In that year, the vast majority of those applying for college were white northern males from middle or upper class families. The mean was established at 500. For many years afterward, college applicants who took the test were measured against the norms established for this standardization group, despite the rapid change in the demographics of college applicants in the years after World War II. Concerns over declining SAT scores in the 1960s and 1970s might have been better directed to the obsolescence of the norms during periods of changing college enrollment patterns. After national averages dipped, in 1994, to 423 for the verbal test and 479 for the math, the SAT was "recentered" so that the average score on each was once again set at 500. Similarly, the Minnesota Multiphasic Personality Inventory (MMPI) was normed on a criterion group of hospitalized mental patients and a control group of largely white, rural residents of the Midwest, most with an elementary school education. No major re-standardization was attempted until almost a half century later.

Selecting a Standardization Sample

There are several ways of choosing a standardization sample, and there are several ways of describing them. We shall categorize them as "random" and "nonrandom."

Random Sampling

In everyday conversation, the word "random" often is used to mean "haphazard." As it is used in statistics and in mathematics in general, random means something very different. Random sampling is actually a method that is carefully designed to give every member of the target population a chance to be included.

For random sampling in general, the first task is to identify every member of the target population so that each is given a chance to be chosen. This task is relatively simple in a small population, like a classroom or a school. It is far more difficult when we deal with larger populations. How does one obtain the names of every resident of a city? Even finding the names of telephone owners is not as simple as it might appear; many people may not have landlines or may prefer not to be listed in the telephone directory. As a result, the simple random sampling we describe first is usually used only for populations that are small or whose members can be easily identified, such as the members of the American Dance Therapy Association.

Simple Random Sampling. From our population list we must now select the members of the sample. Usually, this is done by referring to a table of random numbers. Such tables, appearing in almost all statistics textbooks and on the Internet, are constructed so as to generate a sequence of numbers, arranged in rows and columns that would yield no identifiable pattern if plotted on a graph.

A researcher who wanted a random sample of 50 students from the 500 students matriculated in a particular program at the University of Kansas would secure a list of such students and assign each a three-digit number starting with 001 and continuing to 500. This researcher would then turn to a table of random numbers, put his or her finger on any number in the table, and then continue in any direction – left to right, for example, or top to bottom, taking every number that comes up between 001 and 500 on the list of students. Referring to our own list of random numbers (Downie & Heath, 1970), we started at row 40, column 8, and found:

4 4 2 1 4 0 5 8 2 3 0 8 5 9 4 5 8 6 2 3 0 6 2 9 8 6 3 0 4 1 0 7 6

Consulting our list of students, we would choose for our sample the student to whom we had assigned number 442, followed by 140. The next number, 582, is too high, so we ignore it and continue with 308, going on across the table until we have 50 names.

Systematic Sampling. A list of random numbers is not necessary for systematic sampling also called interval sampling. Referring back to our list of 500 hundred names, we might point haphazardly to one of the first ten names and then proceed to check off every tenth name until we got our sample of 50. The advantage of systematic sampling is that we can avoid the time and effort involved in using the table of random numbers. The disadvantage is that there is a danger of missing altogether members of particular minority groups, who might fall through the cracks. This problem is addressed in the type of sampling we address below.

Stratified Sampling. The population of the university program in which we are interested may be disproportionately male or disproportionately female. Or there may be very few (or very many) members of specific ethnic, religious, nationality, or socioeconomic groups. To ensure that we get a proportionate number from each such group, we can stratify the population, dividing the names into more homogeneous subgroups, or strata, assuming that these can be identified. For each subgroup, we can then take a simple random sample, in the same proportion that the subgroup appears in the general population under study. Each subgroup is treated as a complete population whose members are assigned numbers. After the names have been selected, they are combined into a total stratified sample that is considered representative of the entire population.

Cluster Sampling. For extremely large groups, cluster sampling is one way of limiting the effort and time that is required to gather a representative sample.

Let's assume that we want a sample that is representative of students in state universities throughout the United States. Cluster sampling involves two steps. First, we choose a random sample of universities. We might do this by assigning numbers to all the state universities and then relying on either a simple random approach or a stratified approach based on the regions of the country. For each university selected, we would now choose a simple random sample of students. This cluster approach means that we can avoid covering every state university in the country.

Nonrandom Sampling

Nonrandom sampling is far easier to do than random sampling, but also more likely to result in a biased sample that is not representative of the target population.

Quota Sampling. To be sure that we get samples of various ages, genders, religious, ethnic or social classes, we can sample these groups in the same proportion in which they occur in the population. So, if we know that 45 percent of the students in our program population are women, we make sure that we select a sample where 45 percent are women. At first glance, quota sampling would appear to be similar to the stratified sampling we described above. However, in quota sampling, the sample is drawn by whatever method the investigator chooses; there is no systematic method involved to get an accurate representation of the women or the men in our sample.

Purposive Sampling. Also known as "judgment sampling," this method relies on common sense, or intuitive judgment, on the basis of which to select a sample. For example, if we are interested in a population of middle class Americans, we might proceed on the assumption that people who read *Newsweek* and *People* magazines are representative of that class. Or, if we subscribe to the idea that was popular some years ago, that "As New Hampshire goes, so goes the nation," we might use the New Hampshire primary elections as our guide to primaries across the nation. The danger in this form of sampling is that in time the sample may no longer be representative of the larger population. Some years ago, when it became apparent that the representative nature of New Hampshire primaries no longer could be taken for granted, a wit revised the saying to "As New Hampshire goes, so goes Vermont."

Purposive sampling is particularly useful for sampling extreme or variant cases. For example, if we wanted to find why some programs have long waiting lists and why others have recruitment problems, or why some seem to have high levels of success, while others seem to go nowhere, we might legitimately use purposive sampling.

A variation of purposive or purposeful sampling is sometimes called critical case sampling. If valid generalizations can be drawn from polarized or apparently contradictory samples, it can logically be assumed that the generalization would be true in all cases. For example, when Galileo found that a feather and a heavy ball fall at the same rate in a vacuum it was reasonable to infer that the same generalization could be applied to all the objects that are between the two in weight.

Convenience Sampling. Also known as "accidental" or "incidental" sampling, this is a form of sampling that saves time, effort, and money, but is very likely to result in a biased or unrepresentative sample (Patton, 2002). The sample is drawn from whatever subjects are at hand. We have already discussed the numerous samples that are recruited from the ranks of captive audiences, such as psychology students, or members of the social organizations to which the researcher belongs, or pedestrians who happen to walk by when the researcher is handing out survey questionnaires. We get examples of convenience sampling when assessment procedures are normed on the patients in the test developer's hospital or clinic. These cannot be assumed to be representative of the larger population. Unfortunately, convenience sampling is all too common and characterizes the standardization of some widely used instruments, including the original MMPI. In some cases, however, convenience sampling may be the only reasonable recourse. For example, someone who wants to draw a sample of schoolchildren must often rely on the cooperation of school boards, administrators, and teachers. Such a task may be extremely difficult, and the test developer or researcher must often fall back on convenience sampling.

This last criterion for a standardized test, the "norming" of the test, is the most troublesome. Because of the difficulty in finding standardization samples that match the characteristics of particular clients, there is always the possibility that the scores are not compatible. To avoid these difficulties with normative comparisons, many clinicians use standard scores only for comparing their clients' scores with their previous scores. This is particularly useful for monitoring progress.

Standard Error

When the news media report the results of surveys or of predictions, they almost always report a "margin of error." Where does that figure come from and what does it mean?

Communications engineers talk of "signal" and "noise" when they discuss the accuracy of transmissions. Lee Cronbach (1970, p. 156) used the term signal to describe the information we want: the universe of scores that a test-taker might have made if he or she had been tested many times. The noise is the distortion caused by interference or errors, such as the scores made by the subject when he or she was angry about something or had had a bad hair day.

The "margin of error" can be calculated mathematically by using the standard deviation we have been discussing. It is useful in helping to answer a variety of questions that can arise in testing: How much confidence can we have that a client's test score reflects his or her "true" score or "universe" of scores? What are the odds that a change in a client's test scores represents a real change rather than a predictable change due to chance? How accurately do the scores of a standardization sample represent the scores we could expect from other samples?

You should remember that almost every statistic with which psychometricians deal is a sample. A test score is a sample of the scores that the test-taker might have made, and a standardization sample is a sample of the universe from which a multiplicity of samples could have been drawn. As a result, there are many standard errors that can be calculated: standard error of a score, standard error of the difference between two scores, standard error of the difference between two means, standard error of a correlation coefficient – and on and on, each used for a different purpose. For example, the standard error of the difference between two means can indicate to a researcher whether a difference in scores between a criterion group and a control group represents a real difference between the two populations or sampling error.

To clarify the use of standard error, let's discuss several applications.

Standard Error of Measurement

Also called the standard error of a score, this is the flip side of the test reliability that we discussed in Chapter 3. We pointed out that the reliability of a test or procedure refers to its ability to come close to a test-taker's "true score." The standard error of measurement, or SEM, is calculated in such a way that as the reliability increases, the standard error of measurement shrinks.

The thinking behind the computation of sampling error is this: if a test-taker were to respond to a long series of samples from the same content area, the responses would scatter on each side of his or her hypothetical "true score," depending on a number of variables, including the subject's emotional state, the testing conditions, and the way the test was administered. So the mean of all the possible responses would be a reasonable approximation of the true score. We can't know the test-taker's true score, but we can calculate the probable spread of responses around the score the patient or client actually obtained. If we know, or can calculate, the reliability of the test and the standard deviation for the distribution of scores on the test, we can calculate the standard error of any particular score.

Let's illustrate the way the SEM is calculated. Lorraine takes a hypothetical test to measure "helplessness" for which the mean score is set at 100 and the standard deviation is 20. Let's assume that Lorraine's "true" score is 110. What is the actual score that she is likely to make on the test?

If we know that the test's reliability coefficient is .84, we can calculate that one standard deviation represents eight points on the test (the standard deviation times the square root of one minus the reliability coefficient). Since the standard error of measurement is, in effect, a standard deviation of the test scores that Lorraine might have made, we can say that:

- the chances are 68 percent, or about two out of three, that Lorraine would obtain an actual score of between 102 and 118.
- the chances are about one in six that she would obtain an actual score below 102, and about one in six that she would get an actual score above 118.
- there is a slim possibility (between two and three out of a hundred) that she might obtain a score below 96 or above 126.

Since we don't know Lorraine's true score, we used the test score she achieved on the test as though it were her true score. The spreads will be close enough for us to estimate the standard error of measurement.

Actually, a therapist is not likely to calculate the magnitude of error for a client, and we included the discussion of standard error of measurement to illustrate this point:

Any score that a patient or client obtains approaches his or her "true" score only in terms of probabilities. Too much confidence should not be put in the precision of a single score, which should be viewed cautiously as a hypothesis about the client rather than a description.

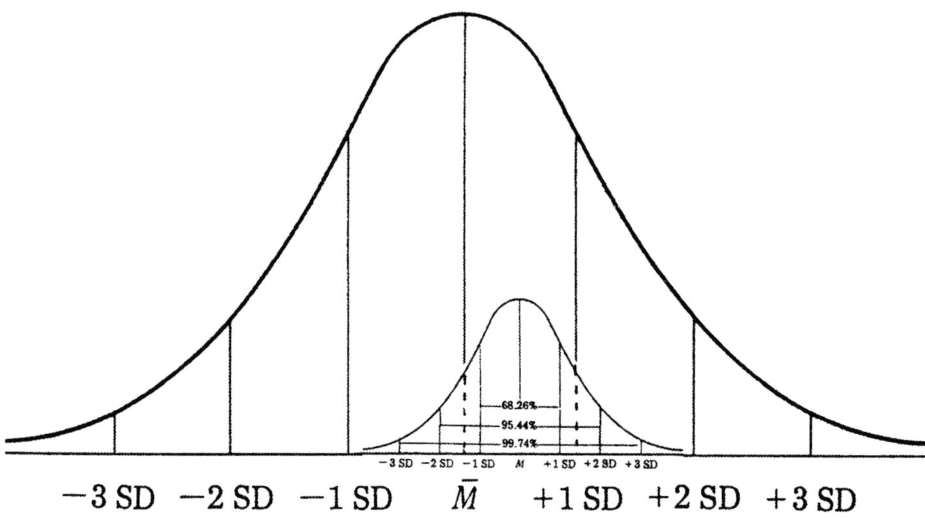

Figure 5.5. The SEM curve for Lorraine's test scores. The distribution of scores Lorraine could obtain on a test on which her "true" score is 110. The odds are two out of three that her actual score would be between 102 and 118.

Standard Error of the Difference Between Two Scores

This concept of a distribution around a "true" figure can help us determine, among other things, how to interpret variations in the test scores that are made by clients and patients and to determine whether any change that we see in patients could be the result of chance or sampling error, rather than of the treatment that has been offered.

Take the case of a client who obtained a score of 124 on a test of self-esteem. After a month of treatment, the client takes the test again, this time scoring 133. Does this change testify to the value of the treatment the client has been receiving?

A knowledgeable therapist might not be sure. Is there any way of calculating whether the change of nine points represents a real change in the client or just a result of chance? The manual reported a test reliability coefficient of .92 and a standard deviation of 14. Using the appropriate formula, this works out to a standard error of 5.6. This means that a difference of less than 11 points is not likely to be statistically significant. It could have been the result of chance variations in the two scores, within the likely "margins of error." In other words, the client might have achieved a score of 133 even before the treatment began.

Again, while a therapist is not likely to calculate the standard error of the difference between two scores, some test manuals provide tables in which score intervals are interpreted with regard to their meanings.

Standard Error of the Difference Between Two Means

By now, it should be clear that the concept of standard deviation can be applied to a wide number of specific situations. However, there is one more that we want to mention, because it is important in determining whether a test designed to discriminate between two populations does so.

The standard error of the difference between two means permits a researcher to know how much confidence he or she can have in the test's ability to differentiate between two populations. Let's suppose that a test is given to a population that is believed to consist of people who are violence-prone. The same test is given to a control group of people who are considered "normal."

The researcher finds a difference in the means of the two groups. But how is he or she to know whether that difference represents a real difference between the two populations, or sampling error? The formula for finding the standard error of the difference between two means will yield a z score. The researcher, referring to a table, will learn the degree to which the difference is "statistically significant," a term that we'll explain shortly. A statement indicating the test's level of confidence in differentiating between two populations should appear in the test manual. This is an indication to the therapist of how much confidence can be placed in the test's usefulness in differential diagnosis or the assessment of a personality trait.

CORRELATION

Correlation has to do with the way two things relate to each other. In many ways, this concept is the basis for psychometrics. We can't presume to predict someone's behavior or status from a test score unless we can show some relationship between the score and the behavior, nor can we see how consistently a test measures what it is supposed to measure.

Reliability and validity are expressed in terms of the ways two sets of data are related. Suppose an art therapist had developed a drawing test of cognitive development in children and wanted to know how these scores related to the same children's scores on an intelligence test in order to establish construct validity. Or the therapist might want to know the degree to which the scores relate to the way the child behaves. The therapist would also be interested in establishing the test-retest reliability of the instrument, and the internal consistency of the test, as well as the inter-rater reliability of the test.

Just as the mean and the standard deviation describe any given distribution, the correlation coefficient, symbolized by *r*, describes the relationship between two distributions. The correlation coefficient can vary from +1.00, describing a perfect positive correlation to -1.00, describing a perfect negative correlation. Most correlations are therefore expressed in fractions between the two. A modest correlation, such as .50, would let us know that test scores bear some relationship to the behavior being predicted or to other test scores, but that there are numerous exceptions.

There are several ways of calculating the correlation between two variables, each useful for a specific kind of application. The most commonly used is the Pearson Product-Moment correlation, also known as the Pearson *r*. The Pearson *r* is used when both sets of data are continuous, meaning that a score can take any numerical value on a continuum and that the numerical ordering is on an interval scale. A number of formulas can be used for calculating the Pearson *r*.

Correlations to Measure Reliability

Many, if not most, of the correlation coefficients that you are likely to find in test manuals or in reviews of objective tests have to do with reliability. In Chapter 3, we saw that there are basically three approaches to estimating reliability of the test itself: test-retest, alternate forms, and internal consistency. In addition, those who use tests are also interested in inter-observer reliability, the consistency with which examiners agree not only on scoring but on interpreting the scores.

Each form of reliability depends on the process of correlation. The approach to correlation and the formula that is used depend on the purpose of the test, the nature of the test, and the way the correlation coefficient will be used. For a test that is to be used on a one-time basis, as during an intake assessment, we might be most interested in the internal consistency of the test. For a test that is to be repeated – to monitor a client's progress, for example – we would expect information on the test-retest reliability or the alternate form reliability.

The Pearson *r* is the most versatile correlation coefficient. It can be used to measure test-retest reliability and alternate form reliability (including split-half reliability). However, there are three other formulas that you are likely to find mentioned in the literature on reliability.

The Spearman-Brown Formula

We pointed out that changing the length of a test almost always affects its reliability. When we calculate split-half reliability, therefore, we are dealing with two subtests, each of which is half the length of the actual test. The Spearman-Brown formula is used to correct the reliability of each half-test so that it is equivalent to the reliability of the whole test. The coefficient number for the half-test is generally adjusted upward to reflect what the figure would have been if the number of items had been doubled.

The Kuder-Richardson Formula

Actually, there are several Kuder-Richardson formulas, the best known of which is the Kuder-Richardson formula 20, usually referred to as KR-20. Its name comes from the fact that it was the 20th formula of a series designed to estimate split-half reliability in a test in which the items are dichotomous. Because the items are not consistent with each other, the split halves might not measure the same traits or qualities. The KR-20 is designed to correct for this mismatch.

Coefficient Alpha

Cronbach's coefficient alpha is used for a variety of purposes. However, it is most widely used to estimate the internal consistency, or inter-item consistency, of a homogeneous test in which all the items are assumed to measure the same trait or quality. For this reason, it is often used for calculating split-half reliability.

Other Correlation Coefficients

The Pearson *r* is so widely used in calculating a coefficient that it is expressed as a simple *r*. A number of other methods are used for specific situations when the data don't conform to the requirements of the Pearson coefficient, and they are usually identified in a subscript following the *r*.

Spearman Rho

This coefficient, developed by Charles Spearman, is also called the "rank-order" correlation coefficient. It is used when the samples are small and when the data are arranged in ordinal, or rank-order, form.

Biserial

This method is used when the two sets of data are continuous but one has been "dichotomized." For example, age groups may be reported as "under 65" or "65 and older." Or a specific type of behavior may be considered normal when it occurs infrequently, but abnormal if it occurs frequently. Depending on an arbitrary point in the frequency of occurrence, the behavior may be reported as "symptomatic" or "asymptomatic." If we wanted to find a correlation between scores on a test and behavior that we designated as symptomatic, we would use a biserial coefficient.

Point-Biserial

This coefficient is used when one set of data is continuous and the other set is truly dichotomous, such as gender or pregnant/not pregnant. The nature of the dichotomy may be ambiguous and open to some interpretation. For example, the point-biserial approach is frequently used for categories where the dividing line may not be absolute, such as the separation of a population into those who abuse drugs and those who don't, or criminals and law-abiding citizens. In such cases, the dividing line must be carefully defined. For example, "law abiding" may mean citizens who have not been convicted of a felony but who may have been convicted of a misdemeanor, such as highway speeding.

Phi Coefficient

Symbolized by the Greek letter *phi*, this coefficient is used to find the relationship between two variables that are both dichotomous.

Correlation of Scores Between Two Tests

One word of caution is needed in the use of correlation coefficients. The reliability of a coefficient that describes the relationship between two sets of data depends largely on the reliability of each set of data being examined. Let's assume that a therapist wants to use a combination of a reading test and an intelligence test as a measure of a child's reading retardation. Each of the two tests has a respectable reliability coefficient of .90, and the correlation between them is a reasonable .80. If the therapist wanted to use the difference between the standard scores as a guide to the level of reading deficiency, the reliability of this difference score, the mathematics of which we won't go into now, would be only a moderate .50. The possibilities of error in the two tests themselves, and in the correlation between them are magnified.

Levels of Confidence

The term confidence level means just that. It informs us of the confidence we can place in figures derived from statistical calculations, and it is expressed in probabilities. So, as we have seen, we can state with 68 percent confidence that any score on a single test will occur within plus-or-minus one standard deviation from the mean of that test, and with 95 percent confidence that it will occur within plus-or-minus two standard deviations.

However, as the term is often used in test manuals and reports on research findings, it usually refers to the odds that a statistic could have occurred by chance. Sometimes referred to as the significance level, it is a simple and easy way of understanding the probability that a correlation could be a mathematical fluke or coincidence, or that a difference in the mean scores of two populations is a real difference and not the result of chance or sampling error.

To find the confidence we can put in a correlation, we need two figures: the correlation coefficient and the number of scores. Turning to the table of significance in any statistics textbook, we refer to the appropriate row and column to learn that a Pearson *r* of .899, for ten scores is "significant at the .01 level." This means that the likelihood of a correlation like this resulting from sampling error, or chance, is less than one in 100. It is conventional to consider a confidence level of .05 (often expressed as "$p < .05$") the dividing line between correlations that are deemed "statistically significant" and those that are likely to have been the result of chance.

On the practical level, most therapists will have contact with confidence levels or significance levels only when they read the descriptions or reviews of tests. Test manuals often include information on the validation of tests that inform readers that correlations (or differences) were found to be "statistically significant."

SUMMARY

Statistics permit researchers to organize large amounts of information in such ways that the relationships between them can be understood. This chapter was designed to introduce readers with little or no background in statistics to the basic concepts in the field. Our underlying purpose was to help such readers understand the terms and references that they are likely to encounter in test manuals and reviews.

All statistical calculations in the measurement of human characteristics begin with frequency distributions. Measurements or scores are arranged in order so that patterns can emerge. From such arrangements, we are usually interested in finding the qualities that describe the distribution, particularly the central tendency, the range, and the variability.

The most important measure of variability is the deviation from the mean, which informs us of the way in which the scores are clustered around the mean. The most useful way of dealing with this dispersion is the standard deviation, which provides a common method for comparing measurements or scores from different sources.

One major function of the "bell-shaped" curve that depicts graphically a normal distribution is to interpret and clarify the meaning of the standard deviations. One standard deviation in either direction from the mean encompasses 34.13 percent of all the measurements or scores. This means that about two-thirds of all the measurements fall within one standard deviation above and below the mean. Ninety-five percent will be included in two standard deviations plus and minus, and very close to 100 percent of the cases will be no more than three standard deviations plus and minus. The system provides a way of seeing clearly just how a particular person's measurement or score deviates from the average.

Because a "raw score" provides little normative information, raw scores are usually converted into "derived" scores, such as percentiles, CEEB scores, IQ scores, *z* scores, and *T* scores, most of which are based on standard deviations. Scores that are obtained on standardized tests, then, can be compared.

A standardized test must meet three criteria:

- It must be based on a standard task.
- It must be administered with standard directions under standard conditions.
- It must have been "normed," or standardized on a sample of subjects who are representative of the population for whom the test is designed.

A number of methods have been developed for choosing representative samples. Many of the more useful and accurate methods are based on one or another of the forms of random sampling. In addition, there are numbers of statistical methods for calculating the probability that any obtained score is the "true" score, both in sampling and in testing. These "standard errors" for estimating the role of chance in distorting the results are usually based on the concept of standard deviation.

The whole field of testing is based on the idea that there are relationships between sets of data and that these relationships can be identified (correlated) and used to measure the reliability and validity of the tests. A number of correlation methods have been developed for specific instruments and purposes. The most widely used were explained in this chapter.

REFERENCES

Bronowski, J. (1973). *The ascent of man*. Boston: Little, Brown.

Cronbach, L. J. (1970). *Essentials of psychological testing* (3rd ed.). New York: Harper and Row.

Gould, S. J. (1985). The median isn't the message. *Discover, 6*(6), 40–42.
Gruber, H. E. (1979). A Dr. Strangelove of the mind. A review of *Cyril Burt, psychologist,* by L. S. Hearnshaw. *New York Times Book Review,* Dec. 16, 1979, p. 3.
Kamin, L. J. (1974). *The science and politics of IQ.* Hillsdale, NJ: Erlbaum.
Patton, M. Q. (2002). *Qualitative research and evaluation methods* (3rd ed.). Beverly Hills, CA: Sage.

Chapter 6

OBJECTIVE TESTS

Objective psychometric testing was developed for the measurement of intelligence, abilities, and aptitudes. Despite disagreements about what these tests really measure, the results remain fairly stable over time and across situations.

Personality and psychopathology are far more complex areas, and the ability of tests to assess traits or characteristics such as anxiety or dependence is far less accurate or useful. Scores must be validated and interpreted in the context of the individual, the situation, and the time. As Gary Groth-Marnat put it, ". . . a *T* score of 75 on the MMPI scale 9 (mania) takes on an entirely different meaning for a highly functioning physician than for an individual with a poor history of work and interpersonal relationships" (1990, p. 4).

So-called "objective" testing does not attempt to eliminate subjectivity. Subjectivity is built into any procedure. It emerges in the organization of the procedure, its construction and design, the choice of items, the administration, the scoring procedures, and the interpretation of the scores. Objective testing simply tries to minimize the variability of scorer judgments. This is done mainly by making the scoring of responses uniform. Answers to questions or tasks are scored in terms of how they meet predetermined criteria. In addition, objective approaches may attempt to provide some way of estimating whatever variability does exist in order to provide an indication of the confidence that the examiner can put in any particular instrument or procedure.

TESTS AND TYPICAL BEHAVIOR

Lee Cronbach (1970) distinguished between two major categories of tests. Intelligence tests, aptitude tests, and achievement tests are tests of maximum behavior. They seek to find out what someone can do. In contrast, personality tests and most tests used for assessment or diagnosis are tests of typical behavior – what someone usually does, which is far more difficult to identify. Someone with an IQ of 80 is not likely to be able to fake an IQ of 110. But people can easily fake, distort, or withhold information about their typical behavior, either deliberately or unconsciously. Moreover, some of the traits or behaviors that we want to identify show up only in specific contexts: at work, in the family, or at school.

The obvious way to ascertain someone's typical behavior is by observing him or her over an extended period of time and in a variety of contexts. However, it is difficult to get a fix on typical behavior without bringing into play the dynamics of the Hawthorne Effect, a working out of the Heisenberg Principle that you can't be sure that what you observe would be the same if you didn't observe it. The Hawthorne Effect is a phenomenon named after a well-known study at the Hawthorne, New York plant of the Western Electric Company on the effects of lighting changes. Every change – increasing the light, decreasing the light, going back to the original lighting – improved production.

Therapists generally note and consider the ways their patients and clients behave during a therapy session. While such observations are essential in evaluation, they are not truly observations of typical behavior. Moreover, even this kind of limited direct observation is often not feasible during an intake assessment, or in making preliminary decisions about assigning a client or patient to a therapy, or in determining a course of treatment when a decision must be made within a short period of time. Even for outpatients or for the clients of therapists in private practice, such direct observations are not likely to extend over enough time or to provide a variety of situations to get a fix on typical behavior. It is particularly difficult to reproduce the social situations in which typical behavior may occur.

Performance or Situation Testing

Abandoning the attempt to ascertain "typical" behavior in general, the performance tester may create a situation in which he or she can sample subjects' behaviors under specific standardized conditions so that they can be compared with those of others. While this technique is useful in testing for leadership or resourcefulness or job performance, it is not very useful in most therapeutic situations unless the client's problem is situation-specific, as in test anxiety, for example.

Some arts therapists contend that the way a patient or client works on a drawing or moves is an analog, or an "equivalent" of experience outside the studio. In fact, the creative therapy approach is based in part on such an assumption. While this may be a legitimate approach to therapy, it addresses neither the problem of "typical" behavior outside of the studio or office, nor that of objective assessment.

Self-Report Questionnaires

For the most part, psychologists and other therapists have tended to substitute reported behavior for behavior that they actually observe; this is done, usually, by asking the patient or client to respond to items in a questionnaire or self-report. Some of these must be scored and interpreted by psychologists or trained examiners; others are either self-scoring or easily administered. These are among the most commonly used assessment instruments and, in many settings, they are almost always included in the assessment procedure.

There are different kinds of self-report measures, including inventories, checklists, scales, and indexes. Inventories and checklists usually present a range of behaviors, thoughts and feelings that are identified by the patient or client as being representative of his or her behaviors, thoughts and feelings. Scales and indexes often ask questions that are scored on a numerically continuous basis; that is, they don't usually ask for answers that are dichotomous (yes-no, for example). The terms scales and indexes are sometimes used interchangeably, although there are some technical differences between them.

Limitations of Self-Report Questionnaires

There are problems in interpreting the information derived from self-reports. In reporting typical behavior, the patient or client would appear to be the single best observer. In many ways this is true. But there are a number of problems that arise when we ask someone to report on his or her own behavior.

Ambiguity

We have pointed out the difficulty involved in avoiding ambiguity in the posing of a question. Reviewing an instrument designed to detect borderline patients, Charles A. Peterson (1978) cited one question: "Have you had any strange or dramatic sexual or religious experiences or adventures?" Peterson wondered, "Are we talking sodomy in Georgia, or hot tubs in Marin County?" (p. 265). A question like, "Do you take suggestions from others?" can rarely be answered with a straight "yes" or "no" and, as Cronbach put it, requires the test-taker to "average his memories" (1970, p. 494). What percent of the time is meant by words like "usually," "often," "frequently," "seldom," and "rarely?"

Some techniques have been developed to overcome the ambiguity inherent in most questions. Many of these operate by bringing clients into the process, as in asking them to help interpret their perception of the question or their response. One such technique, the "couplet" response, will be described later.

Impression Management

Early scholars of social behavior (Goffman, 1959, 1963; Braginsky, Braginsky & Ring, 1969) coined the term impression management to describe the common tendency to influence the impressions that others have of us. We dress, speak, and act in ways that are designed to convey an impression to others. We may withhold or suppress information that is inconsistent with such impressions, we may shade the truth, and we may adjust our movements and our facial expressions to reinforce that image. Not all of these techniques are conscious or deliberate. Some, in fact, may be viewed as aspects of personality (Nunnally, 1978).

Faking. Test-takers may have reasons to elevate scores or to depress them. An applicant for a job is likely to "fake good" in an attempt to enhance his or her attractiveness to the employer. On the other hand, a criminal who is undergoing a court-ordered psychiatric examination may "fake bad" in order to bolster a plea of insanity. Patients and clients may exaggerate symptoms in an attempt to enlist sympathy or to get accepted to a therapeutic program.

Such exaggeration may or may not be deliberate. Cronbach (1970) described the so-called "hello-good-bye" effect. This refers to the tendency of patients seeking treatment, when their symptoms are at a peak and very much on their minds, to present a picture of distress. On the other hand, when the patient is discharged, "the self-description glows with the psychological counterpart of 'Thanks, Doc. I feel fine . . .' It would be ungrateful indeed for the departing client to dwell on the symptoms the therapy left untouched" (p. 496).

Response Sets. When test-takers respond in characteristic ways, regardless of the content of the question, they are described as exhibiting "response styles" or "response sets" (Jackson & Messick, 1962). Response style is some times seen as a manifestation of personality, reflecting processes that the psychoanalytically oriented see as unconscious and behaviorists see as learned.

Many of these response sets are so common among test-takers that they have been identified, studied, and even measured. Allen L. Edwards (1957, 1966) studied one of these in depth, which he called social desirability. He found that the responses individuals make on any kind of personality inventory reflect, at least in some degree, their perception of socially acceptable answers as much as (and often more than) what they truly feel or believe.

Among other response sets that have been identified and described are: Acquiescence, or a tendency to answer "true" or "agree" or "like," rather than "false" or "disagree" or "dislike." Resistance or the tendency to disagree has also been noted. Caution, or a reluctance to commit oneself is another; a cautious response style might result in a disproportionate number of "cannot say" responses. Deviance, or the tendency to give uncommon or unusual answers, which may confound interpretation, can also be present.

There are three basic approaches to the problem of response bias. One is to view response bias as a minor nuisance, the influence of which can be minimized by careful test construction: by modifying the wording of items, by disguising an item to mask the true purpose, by asking "subtle" questions whose relevance to the trait that is in question is not clear, or by employing forced-choice items which force a test-taker to give the "best" answer of a series ("Which of the following most closely describes your situation?").

A second is to build "validity" or "correction" scales into the test to alert the examiner that response bias has influenced the score, and even to correct for bias. This method is in fact employed in the Minnesota Multiphasic Personality Inventory. A third is to identify and measure the response set itself as a manifestation of a personality trait. To some observers, this response style may tell more about the test-taker than the actual responses. In fact, some response styles may be diagnostic indicators of psychiatric disorders.

APPROACHES TO OBJECTIVE SELF-REPORT CONSTRUCTION

There are three major approaches to the construction of self-report instruments. Below, we describe them and provide examples of each.

Logical or Intuitive Test Construction

Also known as "content," "intuitive," or "rational" approaches, logical test construction involves creating collections of items that have been selected because they seem to be appropriate on a commonsense or intuitive level. For example, if you wanted to develop a test to identify compulsive overeating, intuitive logic is likely to suggest that the test include such items as:

1. I often think about food while I am at work. (T) (F)
2. I usually nibble on snacks while watching TV. (T) (F)
3. I often snack or eat between meals. (T) (F)
4. I frequently eat when I'm upset or nervous. (T) (F)

This kind of test is direct and it provides test-takers with the security of knowing that they are in control. There are no hidden purposes or agendas, and the responses are accepted at face value.

However, the very openness of this "face validity" approach creates a number of problems, including all of those we described earlier. While validity scales can be used to detect faking or the influence of response sets, the approach to the construction of most tests in this category is to modify the test construction and to consider the scores in light of personal history and other assessment instruments. This is a reasonable precaution for any test.

One device that is sometimes employed in such tests to minimize the effect of response bias is to use forced-choice items. Such questions force the test-taker to choose one of several choices. If all the items have the same level of social desirability, there is no clear way to fake and no reason for it. Moreover, there is no way to evade the question with "cannot answer."

A very different approach was developed by Frank B. McMahon (1969). Decrying the tendency of psychologists to see a client as "a spidery maze of disguised sickness" who must be outfoxed (p. 55), McMahon created what he called a "couplet" style of questioning, designed to clarify the way the test-taker interprets the question. For example:

> In my family there is not much love and companionship. (T) (F)
> IF TRUE: I get enough love and companionship from
> others (friends, other relatives, etc.). (T) (F)

The couplet style, said McMahon, does two things: it signals areas in which the patient wants further discussion and it relies heavily on the patient to clarify the answer, so that the examiner does not draw unwarranted conclusions (p. 57). Below, we describe a widely used instrument built on a logical, or intuitive, base.

The Beck Depression Inventory

The Beck Depression Inventory (BDI) was first developed in 1961 (Beck, Ward, Mendelson, Mock, & Erbaugh, 1961). Based on depressed individuals' idiosyncratic descriptions of their symptoms, the original descriptions were collapsed into 21 items, a characteristic that was kept in the second edition (Beck & Steer, 1996). Keyed to the diagnostic criteria of the *DSM* to improve content validity and changed with subsequent *DSM* editions, the BDI was designed to assess existence and severity of symptoms of depression in psychiatrically diagnosed adolescents and adults. Currently the second edition of the BDI (BDI-II; Beck, Steer, & Brown, 1996) and a range of short and other forms are in use.

The 21 items or sets of statements are answered on a scale of 0 to 3. The test-taker is asked to report on his or her feelings for the last two weeks. Each of the sets consists of four statements ranging from 0, or no complaint ("I do not feel sad"), to a major complaint ("I am so sad or unhappy that I can't stand it"). Items deal with cognitive and affective subjects, such as pessimism, guilt, crying, indecisiveness. Other items deal with somatic and performance elements, such as sleep difficulties and loss of interest in sex. If a subject chooses more than one statement in an item, the highest answer is calculated into the score.

Psychometric Properties. While the items were developed on the basis of intuitive judgment, data on six patient groups were gathered in validating the instrument, including those with depression, dysthymia, and alcohol abuse (Sundberg, 1992, p. 81). Content, construct and concurrent validity studies were undertaken and were generally supportive of the BDI's value. Content validity has been based, not surprisingly, on the BDI's correlation with *DSM* criteria.

The BDI has been widely used for many years. An analysis of a number of studies (a meta-analysis) using the original BDI showed an acceptable mean correlation between the BDI and clinical ratings of depression in psychiatric samples (.72) and a moderate correlation (.60) with normal subjects (Beck & Steer, 1988). The internal consistency, calculated by Cronbach's coefficient alpha for 25 studies, ranged from .73 to .95, with a mean coefficient for psychiatric populations of .86 (Conoley, 1992, p. 78). While test-retest reliabilities were reported, they were of dubious value, because the symptoms of depression are so variable over time.

Assets and Limitations. The BDI is brief, it can be answered in five to ten minutes, and it is a simple and direct measure for depression that is useful as part of an evaluation. However, there are some cautions to be noted. Collie W. Conoley, reviewing the BDI in the *Eleventh Mental Measurements Yearbook* (1992) wrote: "Caution is imperative in using the BDI with persons who might wish to hide their suicidal intentions or, conversely, would like to overestimate their depression" (p. 78). The BDI manual warns against using the BDI for screening to identify depressed persons, especially in the elderly population (Sharp & Lipsky, 2002).

Criterion-Keyed Test Construction

This approach, also referred to as "empirically keyed" or the method of "contrasted groups," or "defined groups" is frequently used for differential diagnosis as well as for screening. It is based squarely on statistical correlations. As with rational test construction, the items in a criterion-keyed test are usually developed intuitively. What distinguishes this type of instrument is that the items are subjected to rigorous statistical analysis.

Let's suppose that you think that the kind of music that people prefer reflects their levels of self-esteem. So you have developed a self-report instrument that asks people to listen to a varied selection of musical compositions and to check those they like or dislike. You will then try the procedure on at least two groups. The first group or "criterion" group consists of subjects who have already been diagnosed as suffering from low self-esteem. A "control" group (or groups) of people who are presumed to be "normal" in terms of self-esteem makes up the second group. After comparing the scores, you will discover whether they do, in fact, discriminate between members of the two groups. If you find even a modest correlation, you will continue to refine your instrument by keeping those items that discriminate in a statistically meaningful way between the members of the two groups and discarding those parts of the procedure that do not.

In contrast with the logical or intuitive approach, the empirically-keyed items that are finally incorporated do not necessarily have high face validity. The questions don't have to possess any apparent commonsense relationship with the construct for which we are probing, and they are not necessarily assumed to represent samples of behavior. If we find that people with low self-esteem tend to answer "I don't know" more frequently than members of the control group, this response would be noted as a possible sign, or indicator, of low self-esteem, regardless of the content of the question. In using this approach, we avoid the problem of guessing whether the test-taker is telling the truth. As Leona E. Tyler (1963) put it, "We search for behavioral correlates of what persons say about themselves, and give up the essentially unanswerable question about whether consciously or unconsciously, they are telling the truth" (p. 77).

Because empirical keying is a powerful approach to discrimination, this kind of item analysis may be used to develop "validity scales." Such scales don't address the clinical issues, but they do serve as indicators of the test-taker's response style that may have distorted the scores, for example, the tendency to give socially desirable answers rather than true answers.

Among questionnaires, empirically keyed tests are probably the most valid and reliable of the instruments used for personality assessment and differential diagnosis. The Minnesota Multiphasic Personality Inventory (MMPI) is a self-report inventory "primarily designed to aid in clinical diagnosis and in the assessment of general psychopathology of adults," (Rush, First, & Blacker, 2007, p. 89). The MMPI uses an interesting combination of sample and sign approaches.

The MMPI

Originally developed in the 1930s by psychologist Starke R. Hathaway and psychiatrist John C. McKinley as the Medical and Psychiatric Inventory, the test was renamed when it was published in the early 1940s by the University of Minnesota Press.

Starting with a collection of about 1000 statements about feelings, attitudes, and symptoms, Hathaway and McKinley asked a group of diagnosed psychiatric patients to answer "true" or "false" to each item. Another group of people – a "normal" control group – was drawn from hospital visitors, normal clients at the University of Minnesota Testing Bureau, local WPA workers, and general medical patients who were asked to answer the same questions. The results were tabulated and analyzed to discover statistically significant differences between the criterion group (actually eight distinct clinical groups from the university hospital) and the control group. For example, a response was scored on the scale for Hypochondria (Hs) only if members of the criterion group – patients diagnosed with hypochondria – gave that response more frequently than did normal control group. The 504 test items that were finally selected were later expanded to 566 through the addition of two scales and the repetition of 16 items in different content areas. There were 26 such content categories, including general health, family issues, sexual identification, religious attitudes, and psychiatric symptoms (Cohen et al., 1992, p. 417). While most of the questions were relatively obvious and dealt with psychiatric, psychological, neurological, or physical symptoms, some were obscure or "subtle," dealing with topics whose relevance to the problem was not intuitively obvious. For example, one item dealt with teasing animals.

On the face of it, this question does not seem to be related to depression, but it was included in the depression scale simply because empirically it was answered "false" more frequently by depressed than by normal subjects.

The experiences clinicians had with the MMPI added valuable information about interpreting the scores. It was found that certain combinations, or profiles, of scores might be far more revealing than any single score. A high score on the Schizophrenia (Sc) scale was not necessarily indicative of schizophrenia, because the various scales were usually viewed as continua; the very fact that 16 items were repeated in different scales indicated that the categories overlapped. Because literal interpretations of the names of the scales would be inaccurate, MMPI scales were usually referred to by number rather than by name.

Since the development of the MMPI in 1940s, a multitude of new supplementary scales were designed for use with various populations, or for personality traits that had not been treated in the original scales (anxiety, repression, ego strength, and over-controlled hostility, for example), spurring the publication of a number of guides (often referred to by clinicians as "cookbooks") that provide diagnostic interpretations of MMPI profiles.

The MMPI-2

As a result of criticisms, the MMPI-2 was developed in 1989. In order not to lose the benefit of the enormous research base collected over half a century and not to lose the clinicians who were dedicated to the original MMPI, the restandardization committee decided to maintain the basic format, including the original validity scales, to which three new validity scales were added. Objectionable content was deleted from some of the original clinical scales, and additional supplementary scales were added, to assess personality factors such as fears, obsessions, health concerns, anger, cynicism, self-esteem, and social discomfort, using both rational and statistical procedures. The MMPI-2 consists of eight basic syndrome scales:

Hypochondriasis (Hs)	Paranoia (Pa)
Depression (D)	Psychasthenia (Pt)
Hysteria (Hy)	Schizophrenia (Sc)
Psychopathic Deviate (Pd)	Hypomania (Ma)

The two basic clinical scales are Masculinity-Femininity (Mf) and Social Introversion-Extroversion (Si). There are three scales to address test-taking attitudes, Lie (L), Infrequency (F), and Correction/Defensiveness (K). Additional scales can be scored to assist in interpretation of the basic scales, for example, Type A Behavior and Bizarre Mentation, and multiple other scales (Rush, First, & Blacker, 2007).

Restandardization. The most significant change distinguishing the MMPI from the MMPI-2 is the restandardization that took place on 1,462 women and 1,138 men from seven states, recruited through newspaper advertisements and random sampling solicitations. The restandardization group was matched up to the 1980 U.S. census data on demographics, including age, sex, ethnicity, and family income (Butcher, 1990). However, while the original MMPI was skewed towards a normal sample with a limited education, the MMPI-2 is skewed towards a population that is educated beyond the general population, with a higher occupational status, raising some concerns regarding the test's suitability in interpreting test results from lower socioeconomic groups (Archer, 1992).

Assets and Limitations. While the revisions may have addressed some of the problems, others persist, including the overlap in content between scales, limiting the usefulness of the MMPI-2 for differential diagnosis between psychiatric groups; the traditional scale labels, many of which are based on obsolete psychiatric concepts and names, and some of which no longer even appear in the *DSM* (Groth-Marnat, 2009). Although MMPI scores can be used with various cultural groups, clinicians must be careful in interpreting scores. While scores can be useful in yielding valuable personality data, they may also reflect cultural norms. While, there are many available language translations of the MMPI-2 their cultural appropriateness can be questionable unless norms have been developed for that culture.

Despite its considerable shortcomings, it has been found that even the original MMPI could exhibit a significant degree of incremental validity for personality assessment, when it was combined with social history (Garb, 1984). It has been found that diagnostic accuracy increased when MMPI test results were combined with other patient data (Schwartz & Wiedel, 1981). While the test takes 1-1.5 hours to administer and has more than 100 scales, it can be quickly scored via computer and for this reason is still considered an efficient clinical assessment tool (Rush, First, & Blacker, 2007).

Theory-Based Test Construction

Until the development of the Minnesota Multiphasic Personality Inventory, most inventories were scored on the basis of how well responses conformed to a theory of personality or of disorder (Levitt & Duckworth, 1984, p. 467). In fact, theory-based instruments are sometimes called "construct" tests.

The Myers-Briggs Type Indicators

The Myers-Briggs Type Indicator (MBTI) was developed by Katharine C. Briggs and her daughter, Isabel Briggs Myers, after 20 years of research and informal testing. It has been widely available, however, only since 1975. The MBTI is a forced-choice self-report inventory, basically self-administered, that classifies individuals according to an organization based largely on Carl Jung's theory of conscious psychological types. The instrument rests on an assumption that behind the apparent random and diffuse behaviors of individuals is an order based on their conscious choices.

Individual differences in perception and judging, according to Isabel Myers (1962, p. 1), result in "corresponding differences in their reactions, in their interests, values, needs, and motivations, in what they do best, and in what they like to do." In contrast with traits, which are often described as inhering in people, personality types claim to be nothing more than descriptions of the ways people characteristically behave, on the basis of their choice of styles.

The MBTI measures four independent dimensions of an individual's preference styles. Each dimension is presented in dichotomous terms; the test-taker must choose between one preference or its opposite, on the ground that each individual relies primarily on his or her preferred processes.

The Extroversion-Introversion (E-I) Scale. This dimension relates to a general attitude towards the world. People are seen as either basically extroverted (E) or introverted (I). This E-I dimension relates, not specifically to gregariousness or shyness, as is commonly believed, but to where an individual chooses to direct his or her attention and energy. Extroverts will focus on other persons or events, will prefer to communicate by talking rather than writing, and need to experience the world. Introverts will focus on their inner world, preferring to understand before doing, "and so need time to reflect before acting" (Myers & Myers, 1987, p. 2).

The Sensing-Intuition (S-N) Scale. This dimension (one of the two "function" processes) relates to the ways individuals acquire information or find out about things. Those who rely on sensing (S) focus on factual data and are careful with detail. Those who rely on intuition (N) try to go beyond the specifics and the evidence of their senses, to grasp the larger meaning, the implications in, and the overall possibilities of the data.

The Thinking-Feeling (T-F) Scale. This is the second of the function processes. It relates to the ways people make decisions. Thinking (T) types prefer reason and logic, relying on analysis and a weighing of the evidence, and focus on the logical consequences of a choice or a behavior. Feeling (F) types rely on person-centered values. They value harmony and are more likely to focus on the interpersonal consequences of their behavior more than on its logic.

The Judging-Perceiving (J-P) Scale. This scale deals with the fundamental way people orient toward the outer world. Judging (J) types prefer order, structure, and organization. They want to make prompt decisions and come to closure. Perceiving (P) types prefer a flexible, spontaneous approach. They are willing to suspend judgments and keep options open, preferring to understand rather than to control, adapting to situations as they develop.

Because each person's typology is based on combinations of the four preferences, there are 16 possible types, none of which is deemed superior to another.

The J-P scale, while it deals with an independent dimension, also provides a key to the integration of the two function scales, S-N (related to perception) and T-F (related to judging). People do use both of these functions, but they are more comfortable with one – the dominant process – and tend to use it more frequently than the other, the auxiliary process. The J-P scale serves to indicate which is the dominant process and which is the auxiliary.

There is an intricate and complex relationship between the dominant and the auxiliary process. For extroverts, the dominant process will take precedence in the behavior presented to the outside world, the realm in which they are most at home, and the auxiliary in the internal world. For introverts, the opposite obtains, with the dominant process taking precedence in the world within, in which introverts tend to direct most of their energies.

The key to determining which of the two functions is dominant is the JP scale. The extrovert who has a judging preference relies predominantly on either thinking or feeling, and the perceptual function, S or N, becomes secondary. So someone with a profile of ESFJ will be an extrovert whose preferred decision-making process is feeling, with an auxiliary perceptual process of sensing.

For introverts, the process is somewhat different. Since the J versus P preference indicates someone's reaction to the outside world and since the introvert operates largely in the inner world, the introvert's J or P score points to the auxiliary rather than the dominant process. So, for an INTP, the P tells us that N is the auxiliary process (apparent in observed behavior), and thinking the dominant inwardly directed process.

Applications and Uses. The MBTI has been used for a remarkable variety of purposes. Obvious applications are to predict an individual's behavior, to act as a guide in career planning, and to predict compatibility between people. However, in addition, it has been used as the basis for modifying or strengthening someone's coping strategies; for remediation; for conflict resolution; for career planning; for personnel selection; for counseling with individuals, couples and families; for leadership training; and for teaching (McCaulley, 1981, 1990–1991). While it was designed for personality assessment in finding differences between normal people, Myers (1962) suggested it might be useful in psychotherapy in "normalizing individual differences" (p. 78), although the application is not entirely clear.

Technical Data. While the MBTI is based on theory, it has been the subject of considerable empirical validation over the years. There are two ways of scoring the MBTI. The one much preferred by the authors is a dichotomous typology; that is, someone is assumed to be of one or the other type. These are seen as qualitatively different rather than as extremes on a continuum. The other, far more useful method for psychometricians, is a continuous score along the E-I dimension. Anthony J. DeVito, who reviewed the MBTI in the *Ninth Mental Measurements Yearbook* (1985), wrote, "The continuous score is least emphasized in practice because it is a departure from type theory, yet it is this score that is most useful in evaluating the instrument's psychometric properties and analyzing research findings" (p. 1030).

Test-retest reliabilities conducted by the authors and their associates are troubling to many psychometricians because of the emphasis on treating the scores in terms of dichotomies. Mary H. McCaulley, president of the Center for Applications of Psychological Type, described "the critical question" in test-retest reliability as "how often on retest do individuals come out the same type – that is, fall on the same side on each of the four dichotomous preferences – as in the original testing" (1981, p. 318). In nine samples for which retests were administered from intervals of five weeks to six years, a range of from 31 percent to 61 percent of the subjects came out in the same type (1981, p. 318). The manual reports data on alpha coefficients of internal consistency, which tend to range from acceptable to high levels (Myers, Kirby, & Myers, 1998).

Validity studies have focused on several dimensions of the test. The MBTI manual reports reasonable concurrent validity with other tests that focus on similar constructs. Validity information in the manual for the MBTI Form M breaks down information according to various personality assessments and by individual categories in those assessments (Consulting Psychologists Press, 2009). Older studies of other forms of the MBTI found evidence of construct validity in the career choices of individuals who chose the fields that might be expected in terms of their types (McCaulley, 1981, 1990–1991; Kelly, 1985).

Of particular interest to arts therapists, perhaps, is the implication of several studies involving behavioral correlations of the MBTI. Carskadon (1979) found strong correlations between the Jungian typology and the behaviors that were suggested. For example, people who were identified as extroverts by the MBTI were found to exhibit the kinds of behaviors which we associate with extroversion: physical proximity to others, tendencies to talk more, and better recall of people's names, for example. Some movement analysts have been involved in attempts to correlate the results of movement analysis with typological constructs.

Assets and Limitations. The outstanding asset of this instrument is its non judgmental quality, unusual in personality instruments. As a result, the MBTI lends itself to the sharing of results with clients. While it is widely used in business, in education, and in marriage and personnel counseling, the MBTI has gained limited acceptance among psychologists and psychiatrists. Jungian theory is not widely accepted among psychologists. As a result, they cannot accept validation of the underlying constructs.

However, the research that has been conducted on the MBTI has yielded considerable empirical data that should make the instrument useful even for those who reject the theoretical base (see for example, Quenk, 2009). Nevertheless, differences in perception of the instrument create a barrier between those who are theory-oriented and those who are psychometrically inclined. "The principal stumbling block to more widespread acceptance of the MBTI," wrote Jerry Wiggins (1987), "lies in the structural model of bipolar discontinuous types to which the test authors are firmly committed" with its assumption that the poles "are all assumed to be genuine dichotomies with true zero points" (p. 538). DeVito contended that, for all its psychometric strength, the failure to provide normative data for continuous scores keeps the MBTI from meeting the criteria for being a psychological test (p. 1032). Since the authors do not see the procedure as a test, anyway, this may not be a serious shortcoming from their point of view. Fortunately for those who are interested in psychometric approaches, there are numbers of externally developed validity and reliability studies.

PROGRAM TESTS AND ALTERNATIVE FORMS

"Program" testing is a term that Lee Cronbach (1970) used to describe tests that are designed to fit the needs of a particular program, institution, or clientele. Program tests are frequently adaptations of existing tests, with changes in the length of the test, the design of tasks or items, or the administration or scoring of the test.

Those who design program tests sometimes assume that their modified instruments can ride on the validity or reliability of the prototype. However, the reliability or validity of a procedure refers only to that specific procedure as it was studied. Any time a procedure is changed in any significant way, its psychometric properties change. We cannot assume that the reliability coefficients that were calculated for MMPI automatically apply to MMPI-2. Nor can we assume that different forms of a test that bear the same name – Forms F, G, and M of the MBTI, for example – are necessarily equal in reliability or validity.

There may be legitimate reasons why a therapist may want to modify or adapt a test. For example, the clientele for which the test is to be used may be different demographically from the standardization sample. In such a case, the first order of business should be to consult the test manual. Some carefully researched tests may offer local norms as well as national norms. However, if the therapist believes that the only reasonable alternative is to adapt an existing test, he or she should be aware of two problems. One is the possibility of copyright infringement, the other the loss of the psychometric properties of the original. Every test must be standardized and validated on its own, even if the two tests share the same principles or the same format.

This last caution applies as well to using a test that bears a resemblance to one that has been carefully normed and validated. From time to time, test manuals may be misleading in their citation of research data. Cronbach (1970, p. 118) cited one manual for a test battery that described what appeared to be impressive evidence of validity. However, nearly all the "evidence" had been collected on an entirely different set of tests, used for a very different purpose. Presumably, the assumption was that, since the tests bore a superficial similarity, the validity data were equally applicable.

Even when tests are based on the same theoretical principles and designed for the same purpose for the same clientele, changes in the wording of questions or the numbers of questions will affect both reliability and validity. For example, the 70-item Keirsey Temperament Sorter (Keirsey & Bates, 1984) was designed to discriminate among types in terms of the same four Jungian-based dimensions as the MBTI, to which it bears a superficial resemblance. However, the items are more ambiguous and open to various interpretations. For example, question 19 asks, "Are you more comfortable in making (a) logical judgments (b) value judgments" (p. 6). How do you answer if you think that you make choices about the clash of values in a logical fashion? And question 51 asks if you are more likely to trust your experience or your hunch. How do you answer that question if you trust your hunches because they are based on your experience?

There are other differences between the two, in length, in form, and in scoring. All of these mean that we cannot assume that the two instruments can be said to have the same validity or the same reliability. Any time a therapist creates or uses a program test, or an adaptation of an existing test, or a test that is similar to the one that is known to have been carefully researched, or even an alternate or equivalent form of the same test (as in the case of the MMPI and the MMPI-2), the best advice is to proceed with caution unless the psychometric qualities are known.

THE TEST MANUAL AS A SOURCE OF INFORMATION

The test manual is your first source of information about a test; often it is your best source. Nevertheless, all test manuals are not equally useful and, as Buros and others have pointed out, some may actually be misleading. The easy accessibility of the Internet can make locating test information and test reviews easier than in earlier decades. The interested user can find detailed information, either through *Mental Measurements Yearbook* online, or other similar online sources.

Use and Applications

A test cannot be described as a "good test" in the abstract. Without a clear idea of how you want to use the test, with what population, and for what reason, there is no way to evaluate the test. While the test manual may indicate the purpose or purposes for which the authors believe the test is useful, the key to its utility for you is its "fit" with the decisions that you must make.

Often reviews of the test, and frequently the test manual itself, will suggest how the test has been used and applied in specific situations. Again, the test's track record and the research that has been conducted provide raw material for seeing whether or not the test is a good match for your purpose.

Administration and Scoring

The issue of administration is one that goes beyond convenience, although this is certainly a consideration. The way the test is administered should be appropriate in terms of the purposes for which the test is to be used, not necessarily the purposes for which the test was designed. For example, no matter how accurate or useful a test might be for a lengthy in-depth assessment, if the purpose for which it is used is to make rapid decisions about admission or assignment, the time involved and the complexity of the test are issues to be considered. For the most part, practitioners in private practice may also prefer tests that are easy to administer and that are not time-consuming. A great many self-report inventories are available that can be useful screening or rating tools for clinicians on specific concerns. As discussed by Groth-Marnat (2009) a proliferation of tools for planning and monitoring treatment has taken place since the 1990s due in part, to the expansion of managed care and the focus on cost containment. An example is the Beck Anxiety Inventory (Beck & Steer, 1993), which is useful for measuring severity of anxiety and panic disorder symptoms. A good resource for these types of tools is the *Handbook of Psychiatric Measures* (Rush, First, & Blacker, 2007).

For any tool one chooses, the directions should be clear and appropriate for your clientele, in terms of language, levels of education and socioeconomic class, cultural or other biases that may be present both in the instructions and in the items themselves. You should evaluate both the directions that are given the test-taker and the actual content of the items. One clue to these questions is the composition of the standardization sample, which should be presented in the manual.

There are tests available that are so complex that they require special skills or training on the part of the examiner. Beyond the issue of mere complexity, the laws in some states mandate that certain tests may be administered only by licensed psychologists. This is a major consideration that you should address even before you begin to search for an assessment instrument. Scoring, too, may be an issue. Some tests cannot be scored except by someone who is highly trained in the system. This should be made clear in the manual.

Technical Data

The issues of validity, reliability, and standardization that we have discussed in the last few chapters should be addressed in this section of the manual.

Validation

In Chapter 3, we raised questions you should ask about construct validity and criterion validity. At this point, armed with some knowledge about the statistical methods for establishing validity, you should be better prepared to ask more specific questions.

Standardization. What was the composition of the standardization group? How was it selected? Are data presented that would help you decide how representative it was of your patients or clients?

Criterion Validity. What evidence is presented in the manual to support the validity of the test in terms of specific criteria? Do the studies offer evidence of the predictive value of the instrument? What populations were studied, and do they represent your clientele? Are the coefficients high enough for you to feel comfortable with the correlations? Does the manual indicate the time between the test and the criterion? What other empirical evidence is offered to suggest that the test does what you want it to do?

Reliability. What evidence is presented to support the reliability of the test itself? What evidence is presented to support the inter-observer reliability? Is special training required to approximate the reported inter-observer reliability?

Basically, you should read the manual with one central question in mind: to what extent does the test help you to make the decision that you have to make about your patient or client?

SUMMARY

Objective tests are "objective" in only one sense: subjectivity in scoring is minimized, because the criteria have been predetermined and are uniform. If an instrument or procedure has been standardized, objective approaches may also help provide a way of ascertaining how much confidence the test user can put in its reliability.

Assessment is based on ascertaining and analyzing someone's typical behavior. Assessment is usually based on behavior that is reported by patients and clients. In objective testing, this is usually done through self-report questionnaires that may take the form of inventories, checklists, scales, and indexes.

Self-report questionnaires have some inherent weaknesses, including the ambiguity that is built into questions and items, and the problem that test-takers may not all interpret questions uniformly or as the test-maker had intended. The accuracy of self-reports is also compromised by such factors as faking or lying by the test-taker, or by the influence of response sets, or response styles that reflect the particular ways individual test-takers tend to respond.

A number of approaches and techniques have been developed to deal with these problems. They include the modification of test construction and administration, the inclusion of validity or correction scales, and treating response bias as an element of the test.

There are three basic approaches to the construction of objective self-report instruments.

Logical, rational, or intuitive scales and indexes are based on the selection of items that are intuitively derived. They are face-valid and treat answers as samples of behavior. The advantage of this approach is that it is simple and clear, providing clients with a sense of collaboration in their own assessments. Among the limitations are the susceptibility of such instruments to faking and to the influence of response bias.

Criterion-keyed tests, grounded on a method that is also called the method of "contrasted groups" are based on an analysis of responses by a criterion group and a control group. The responses are compared and items that discriminate between the groups are identified. The method is based squarely on statistical correlation.

Theory-based questionnaires rest on the selection of items for which the responses conform with a theory or a particular concept. While the instruments are developed on the basis of theory, they are often validated statistically.

REFERENCES

Archer, R. P. (1992). Review of the Minnesota Multiphasic Personality Inventory. In J. J. Kramer & J. C. Conoley (Eds.), *Eleventh mental measurements yearbook* (pp. 558–562). Lincoln, NE: Buros Institute of Mental Measurement.

Beck, A. T., & Steer, R. A. (1988). *Manual for the Beck Hopelessness Scale.* San Antonio, TX: The Psychological Corporation.

Beck, A. T., Steer, R. A., & Brown, G. K. (1996). *Manual for the Beck Depression Inventory II* (2nd ed.). San Antonio, TX: The Psychological Corporation.

Beck, A., Ward, C. H., Mendelson, M., Mock, J., & Erbaugh, J. (1961). An inventory for measuring depression. *Archives of General Psychiatry, 4,* 561–571.

Braginsky, B. M., Braginsky, D. D., & Ring, K. (1969). *Methods of madness.* New York: Holt, Rinehart, and Winston.

Butcher, J. N. (1990). *MMPI-2 in psychological treatment.* New York: Oxford University Press.

Carlyn, M. (1977). An assessment of the Myers-Briggs Type Indicator. *Journal of Personality Assessment, 41,* 461–473.

Carskadon, T. G. (1979). Behavioral differences between extroverts and introverts as measured by the Myers-Briggs Type Indicator: An experimental demonstration. *Research in Psychological Type, 2,* 78–82.

Cohen, R. J., Swerdlick, M. E., & Smith, D. K. (1992). *Psychological testing and assessment.* Mountain View, CA: Mayfield.

Conoley, C. W. (1992). Review of Beck Depression Inventory, revised ed. In J. J. Kramer & J. C. Conoley (Eds.), *Eleventh mental measurements yearbook.* Lincoln, NE: Buros Institute of Mental Measurement.

Cronbach, L. J. (1970). *Essentials of psychological testing* (3rd ed.). New York: Harper and Row.

DeVito, A. J. (1985). Review of Myers-Briggs Type Indicator. In J. V. Mitchell (Ed.), *Ninth mental measurements yearbook.* Lincoln, NE: Buros Institute of Mental Measurement.

Edwards, A. L. (1957). *The social desirability variable in personality assessment and research.* New York: Dryden.

Edwards, A. L. (1966). Relationship between probability of endorsement and social desirability scale value for a set of 2,824 personality statements. *Journal of Applied Psychology, 50,* 238–239.

Goffman, E. (1959). *The presentation of self in everyday life.* New York: Anchor.

Goffman, E. (1963). *Behavior in public places.* Glencoe, IL: Free Press.

Groth-Marnat, G. (1990). *Handbook of psychological assessment.* New York: John Wiley and Sons.

Groth-Marnat, G. (2009). *Handbook of psychological assessment* (5th ed.). New York: John Wiley and Sons.

Jackson, D. N., & Messick, S. (1962). Response styles and the assessment of psychopathology. In S. Messick & J. Ross (Eds.), *Measurement in personality and cognition.* New York: Wiley.

Keirsey, D. N., & Bates, M. (1984). *Please understand me: Character and temperament types.* Del Mar, CA: Prometheus Nemesis.

Kelly, E. J. (1985). The performance of chess players. *Journal of Personality Assessment, 4*(9), 282–284.

Levitt, E. E., & Duckworth, J. C. (1984). Review of MMPI. In D. J. Keyser & R. C. Sweetland (Eds.), *Test critiques,* Vol. I. (pp. 466–471). Kansas City, MO: Test Corp. of America.

McCaulley, M. H. (1981). *Jung's Theory of psychological types and the Myers-Briggs Type Indicator.* Gainesville, FL: Center for Applications of Psychological Types.

McCaulley, M. H. (1990–1991). *The Myers-Briggs Type Indicator: A Measure for Individuals and Groups.* Gainesville, FL: Center for Application of Psychological Types. Reprinted from *Measurement and evaluation in counseling and development,* 22 (January, 1990) and 23 (January, 1991).

McMahon, F. B. (1969). Personality testing – a smoke screen against logic. *Psychology Today, 2*(8), 54–59.

Myers, K. C., & Myers, I. B. (1987). *Myers-Briggs Type Indicator, Form G self-scorable question booklet.* Palo Alto, CA: Consulting Psychologists Press.

Myers, I. B. (1962). *Manual: The Myers-Briggs Type Indicator.* Princeton, NJ: Educational Testing Service.

Myers, I. B., Kirby, L. K., & Myers, P. B. (1998). *Introduction to type.* Mountain View, CA: CPP, Inc.

Nunnally, J. C. (1978). *Psychometric theory* (2nd ed.). New York: McGraw-Hill.

Oakland, T., & Dowling, L. (1983). The Draw-A-Person Test. Validity properties for non-biased assessment. *Learning Disabilities Quarterly, 6,* 526–534.

Peterson, R. A. (1978). Review of Rorschach procedure. In O. Buros (Ed.), *Eighth mental measurements yearbook.* Highland Park, NJ: Gryphon Press.

Quenk, N. L. (2009). *Essentials of Myers-Briggs type indicator assessment.* Hoboken, NJ: John Wiley & Sons.

Rush, A. J., First, M. B., & Blacker, D. (2007). *Handbook of psychiatric measures* (2nd ed.). Washington, DC: American Psychiatric Publishing, Inc.

Schwartz, S., & Wiedel, T. C. (1981). Incremental validity of the MMPI in neurological decision-making. *Journal of Personality Assessment, 45,* 424–426.

Sharp, L. K., & Lipsky, M. S. (2002). Screening for depression across the lifespan: A review of measures for use in primary care settings. *American Family Physician, 66*(6), 1001–8.

Sundberg, N. D. (1992). Review of the Beck Depression Inventory. In J. C. Kramer & J. C. Conoley (Eds.), *Eleventh mental measurements yearbook.* Lincoln, NE: Buros Institute of Mental Measurement.

Tyler, L. E. (1963). *Tests and measurements.* Englewood Cliffs, NJ: Prentice-Hall.

Wiggins, J. S. (1987). Review of the Myers-Briggs Type Indicator. In J. C. Conoley & J. J. Kramer (Eds.), *Tenth mental measurements yearbook.* Lincoln, NE: Buros Institute of Mental Measurement.

Chapter 7

PROJECTIVE APPROACHES IN ASSESSMENT

The study of human characteristics begins with a paradox. All humans are alike; yet every human is different from every other. No two of the billions of people who live on the earth, or who have lived on it in the past, or who will live on it in the future, are exactly the same or share the same combination of genes and experiences. Individuals are so distinctive that we can pick out a friend, a relative, or even a stranger whose photograph we have seen, in a crowd at an airport or a railroad station. We can recognize people's voices on the telephone, and we can identify the distinctive movements, rhythms, and accents of those we know. Yet, we can generalize about people; we can talk about "human nature," and "average" height or weight, and "typical" reactions and responses.

Do we understand people better by focusing on their similarities or on their differences? Do we find what people have in common and then find how each individual deviates from these norms, or do we start by seeking what is unique in each individual? In the last two chapters, we dealt with normative approaches, which begin by calculating central tendencies.

In the last three quarters of a century or so, some theorists have questioned objective normative assessments which, they contend, tell little about the individual client. Numbers of critics have wondered how students of personality could expect to learn about individual differences by studying the ways in which people are uniform, and by focusing on commonalities "that ignore or subordinate individuality, treating it as a troublesome deviation" from the central tendency (Frank, 1939, p. 393). It is interesting to also note that a similar argument has been associated with therapists' indifference to research (Cruz & Berrol, 2012). Idiosyncrasy, not uniformity, critics contend, is the distinguishing feature of human perception. The way each individual interprets the evidence of his or her senses, they say, constitutes that individual's personality.

In addition to this philosophical objection, many claim that self-report, the basis for ascertaining "typical" behavior, doesn't probe beneath the surface to find the roots of this idiosyncrasy. Many aspects of personality, they contend, cannot be identified through self-reports because of unconscious defenses and conscious resistances.

The growth of projective assessment techniques is one manifestation of these arguments. Traditionally, such assessments were based largely on psychoanalytic theory and viewed fundamentally as clinical assessments. Yet, attempts to establish their validity and reliability forced most of them into the arena of statistical verification. It is here that practitioners who find projective techniques clinically useful come into conflict with researchers who question their assumptions, hypotheses, and conclusions.

It is worth noting before examining the topic in more depth, that some academics in the area of personality assessment recommend doing away with the classification of personality tests as "projective" and "objective" (Meyer & Kurtz, 2006). The argument rests on a point we made earlier that only the scoring is objective for objective tests. In addition, Meyer and Kurtz made the point that projective tests involve a stimulus to which individuals are asked to respond with minimal guidance by the test administrator; in responding to the ambiguity of the situation, it is assumed that respondents include elements of their personal characteristics. This notion is likely to resonate greatly with most creative arts therapists, as the personalization of visual, musical, and movement productions of clients are viewed this way across the arts therapies. Based on this knowledge, we hope the further discussion of projective techniques is germane and helpful.

THE PROJECTIVE HYPOTHESIS

Traditional projective techniques are based on what is often called "the projective hypothesis," which draws heavily from psychoanalytic theory. Those who accept this hypothesis maintain that if we want to get a fix on individual personality, we must observe how individuals manifest their individuality through the environments that they create or with which they surround themselves, all of which are assumed to reveal their personalities (Rapaport, Gill, & Schafer, 1968, p. 224).

But these external manifestations of personality, for the most part, are driven by a pervasive internal component that is usually not accessible for examination. "The most important things about an individual," wrote Lawrence K. Frank (1939), one of the early developers of projective approaches, "are what he cannot or will not say" (p. 395). This internal aspect of behavior consists of the percepts, fantasies, and thoughts that people don't readily expose on a conscious level, and of which they may not even be aware, but that they may reveal symbolically. The challenge to assessors is to coax into the open these covert internal aspects of personality.

PROJECTIVE TECHNIQUES

Projective procedures are those "in which the subject actively and spontaneously structures unstructured material and in so doing reveals his structuring principles – which are the principles of his psychological structure" (Rapaport et al., 1968, p. 225).

Of the various forms of projective procedure, we shall focus in this chapter on "projective tests" that seek to identify patterns of thinking or feeling. David Rapaport defined projective tests as procedures that attempt to "elicit, to render observable, to communicate the psychological structure of the subject, as inherent to him at any given moment, and without study of historical antecedents. The mode of achieving these aims distinguishes the projective tests from projective procedures at large" (Rapaport et al., 1968, p. 226).

Self-report measures that we considered in the last chapter are direct measures; they are self-observations of a subject's typical behavior. Projective tests, on the other hand, are indirect. Instead of getting clients to talk about themselves, projective tests are designed to get them to talk about something outside of themselves: clouds, drawings, inkblots, or other people; or to create objects that they structure according to their internal principles; or to move spontaneously in response to a stimulus, either external or internal. In so doing, according to the projective hypothesis, they will reveal the internal structures that shape their responses to the outside world, often in symbolic representation. Because the process is indirect, the subject may not be aware of all that he or she is revealing and is therefore less likely to fake or censor. The material revealed draws from unconscious at least as much as from conscious sources.

In this chapter, we will survey some of the better known projective techniques. First, however, we will illustrate the process of projective testing by describing briefly the best known of the projective techniques: the Rorschach Inkblot Procedure. Paradoxically, the projective element is only one small part of the Rorschach.

Many states restrict the administration and interpretation of the Rorschach to licensed psychologists. For the most part, art therapists would not be likely to use an instrument that serves only as a stimulus, preferring to have clients create their own products that serve both to reveal the hidden structural principles and to serve as a starting point for discussion. Nevertheless, the Rorschach is the paradigm for projective approaches in general.

The Rorschach

The Rorschach Test, also known as the Rorschach Method, the Rorschach Inkblot Technique, and Rorschach Psychodiagnostics, was named after its creator, Swiss psychiatrist Hermann Rorschach. Interested in the relationship between psychoanalysis and art, Rorschach came to the conclusion that what an individual perceives and the ways in which he or she perceives is dependent on the underlying structure of that individual's personality. Rorschach saw his "experiment" (he did not call it a test) as a standard task in which many aspects of personality could be engaged: cognitive, emotional, perceptual, social.

The stimulus materials consist of ten inkblots, similar to that shown below, printed on separate cards. Five are achromatic, in tones of black and gray, two include red areas, and three are multicolored.

Rorschach himself never prepared a manual with instructions for administration, scoring, or interpretation, but a number of systems have developed over the years that include such manuals. While they differ in many respects, the basics are similar. The cards are usually presented one at a time and in a definite order. The subject is asked merely to describe what he or she sees on the card ("What might this be?" for example). The examiner records the responses verbatim, as well as the

Figure 7.1. A Rorschach-type inkblot.

time it took to respond to each card, the way the card was held, and any unusual body gestures the subject might make. During this first administration, the examiner remains silent, permitting the subject to "project" without any distractions or intrusions. A second administration is conducted. This administration, known as the "inquiry," is an attempt to find why the subject has responded as he or she did, what aspects of the inkblots brought forth particular answers, whether new responses are offered, and whether the subject remembers the first response.

While scoring systems differ, most of them address the following categories:

1. Location. Did the response deal with the entire inkblot, a small part of it, a large part, or the empty spaces? The area chosen is presumed to relate to basic perceptual organizing processes.
2. Content. Did the subject see a human? An animal? An inanimate object? A sexual symbol? A body part? The choice here relates to associative processes.
3. Determinants. What qualities were perceived: color? shape? shading? movement? While all subjects tend to be aware of all the proper-

ties, the specifics of the response show which influenced or determined the response.

4. Form. How precise was the response? Was the concept itself simple or complex? Was it cohesive or fragmented? When the associative response ("that makes me think of . . .") overrides the perceptual one, this is considered evidence of psychopathology (Rapaport et al., 1968, p. 284).

5. Originality. Was the response "popular" (predictable)? If "original" (rare), was it linked to reality, or was it bizarre?

On the basis of clinical observation, Rorschach discovered over the years that most normal individuals responded first to the whole figure, and then proceeded to talk about details, usually from the larger to the smaller ones. He interpreted a reversal of this pattern as an indication of abnormality. He also interpreted a focus on the empty spaces in the pattern an indication of abnormality. A low number of responses (the average was about 30) Rorschach associated with depression. However, Rorschach recognized that an individual who responded to all 10 images with the perfectly normal (popular) reading might be displaying compulsive tendencies; most "normal" responses, he found, were symmetrical (well balanced) and not perfectly consistent. Depressed subjects were overly concerned with clear form and their answers were stereotyped.

In particular, Rorshach saw color perception as a clue to emotional control: the withdrawn person disregarded color; depressed persons focused on the blacks and grays; and impulsive subjects responded in an uncontrolled, diffused way. One card, in a combination of gray, blue-green, pink, and orange-brown colors, caused "color shock" in those with neuroses.

The 10 images used today are those that Rorschach himself selected, after years of experimentation, but the way the inkblots are used has undergone numbers of changes since they were first published in 1921. Rorschach himself had been more interested in developing a system for differential diagnosis than in analyzing the symbolic content of the responses.

However, after Rorschach's death in 1922, five separate scoring systems were developed, making the Rorschach, in effect, five different tests, each with a specific theoretical approach and system of interpretation. As a result, many clinicians abandoned the published scoring systems entirely and based their interpretations on a subjective analysis of the content of the response, often focusing on the symbolism, and interpreting responses in Freudian terms.

In 1974, a "comprehensive system" was developed by John E. Exner, Jr., that integrated the best features of the five existing systems. The Exner system came to be the most widely used method for administering, scoring, and interpreting the Rorschach, although some individual clinicians still use one of the five older systems or their own intuitive interpretation systems.

Psychometric Qualities

Evaluating the reliability of the Rorschach in any of its six forms is difficult at best, a problem that is true of all projective techniques. For one thing, the traditional methods for establishing test reliability don't apply. How can we assess reliability by using the split-half method, when each inkblot is deemed to have its own stimulus properties and is not comparable with another? How can we use test-retest methods in situations where the stimuli are so ambiguous as to call forth responses based on fleeting moods, momentary concerns, and ephemeral associations that may not persist from one test administration to the next?

Studies have not tended to give high grades to the Rorschach in terms of inter-judge reliabilities. While numbers of studies found high correlations in scores of examiners trained in a specific system (Cohen et al., 1992, p. 446), the name of the game in assessment is not scoring but interpreting what the scores mean. Here, the results were not encouraging, with the coefficients in several studies at .33 or lower, making it ineffective in discriminating between groups (Cohen et al., 1992, p. 446).

Culture Bias

It is generally acknowledged that the Rorschach is culture-biased when used as a test. For one thing, an individual's perception is heavily influenced by his or her cultural background, as it is in body language. Primitive desert Moroccans tend to concentrate on tiny, scarcely discernible details, while Samoans ignore details altogether, seeing only a general percept, such as a bird or a fish.

Researchers have found, too, that examiners' interpretations are influenced by the social class of the subject, finding greater evidence of pathology if the client's record indicates that he or she belongs to a lower socioeconomic class. Many responses that are typical of lower socioeconomic class subjects were traditionally interpreted as pathological when they occurred in middle class subjects (Peterson, 1978, p. 661).

Is the Rorschach Really a Test?

Like those blind men we left arguing over the elephant in Chapter 2, various interpreters are looking for different things, suggesting that interpretations of the Rorschach may have meaning and value only for each individual clinician in his or her own practice.

The Rorschach itself is subject to various interpretations and definitions. Charles C. McArthur, reviewing it in the *Seventh Mental Measurements Yearbook* (1972), called it "the richest behavior sample we know how to collect," but he added:

> The Rorschach is not a "test" in the sense of "tests and measures." It is a behavior sample – a standardized sample, however. . . . Paradoxically, a literature has grown up around the "psychometrics" of this nontest. . . . The Rorschach is not psychoanalytical [despite] recent distortions by those who "interpret" only content. . . . The Rorschach is not a projective test. The projective mechanism occurs in only one kind of response. Above all, it is not psychometric, nor even a measure. . . . Labeling the Rorschach as "The Rorschach Test". . . has thus erected for the delight of the captious a straw man easy to knock down. (pp. 440–441)

In the *Eighth Mental Measurements Yearbook* (1978), Richard H. Dana wrote of the changing perceptions of the Rorschach. "Psychologists no longer demand that the Rorschach provide a clinical diagnosis," he wrote. "Rather there is an expectation that Rorschach data provide an information source, or structured interview" (p. 1040). But in the same Yearbook, another reviewer warned that just calling the Rorschach a structured interview rather than a test did not mean that "subjective and nonvalidated uses of data are acceptable" (Peterson, 1978, p. 1043). Pointing to the susceptibility of clinicians to illusory correlation (see Chapter 4), he wrote:

> The general lack of predictive validity for the Rorschach raises serious question about its continued use in clinical practice. Since it is unlikely that the strong adherents of the Rorschach procedure will discontinue using it, it is incumbent upon them to provide the predictive va-

> lidity data upon which they base their interpretations and predictions. Without such data, the Rorschach user can only claim acceptance of his or her information on the basis of theory-based, expert opinion (p. 662). Lauded and condemned, the Rorschach is one of the most reviewed, researched, and analyzed techniques used in assessment. Despite the skepticism of researchers, the Rorschach remains among the most widely used instruments in personality assessment. Two authors of a survey that found enthusiastic support for the Rorschach among practitioners hypothesized that clinicians were probably unaffected by critical research findings "because they accord greater weight to personal clinical experience than to experimental evidence" (Wade & Baker, cited in Cohen et al., 1992, p. 449). However, Charles McArthur, agreeing that the Rorschach was a psychometrician's despair, contended that psychometricians and clinicians operate in different worlds. The mystery of why the Rorschach will not die has baffled psychometrically oriented reviewers for years. Is it because Rorschachers don't read the literature? (They do.) Is it an instance of the madness of crowds? (McCall, 5:154) (We hope not!) The best answer is to be found in the Rorschach experience. . . . What "test" lets us know a man, live and functioning? To make his acquaintance? To see him operate? . . . [The Rorschach] is the only game in town. (1972, p. 442.)

Most of the tests produced since Hermann Rorschach produced his inkblots have used more representational images, such as pictures on which the subject is assumed to project meaning. These images are usually seen as stimuli for the client's responses. Such tests as the Rosenzweig Picture-Frustration Study and the Thematic Apperception Test are frequently used as part of a psychological battery for general screening.

PROJECTIVE DRAWINGS

Most art therapy assessment techniques involve drawings by clients and patients. These drawings fall into two basic groups: directed and spontaneous. While spontaneous productions are far more likely to evoke the projective principle, they have serious limitations as assessment instruments because of the large number of variables that may account for the result. So it is difficult to compare the drawing with those the patient has produced before or to score it in terms of specific criteria. Such drawings can be assessed only in global terms. Consequently, any attempt to compare a drawing with anything else, including another drawing, must rely on directed tasks.

It is possible that limiting the spontaneity of the task may inhibit the projective element of the drawing. However, drawing tests are almost all referred to as "projective" drawings, whether or not they are actually based on the construct of projection. Their validation is based, for the most part, on attempts to find empirical correlations between elements of form – size, shape, color, line – and specific traits, disorders or deficiencies. It is both the quantification and the norm-referenced validation that has brought criticism from psychometricians.

Figure drawing procedures were developed largely by psychologists, who were searching for nomothetic principles or generalizations. Scoring, therefore, tends to be uniform, so that results can be compared. Chapter 11 will explore approaches used in art therapy that while founded on projective approaches described here, have developed distinctively to use art-based measures for assessment and research.

Historical Development

Psychiatrists, psychologists, anthropologists and educators have been intrigued for over a century by the relationship between the kinds of drawings that individuals produce and both their intelligence and mental status (Anastasi & Foley, 1941; MacGregor, 1989). To the degree that such a relationship could be established, the drawings could be considered reflections of cognitive or emotional development, or diagnostic indicators of psychiatric disorders.

As early as 1876, Max Simon suggested the diagnostic value, not only of the drawings produced by psychotic patients, but the clothes they wore and other manifestations of their perceptual and emotional states (Anastasi & Foley, 1941, p. 9). Later researchers systematized and standardized methods for identifying indicators of psychosis by analyzing patients' drawings (Anastasi & Foley, 1941; Gantt, 1992). Drawings by patients, unlike their movements, their music preferences, or their music productions, provide an artifact, a record of the patient's thoughts and perceptions that can be preserved for diagnosis and that do not rely on a middle language of notation.

Coinciding with the study of drawings for signs of psychiatric disorder, a good deal of research was conducted between the late 1880s and

1910 on the psychology of children's drawings. The research findings established that children passed through an orderly sequence of developmental stages in their drawings that reflected their intellectual development (Fredrickson, 1985).

Drawing Tests of Cognitive Ability

Based largely on this body of knowledge and on her own observations, Florence Goodenough developed the first formal drawing test, the Draw-A-Man Test, in 1926. This test was conceived as a nonverbal test of intelligence, and measured accuracy of observation and the development of conceptual thinking. Neither the content of the drawing nor its artistic merit was a major consideration. The test was expanded in 1963 and is now known as the Goodenough-Harris Drawing Test. To date, it is considered the most psychometrically sound of the drawing tests, especially with a "quantitative scoring system" developed by Jack Naglieri (1988). Despite the fact that it is considered an intelligence test rather than a personality test, it set the standard for human figure drawing tests that are used for a variety of purposes.

The Goodenough-Harris Drawing Test

Goodenough's test has been followed by several drawing tests of cognitive ability, but with revisions by Dale B. Harris, it remains the best known and most widely used of such tests. Goodenough found that her evaluations of these drawings paralleled the results of psychometric studies of children's intelligence. She confirmed the findings of previous researchers that the quality of the drawings improved incrementally with age. By "quality," Goodenough referred to both the coherence of the drawings and the presence of more fully developed detail; she found that maturation was demonstrated largely in cognitive, not in artistic, development. Her system scored 51 items that included the presence of body parts (such as ears, neck, elbow, and fingers), and the quality of connections and proportions.

In 1963, the system was revised and expanded by Harris, who added two new forms: a more detailed scoring system (with 73 scoring items) and a broader standardization base. To the drawing of a man, Harris added a Draw-A-Woman Test and a Self-Drawing Test (Harris, 1963a, 1963b). The system was scored on a 12-point quality scale for the drawings of the man and the woman, ranging from one for the lowest quality to 12 for the highest. No scale was provided for the drawing of the self, which was developed as a possible projective test of personality.

The Goodenough-Harris Drawing Test was standardized on a sample of 2,975 boys and girls from age five to 15, in rural and urban areas of Minnesota and Wisconsin. Harris revised the IQ from the obsolete mental age/chronological age system to a deviation IQ system. Obtained raw scores based on the scoring scale were converted to standard scores with a mean of 100 and a standard deviation of 15, the same psychometric base as that for many verbal intelligence tests.

In addition, Harris developed a set of 24 Quality Scale cards of standardized drawings to be used for reference, with examples for each age level. The Quality Scale cards were designed as a simple, global and qualitative substitute for the detailed point-scoring system, recommended for use only by those who were already experienced in the detailed point-scoring system.

The Goodenough-Harris is used primarily by psychotherapists, school psychologists, and certified psychometricians (Frederickson, 1985), whose interest is in the measurement of intellectual development, not of personality. It is frequently used with language-impaired or other children for whom a verbal intelligence test might not be appropriate.

Psychometric Properties. While the Goodenough-Harris Test was standardized, it still shares many of the weaknesses of other drawing tests in terms of test reliability. Children rarely draw in a consistent fashion, and the contents of the drawings vary greatly. While a drawing of a cowboy and a fireman can be compared on a global qualitative basis (bizarreness, creativity, etc.) for test-retest reliability or internal consistency, it is difficult to compare them on a point-for-point basis; reported coefficients are low to moderate. Inter-rater reliabilities, however, are impressive, with Harris (1963a) reporting Pearson correlations of .91 to .98, and an independent researcher reporting median Pearson correlation coefficients of .90 for the drawing of the man and .94 for that of the woman (Scott, 1981).

Some reviewers have criticized the test on the ground of the structure of the instrument. There appears to be no theoretical or empirical support for the choice of the three figures, particularly the self-drawing; internal consistency coefficients (coefficient alpha) show that whatever the self-drawing measures, it isn't the same as what is measured by the drawings of the man and the woman (Cosden, 1992).

Nevertheless, the test is considered a psychometrically valid way of scoring projective drawings (Groth-Marnat, 2009). That may be because, with the exception of the self-drawing, the Goodenough-Harris isn't a projective test.

Figure Drawings as Tests of Personality

It was predictable that drawings would be seized upon by psychotherapists as ways of gauging personality. Considering that there is no consensus on the nature of personality to begin with, it was also predictable that this is the area that has generated the most heated conflicts between clinicians and researchers.

The Machover Draw-A-Person Test

In 1949, Karen Machover published the Draw-A-Person (DAP) projective test based on psychoanalytical principles. Considerably revised and expanded by others (Hammer, 1958; Handler, 1985; Koppitz, 1968, 1984; Urban, 1963), the DAP is probably the most widely used projective drawing test for purposes of personality assessment.

Machover hypothesized that "The human figure drawn by an individual who is directed to 'draw a person'. . . is the person, and the paper corresponds to the environment" (Machover, 1949, p. 35).

Thus, when a subject erases his arms and changes the position of them several times, it may be literally interpreted that the subject does not know what to do with his arms in his behavior. If the fist is clenched, he may literally be expressing his belligerence (Machover, 1949, p. 183).

The administration of the test is simple: the client is given a blank sheet of paper and told to "draw a picture of a person." When this drawing is finished, the client is asked to draw a person of the opposite sex.

The drawing task is usually followed by an "inquiry phase," in which the client is asked questions about the people in the drawings: "Tell me about this person," "What is he/she doing?" "How is he or she feeling?" The responses are the basis for a diagnostic hypothesis. So, the test actually is used both as an assessment tool and as a device for initiating a clinical interview.

Scoring and Interpretation. Machover developed her test on the basis of a number of hypotheses and assumptions that combined intuitive judgments and her clinical observations. Much of it was based on an assumed isomorphy: a very small drawing reflects low levels of self-esteem, or depression; extremely large drawings suggest compensatory inflation, as in the case of patients with delusions of grandeur or in a manic state; a very large woman drawn by a man suggests domination by the mother or problems with sexual identity; and placement on the page reflects how the subject functions in the social environment.

In addition, the drawings are scored on the basis of such factors as the length of time that was required for completing the drawings, the placement of the figures, the pencil pressure, the presence of erasures, distortions or omissions of body parts, facial expressions, posture, clothing, line quality, shading, and general overall quality.

Numbers of others added their own interpretive scoring systems, so that as the technique is used today, scoring and interpretation are often based on combinations of interpretive hypotheses developed, not only by Machover, but by others as well. For example:

- Large eyes and/or large ears may suggest paranoid tendencies (Machover, 1949).
- Impulsivity is suggested by such qualities as a drawing that runs off the page, a very short completion time, omissions, poor proportions, and aggressive elements.
- On the other hand, eye emphasis, mouth detail, shading, and a long completion time are suggestive of nonimpulsivity (Oas, 1984).
- In addition, Machover (1949) and others hypothesized that shading may represent anxiety, with the specific area shaded suggesting concern about this area.
- Severely shaded or reinforced fingers are regarded as guilt indicators. unusually light pencil pressure suggests character disturbance (Exner, 1962).
- Elongated feet and long and conspicuous ties represent phallic symbols and suggest sexual aggressiveness (Machover, 1949).
- A concave or "orally receptive" mouth indicates fixation at the oral level (Machover, 1949), and outstanding or conspicuous buttons suggest dependent or infantile tendencies (Halpern, 1958).
- Drawing the opposite sex first indicates possible sexual identity confusion (Machover, 1949).

- Placement of the figure in the upper right suggests excessive optimism about the future; placement in the lower left suggests depression and a longing for the past (Buck, 1948).

In a review of the literature on the DAP, Maloney and Glasser (1982) found and compiled a list of nine factors that were found, with varying degrees of success, to discriminate between normal individuals and various groups of psychiatric patients. Signs of maladjustment included:

- Primitive or overly simplified head.
- Simplified body, as in a stick figure.
- Poor overall quality, related to number of details, accuracy, proportion, etc., rated impressionistically on a scale from one to nine.
- Distortion of the body, body parts not connected or connected inappropriately, proportions not appropriate.
- Omissions of significant details, such as hands, feet, arms.
- Overly detailed sexual elements, such as breasts or penis.

Psychometric Properties. The Machover Draw-A-Person Test has fared poorly at the hands of research-oriented reviewers from the time it was published. In particular, Machover was criticized for having made strong assertions about the utility of the test, mentioning "accurate matching" of "thousands of drawings" with case records but failing to provide any data to support such claims. In fact, no data on validity or reliability were offered at all. While many of Machover's assumptions appear plausible, wrote one reviewer in *Psychosomatic Medicine,* and "do not lack conviction, they cannot be accepted as sufficient validating data" (Waldfagel, 1950). Another criticized the interpretations offered by Machover for "its bondage to fixed [Freudian] symbols" (long feet, long ties, guns and swords as phallic symbols) at a time when psychoanalysts had come to recognize the "extremely individualistic language of symbolization" (Kendig, 1949). One reviewer for the *American Journal of Psychiatry* was skeptical about Machover's reliance on her clinical observations for her hypotheses regarding personality. "She seems to expect that her discussion will seem plausible with only this" (Richards, 1949). Summarizing the deficiencies of the Machover Draw-A-Person Test, Philip Kitay wrote:

> The Machover manual is most inadequate in its coverage of theoretical bases and procedures for interpretation, reliability, and validity. It is deficient in regard to . . . exactness of description of drawing items to be interpreted and rationale and empirical evidence for interpreta-

tions offered. Statistical normative data are not presented. (1965, p. 195)

The work of the researchers, in turn, has been criticized by defenders of the projective drawing procedures. Hammer (1981), probably the most prominent proponent of projective drawings, contended that some of the research studies contradicted considerable clinical experience, and suggested that the lack of research support was the result of faulty research methodology.

Despite criticism by psychometricians, the DAP is still used by those who find it a useful, fast, and easy-to-use technique that can provide diagnostic hypotheses for the clinician to confirm or reject on the basis of other evidence. Because it can be used by those who are not trained in or knowledgeable about research methods, not only has it been used by art therapists, but it has served as a model for a number of art therapy assessments.

Its continued use rests largely on an underlying assumption that the psychometric weaknesses of the test could be balanced by the experience of the clinician, especially the experience of one who has used the DAP frequently. Unfortunately, even this assumption has been challenged as the result of experimental research. A number of studies found no relationship between diagnostic accuracy, general clinical experience, familiarity with the DAP, or expertise in projective techniques (Wanderer, 1967; Watson, 1967).

Children's Human Figure Drawings

Elizabeth M. Koppitz attempted to coordinate the principles of the Goodenough and the Machover approaches to figure drawings in the assessment of children. She thought that a single drawing characteristic could not simultaneously be interpreted as an indicator of a developmental stage and of an emotional concern, and she developed a set of parallel scoring systems. Koppitz (1968) based her Human Figure Drawings (HFD) or Human Figure Drawing Test (HFDT) on Harry Stack Sullivan's theory of interpersonal relationship. In her view, drawings reflect not only the child's developmental characteristics at a given age but significant aspects of the child's interpersonal relationships, as well as the fears, concerns, and stresses that emerge as the child tries to reconcile divergent demands and pulls. She developed two sets of indicators: one for developmental signs, one for emotional indicators.

A child is asked simply to produce a single drawing of a whole person. A scoring key is provided for 30 developmental signs and 30 emotional indicators. The scoring is more complicated than merely counting signs; there are significant combinations of signs that must be considered in terms of the child's age level.

Koppitz warned against simple one-to-one interpretations (1968, p. 85), but critics pointed to her own assignment of meaning to specific features or to their absence. A slanting figure, for example, is an apparent "sign of instability and imbalance which interferes with academic achievement" (p. 52) and suggests that the child lacks a secure footing. Tiny figures indicate timidity, large figures suggest aggression, and small heads "indicate intense feelings of intellectual inadequacy" (p. 61).

The attempt to identify signs empirically, wrote Clinton Chase, "is to be applauded; however, the methodologies . . . leave much to be desired from the point of view of the empirically minded reader. Signs and combinations of signs are employed without adequate support of hard data" (1984, p. 193).

Some critics questioned the central assumption that children's drawings alone can be used to describe personality traits. Referring to the approach as "blind analysis," Rhoda Kellog contended that "pictorial capacity . . . does not exist until the child is trained to substitute an adult's idea of how lines 'should be drawn' for his own highly developed and natural ideas about drawing" (1969, p. 189). Kellog argued, too, that any inferences about the intellectual or emotional development of a child based on a single drawing are almost inevitably distorted, because children's drawings of figures are remarkably inconsistent, even over a short span of time.

Dale B. Harris reviewed the HFDT and concluded that despite the attempt to score responses:

> The HFDT is not . . . a test but an evaluation of presumptive clinical evidence. It adds little that is objective or quantifiable to the subjective or "clinical" use of drawings. . . . Depending on the psychologist's use of and belief in qualitative and subjective evidence, the HFDT may be used along with other evidence, qualitative or quantitative, to illuminate and clarify the clinical picture of personality where disturbances are known or strongly suspected. (1978, p. 398)

Figure Drawing Variations

The idea of human figure drawings has been adapted for a variety of specific purposes. The Draw-A-Person-in-the-Rain, which, according to Hammer (1978), has no known authorship, is used to assess responses to unpleasant situations. Interpretations focus on the ways subjects react, in terms of facial expressions; movement; placement; shields, including umbrellas; and additional embellishments, such as clouds, lightning, or rainbows.

Hammer (1978) developed a test, which he called Draw-A-Member-Of-A-Minority-Group, to assess the projection of attributes and prejudices. An examination of personality test titles in any of the standard sources will reveal numbers of variations on the theme of human figure drawings designed for specific purposes.

The House-Tree-Person Technique

A year before Machover published her DAP, John N. Buck (1948) published his House-Tree-Person (H-T-P) Technique. Originally designed as a dual-purpose instrument – to assess intelligence and personality – it is fundamentally a projective tool; the cumbersome scoring procedure for ascertaining cognitive ability is seldom used. The manual was later revised by Buck (1966) and by Buck and Emanuel F. Hammer (1969).

The administration involves asking a subject to draw first a house, then a tree, and finally a person. Buck postulated that individuals invest houses and trees, as well as persons, with symbolic meaning (Buck, 1948, 1966). The house was deemed to mirror the subject's home life and family relationships, as well as his or her own body. The tree represents the subject's sense of growth and vitality. If the three are drawn on one piece of paper (one variation suggested by several writers), the relative sizes and the relationship between them is significant. The procedure was modified later to include an interview following the initial drawings, and a chromatic series of drawings, with eight or more crayons, again followed by a structured interview, with specific questions about the house, the tree, and the person. Examples:

- If there was a fire in the house, what do you think the person you drew would do?

- Would it be easy to climb the tree?
- What sort of things make this person angry?

The interpretations offered by Buck and Hammer and numbers of others have been intuitively developed and are heavy on symbolism. The house represents, according to different writers, either the self (with the roof representing fantasy or intellectual capacity) or the family. The tree, too, is subject to various symbolic interpretations, but is usually seen as a reflection of the individual's sense of ego and self-development, with the roots representing security and contact with reality.

From clinical observation, Hammer (1958) found that the average individual used from three to five colors for the house, two to three for the tree, and three to five for the person. Inhibited individuals tended to use a single crayon and employ it as though it were a pencil. On the other hand, those who had trouble exercising adequate control over their emotions demonstrated an "over-expansive" use of color. Hammer (1958) noted that "one psychotic . . . indicated his inadequate control, as well as his break with conventional reality, by drawing each of the eight windows in his house a different color" (p. 232).

Some other reports included that the use of reds and yellows reflected spontaneity while the use of blues or greens indicated control (Zimmerman & Garfinkle, 1942), that black and brown were symptomatic of inhibition (Bieber & Herkimer, 1948), and that the overuse of yellow might be an expression of hostility and aggression (Brick, 1944).

The reaction to the test depends heavily on the theoretical position of reviewers and readers. If you prefer an intuitive or impressionistic approach, you will probably find the H-T-P a useful technique for exposing a patient's inner personality structure. Those who are inclined to interpret in traditional Freudian terms, especially, are likely to find a wealth of symbols in the drawings, as with the possible phallic connotations of the house's chimney.

On the other hand, if you are research-oriented, you will have a good deal of trouble with the test. The reviews of the H-T-P in the *Mental Measurements Yearbooks* and *Test Critiques* have generally ranged from lukewarm to scathing. Mary Haworth (1965) wrote that "while very little experimental data can be marshaled in support of [interpretations offered by Buck, by Hammer and by Jolles], nevertheless these publications do serve to make explicit many inferences frequently made by clinicians in interpreting the meaning of drawings" (p. 435) and suggested that the test might be used as a "non-threatening 'opener' before more formal testing" (p. 436). One reviewer was less tolerant, writing that the original manual "displays incredible naivete, fanaticism, and arrant disregard for any attempt at scientific validation of the material presented" (Ellis, 1989, p. 592). Buck admitted that "there is almost no statistical proof of the validity of the qualitative scoring points and their interpretations" that would satisfy statistically minded researchers, but he added, "It is the author's belief that the validity of the principle of the H-T-P method as a whole has been satisfactorily established (although the evidence is almost wholly clinical)" (quoted in Killian, 1984, p. 348).

Such comments invited the scorn of Grant A. Killian, who reviewed the test in *Test Critiques* (1984). "One wonders how a test can be valid and not reliable," wrote Killian. "If this projective test is not consistent in its measurement, and if raters cannot consistently agree on scoring, then it cannot possibly measure what it purports to measure" (pp. 348–349).

Despite such criticisms, the H-T-P is not only widely used but has been expanded and modified and a number of variations have emerged over the years. Psychologist Robert C. Burns and psychiatrist S. Harvard Kaufman (1970, 1972) recommended that the tree, the house, and the person all be drawn on the same piece of paper, inviting a more integrated response from the subject, and in 1987, Burns developed his Kinetic House-Tree Person (K-H-T-P), adding the request that the person in the drawing be depicted "doing something." One author developed a projective test that invites the subject to write a story involving a house, a tree, and a person, on the assumption that each has a personality and that they can talk to each other (Diamond, cited by Killian, 1984, p. 339).

Family Drawings

Because so much of an individual's personality and emotional responses are related to the context of interpersonal relationships, a number of assessment devices have focused on getting a sense of the family structure and the client's role in it.

The idea of family drawings was advanced by psychologists and psychiatrists as far back as the 1930s, and family drawings were used for both assessment and therapy on an informal basis. With the increasing popularity of family therapy in the 1960s, Dale B. Harris (1963a) developed a more formal approach as an extension of the Goodenough Draw-A-Man Test, which came to be known as the Draw-A-Family (DAF) Test. Instead of an anonymous figure, or pair of figures, the subject is asked to draw a picture of "your family."

The technique gained wide acceptance among art therapists when Hanna Y. Kwiatkowska pioneered its use for family sessions at the National Institutes of Health. She found that family drawings in sessions in which all family members were involved revealed much about the relationships between family members and about the perceptions of the individuals about the role and status of each member. Kwiatkowska saw her program as a combination of spontaneous art expression and some standardized tasks that made the drawings useful in comparing perceptions. The same tasks were given to each newly admitted family. "Together," Kwiatkowska told an audience of art therapists, "these procedures give us an astonishingly clear view of all [the family's] members and their transactional systems" (1971, p. 139).

Kwiatkowska interpreted the drawings psychoanalytically, as did many psychotherapists who used family drawings. The usual procedure is to look for a general sense of mood and then to weigh the meaning of the size and placement of individual family members. This assessment indicates how the individual sees his or her place in the family. Interpretation is isomorphic: physical proximity or distance are indicators of emotional closeness or distance; the figures that are drawn first or that are larger than the others are perceived to be more influential or important than those that are drawn small or last. Interpretation of the individual figures is similar to that used in the DAP, with the difference that features drawn for an individual family member are not interpreted as self-representations but as the subject's view of the family member's importance or personality.

In the early 1970s, Robert Burns and S. Harvard Kaufman complained that the DAF was static and provided no interaction between family members. They developed the concept of the Kinetic Family Drawing (KFD), primarily for use with children. By asking clients to draw their families "doing something," they wrote, they get "much more valid and dynamic material in the attempt to understand the psychopathology of children in a family setting" (1970, p. 18).

When the drawing has been completed, the client is asked to describe it or to tell a story about it. The interpretation is similar to that in akinetic, or static, drawings, with a focus on the elements suggested by

Karen Machover (1949). Burns and Kaufman were also concerned with the kinetic elements: style, actions, and relationships. A figure isolated from the others might mean that that person is seen as detached from the family (or a sign of wishful thinking, as in the case of sibling rivalry).

To aid in interpretation, Burns and Kaufman prepared a KFD analysis sheet, essentially a guide in checklist form that directs attention to five basic elements:

1. Style. Does the subject compartmentalize? Edge the drawings? Underline individual figures?
2. Symbols. What traditional Freudian symbolism is present?
3. Actions. What are individual family members doing? What actions can be identified between family members?
4. Physical characteristics. For each individual, what characteristics are apparent in terms of arm extensions? Elevation? Which figures are in front, in back, hanging? For which members have body parts been omitted? What erasures are apparent? Which family members have been omitted entirely?
5. KFD grid. How are family members placed? What is their relative size? What are the distances between family members?

As the family drawing systems became increasingly popular, a number of objective scoring systems were developed. Currently, there are five such systems that have been subjected to tests of inter-observer reliability, concurrent validity, and test-retest reliability. In general, it would appear that inter-scorer reliabilities have been reasonable to good, but that test-retest reliabilities have been low (suggesting, to the test's developers, that certain KFD variables are sensitive to children's transitory personality states). Reports on the power of the scoring systems to discriminate between normal and clinical populations have been contradictory and inconclusive (Raskin & Bloom, 1979; McGregor, 1979).

The idea of drawings in which people do something spurred the development of a number of other kinetic systems, including a Kinetic School Drawing (KSD), developed by Prout and Philips (1974), and a Kinetic Drawing System for Family and School (Knoff & Prout, 1985) that attempt to synthesize interpretation of the KFD and the KSD.

Psychometric Properties. Here again, those who want research support will be disappointed. Bert P. Cundick reviewed the Kinetic Drawing System for Family and School: A Handbook in the *Tenth Mental Mea-*

surements Yearbook (1989), began by noting that the handbook provided no guiding rationale for the creation of a task, no norm groups, no real evidence of systematic attempts to determine validity. It was, instead, a "compendium of sources regarding a technique" (p. 422) and a series of questions that might be presented to the child about each person in the drawing. Rather than a scoring system, there are "suggested clinical hypotheses that stem from some published source dealing with the technique" (p. 423) – in other words, what some writer thinks each element might mean.

However, in fairness to the authors, Cundick pointed out, they did not purport to have a test, and their approach "primarily involves a hypothesis-testing model, rather than a procedure focused on differential diagnosis" (p. 423). Richard A. Weinberg (1989), who reviewed the same procedure, found the absence of meaningful psychometric data disturbing, and wrote:

> In his foreword to the Handbook, Robert C. Burns articulates well the historical tension between the science of psychometrics and the clinical artistry of projective techniques. Burns argues for clinical validity "as a beginning to ask more sophisticated and wise questions." Unfortunately, patience wears thin, waiting for other kinds of validity data. To date, as reflected in this Handbook, the accumulated psychometric underpinnings for projective drawings in general, and the Kinetic Drawing System for Family and School, in particular, are lean. (p. 424)

AUDITORY AND MUSIC PROJECTIVE TESTS

In 1955, Crocker (1955) used improvised music as a technique for ascertaining the ways emotionally disturbed and psychotic children perceived reality. A Sound Apperception Test (SAT) was developed as an auditory equivalent of the widely used Thematic Apperception Test (TAT) (although the article describing it was entitled "Music Therapy from Auditory Inkblots," suggesting an equivalency with the Rorschach). Everyday environmental sounds were altered to create six semi-structured sound patterns. Outside of the original norming data (500 normal individuals), little information is available on the SAT, and it does not appear to be widely used.

More familiar to music therapists are projective tests based on musical selections. The best known is probably the IPAT Music Preference Test of Personality, developed by Raymond B. Cattell and his associates (Cattell & Anderson, 1953; Cattell & Saunders, 1954; Cattell & McMichael, 1960). The IPAT Music Preference Test attempted to find if there were differences in music preferences between normal and various pathology groups. Cattell and his associates collected 100 music excerpts that were correlated with a Sixteen Factor Personality Questionnaire. The test attempted to differentiate subjects in terms of eight personality factors (such as introspection versus social contact and adjustment versus frustrated emotionality) on the basis of their preferences for certain kinds of music. Although Cattell and his associates concluded that the test was useful as a diagnostic instrument, researchers have been as critical of it as they have of projective drawings, largely because the supporting psychometric data have been skimpy. Several research studies failed to support Cattell's claims that the test could distinguish between various populations (Healey, 1973; Robinson, 1976). In any event, the question of the test's validity seems to be academic. Many music therapists seem to regard the IPAT Music Preference Test as an interesting theoretical experiment with limited practical utility. Music therapists in general appear to agree that it doesn't provide clear guidance for treatment decisions.

PROJECTIVE TECHNIQUES IN DANCE/MOVEMENT THERAPY

In the 1940s, a group of clinicians and researchers experimented with verbal and nonverbal approaches to projection at Bellevue Hospital in New York City. The group was a varied one and included psychoanalyst Paul Schilder, psychologist Lauretta Bender, art therapist Margaret Naumberg, Adolf Wollman in puppetry, and dance therapist Franziska Boas.

Building on the projective approaches that were already commonly used in creative dance movement, Boas saw projective techniques as a natural extension of the dance experience that could be used for diagnostic as well as therapeutic purposes. She viewed projective devices as ways in which the patient could project thoughts and feelings through psychomotor free associations (Levy, 2005).

However, while the notion of projection as a diagnostic tool was picked up by a number of other dance therapists, including Blanche Evan, who worked with "normal neurotics," and Mary Whitehouse, who applied the Jungian concept of "active imagination" projective techniques in dance therapy were never conceived as assessment or diagnostic tools. Probably because of its roots in creative and modern dance, the projective approach is seen primarily as an extension of the movement experience itself that lends itself to therapeutic purposes, and only incidentally to assessment. The therapist might look for clues in the projected thoughts and feelings to suggest the direction for an ensuing session.

HOW VALID ARE PROJECTIVE TECHNIQUES?

The debate between the groups that have been dubbed "enthusiastic clinicians" and "skeptical academicians" has been raging ever since projective assessment techniques were developed. In large part, the problem is that the two groups operate on different sets of assumptions and expectations.

In reviewing projective techniques, we must distinguish between their use in clinical practice and their use as "tests." These techniques are probably most useful when they are used, to explore individual characteristics. Projective techniques and approaches may be unparalleled as devices for initiating discussions with clients in order to probe for idiosyncratic meanings. However, when the developers of projective "tests" attempt to generate interpretations to be taken and applied to groups of individuals they invite psychometricians and researchers to review their work, and their work is found lacking.

The Goodenough-Harris Test, designed to measure cognitive development, is based on quantitative scoring specifications that were developed empirically. As we saw earlier in this chapter, this test is probably the most psychometrically sound of the figure drawing tests, but at the expense of the projective function. Attempts to use figure drawings to measure personality, on the other hand, have not gained favorable treatment from psychometricians.

Can Projective Techniques Be Tests?

In addition to criticisms of the psychometric properties of projective approaches is the persistent problem of projection by the clinician, largely through the phenomenon of illusory correlation. This is a danger that is recognized by proponents of projective approaches. Hammer (1968) noted that interpretations by clinicians often reflect personality characteristics of the interpreter; those who are hostile, for example, are more likely to find indicators of hostility in their clients' drawings.

Reviewing the empirical evidence for the validity of figure drawings in personality assessment, Kahill (1984) suggested that clinicians abandon "futile attempts" to make figure drawings scientific tests. Instead, the technique "should more properly take its place as a rich and potentially valuable clinical tool that can provide working hypotheses and a springboard for discussion with the patient" (p. 288). Many clinicians who subscribe to both psychodynamic and humanist approaches should have little problem with this approach; in fact, many have been using such techniques in precisely that way. Few would argue with the idea of a figure drawing as a source of interpretive hypotheses. The problem is one suggested by the Chapman and Chapman study (1967, 1971): many clinicians do, in fact, use these as "tests," ignoring the empirical data, and reaching intuitively derived interpretations that are not supported, or that may even be contradicted, by the research findings. Reinforcing this notion that all figure drawing techniques are tests is the fact that many reviewers continue to refer to the technique as tests, and that the *Mental Measurements Yearbooks* list projective instruments as "projective tests," whether or not they are based on the principle of projection.

With the current emphasis on cultural and ethnic diversity in psychology and counseling, as well as, the creative arts therapies, a final issue for the projective tests described in this chapter and objective tests discussed in the previous chapter, is the issue of cultural and ethnic factors. The lack of understanding of the potential impact of cultural and ethnic factors on objective and projective measures has seldom been discussed openly in the literature. For creative arts therapists these are important issues that also affect clinical practice. For example, cultural and ethnic factors can limit what it is permissible to draw and who it is permissible to move, make music, and interact with (see for example, Alyami, 2009; Hervey, 2012).

Added to issues of the appropriateness of the different projective assessments to individuals from a range of cultures are the interpretations of the test administrator and his or her understanding of the lack or representation of different groups in norm samples (when they exist). The test administrator's own knowledge and biases about the culture or ethnicity of the subject are also highly relevant to interpretations from tests. This topic is an important and often unaddressed issue with regards to testing and assessment. We bring it up here as yet an additional caution and also as a call to future arts therapists to incorporate into practice and research.

SUMMARY

Psychometricians look for differences between individuals mainly in the ways they deviate from the mean. In contrast, those who prefer projective techniques seek what is unique in the way each individual structures his or her perception.

The projective approach rests on the "projective hypothesis," which holds that individuals create and interpret their environments in terms of the unique structuring principles that make up their personalities. To make these principles manifest, examiners must provide relatively unstructured raw materials on which the subject can project his or her perceptive structure. Conversely, the subject can be given the task of creating a situation or an object or a movement that will bring the usually covert internal operations into the open. In contrast with self-report measures, projective techniques are indirect measures: the individual deals, not with himself or herself, but with external things. In this way, it is hypothesized, the individual may not be aware of all that is being revealed and will be less likely to fake, consciously or unconsciously.

The best known of the projective techniques is the Rorschach Inkblot Technique. In this procedure, a series of ten ambiguous inkblots is presented to the subject, who describes what he or she sees. The response is scored in terms of location, content, determinants, form, and originality.

Attempts to correlate responses with personality traits or psychiatric disorders have not been considered psychometrically sound, but the Rorschach has remained popular for a variety of reasons that may have less to do with its accuracy in assessment and more with its utility as an interviewing technique.

Figure drawings are a major category of projective assessment technique. Figure drawings have been used as measures of intelligence and as indicators of personality. The Goodenough-Harris Test is generally considered a psychometrically sound approach to the nonverbal measure of children's intelligence. However, when they are used in measuring cognitive development, figure drawings are empirically validated and are not truly projective.

The use of figure drawings in personality assessment has not gained similar psychometric support. Few of the interpretive hypotheses on which these tests are scored have successfully been validated, and psychometricians find considerable fault with both the hypotheses and the underlying assumptions on which such hypotheses rest. These techniques have not been found useful for differential diagnosis.

Nevertheless, like the Rorschach, these techniques remain popular among clinicians, suggesting that their value may lie less in their diagnostic utility than in their clinical value as semi-structured interviews. One reviewer recommended that practitioners abandon "futile attempts" to make figure drawings scientific tests, and turn their efforts to using them clinically as sources for working hypotheses and as guides for interviews. Apparently, this is the way many clinicians already use them.

REFERENCES

Alyami, A. (2009). The integration of art therapy into physical rehabilitation in a Saudi hospital. *The Arts in Psychotherapy, 36,* 282–288.

Anastasi, A., & Foley, J. P. (1941). A survey of the literature on artistic behavior in the abnormal. *Annals of the Academy of Sciences, 42,* Art. I., 3–111.

Bieber, I., & Herkimer, J. K. (1948). Art in psychotherapy. *American Journal of Psychiatry, 104*(10), 627–631.

Brick, M. (1944). Mental hygiene value of children's art work. *American Journal of Orthopsychiatry, 14*(1), 136–146.

Buck, J. N., & Hammer, E. F. (Eds.). (1969). *Advances in House-Tree-Person techniques: Variations and applications.* Los Angeles: Western Psychological Services.

Buck, J. N. (1966). *The House-Tree-Person technique: Revised manual.* Beverly Hills, CA: Western Psychological Services.

Buck, J. N. (1948). The H-T-P technique, a qualitative and quantitative scoring manual. *Journal of Clinical Psychology, 4,* 317–396.

Buck, J. N. (1986). *The House-Tree-Person technique: Revised manual.* Beverly Hills, CA: Western Psychological Services.

Burns, R. C., & Kaufman, S. H. (1970). *Kinetic family drawings (KFD).* New York: Brunner/Mazel.

Burns, R. C., & Kaufman, S. H. (1972). *Action, styles, and symbols in kinetic family drawings (K-F-D).* New York: Brunner/Mazel.

Cattell, R. B., & Anderson, J. C. (1953). The measurement of personality and behavior disorders by the IPAT music preference test. *Journal of Applied Psychology, 37,* 446–454.

Cattell, R. B., & McMichael, R. E. (1960). Clinical diagnosis by the IPAT Music Preference Test. *Journal of Consulting Psychology, 24,* 333–341.

Cattell, R. B., & Saunders, D. (1954). Musical preferences-personality diagnosis: A factorization of one hundred and twenty themes. *Journal of Social Psychology, 39,* 3–24.

Chapman, L. J., & Chapman, J. P. (1967). Genesis of popular but erroneous psychodiagnostic observations. *Journal of Abnormal Psychology, 72,* 193–204.

Chapman, L. J., & Chapman, J. P. (1971). Test results are what you think they are. *Psychology Today, 5*(6), 18–22, 106–110. Also reprinted in D. Kahneman, P. Slovic, & A. Tversky (Eds.), *Judgment under uncertainty: Heuristics and biases.* Cambridge: Cambridge University Press, 1982.

Chase, C. I. (1984). Review of psychological evaluation of children's human figure drawings. In D. J. Keyser & R. C. Sweetland (Eds.), *Test critiques 1* (pp. 189–193). Kansas City, MO: Test Corporation of America.

Cohen, R. J., Swerdlick, M. E., & Smith, D. K. (1992). *Psychological testing and assessment.* Mountain View, CA: Mayfield.

Cosden, M. (1992). Review of draw-a-person: A quantitative scoring system. In J. J. Kramer & J. C. Conoley (Eds.), *Eleventh mental measurements yearbook.* Lincoln, NE: Buros Institute of Mental Measurement.

Crocker, D. B. (1955). Music as a projective technique. *Music Therapy, 5,* 86–97.

Cruz, R. F., & Berrol, C. F. (Eds.). (2012). *Dance/movement therapists in action: A working guide to research options* (2nd ed.). Springfield, IL: Charles C Thomas.

Cundick, B. P. (1989). Review of kinetic family drawing system for family and school. In J. C. Conoley & J. J. Kramer (Eds.), *Tenth mental measurements yearbook.* Lincoln, NE: Buros Institute of Mental Measurement.

Dana, R. H. (1978). Review of Rorschach inkblot. In O. Buros (Ed.), *Eighth mental measurements yearbook* (pp. 1040–1042). Highland Park, NJ: Gryphon Press.

Ellis, A. (1989). Rational-emotive therapy. In R. J. Corsini & D. Wedding (Eds.), *Current psychotherapies* (4th ed.). Itasca, IL: F. E. Peacock.

Exner, J. E. (1962). A comparison of human figure drawings of psychoneurotics, character disturbances, normals, and subjects experiencing experimentally induced fears. *Journal of Projective Techniques, 26,* 292–317.

Frank, L. K. (1939). Projective methods for the study of personality. *Journal of Psychology, 8,* 389–413.

Fredrickson, L. C. (1985). Review of Goodenough-Harris Drawing Test. In D. J. Keyser & R. C. Sweetland (Eds.), *Test critiques,* Vol. II, 319–325. Kansas City, MO: Test Corporation of America.

Gantt, L. M. (1992). A description and history of art therapy assessment in research. In H. Wadeson (Ed.), *A guide to conducting art therapy research.* Mundelein, IL: American Art Therapy Association.

Groth-Marnat, G. (2009). *Handbook of psychological assessment* (5th ed.). Hoboken, NJ: Wiley & Sons.

Halpern, F. (1958). Child case study. In E. F. Hammer (Ed.), *The clinical application of projective drawings* (pp. 113–129). Springfield, IL: Charles C Thomas.

Hammer, E. F. (1981). Projective drawings. In A. I. Rabin (Ed.), *Assessment with projective techniques: A concise introduction.* New York: Springer.

Hammer, E. F. (1958/1978). *The clinical application of projective drawings.* Springfield, IL: Charles C Thomas.

Hammer, E. F. (1968). Projective drawings. In A. I. Rabin (Ed.), *Projective techniques in personality assessment* (pp. 366–393). New York: Springer.

Handler, L. (1985). The clinical use of the Draw-A-Person Test (DAP). In C. S. Newmark (Ed.), *Major psychological assessment instruments.* Newton, MA: Allyn and Bacon.

Harris, D. B. (1963a). *Children's drawings as measures of intellectual maturity: A revision and extension of the Goodenough Draw-A-Man Test.* Cleveland, OH: The Psychological Corporation.

Harris, D. B. (1963b). *Goodenough-Harris Drawing Test: Manual.* Cleveland, OH: The Psychological Corporation.

Harris, D. B. (1978). Review of psycholingual evaluation of children's figure drawings. In O. K. Buros (Ed.), *Seventh mental measurements yearbook.* Highland Park, NJ: Gryphon Press.

Haworth, M. R. (1965). Review of H-T-P. In O. K. Buros (Ed.). *Sixth mental measurements yearbook* (pp. 435–436). Highland Park, NJ: Gryphon Press.

Healey, B. (1973). Pilot study in the applicability of the music preference test of personality. *Journal of Music Therapy, 10,* 36–45.

Hervey, L. W. (2012). Embodied artistic inquiry. In R. Cruz & C. Berrol (Eds.), *Dance/movement therapists in action: A working guide to research options* (2nd ed.). (pp. 205–232). Springfield, IL: Charles C Thomas.

Kahill, S. (1984). Human figure drawings in adults: An update of the empirical evidence, 1967–1982. *Canadian Psychology, 25,* 269–290.

Kellog, R. (1969). Learning through movement: Summary. In I. Jakab (Ed.), *Art interpretation and art therapy: Psychiatry and art.* Vol. II. Basel: Karger.

Kendig, I. V. (1949). Review of MDAP test. *Quarterly Journal of Psychiatry and Neurology, 4,* 252–253.

Killian, G. A. (1984). Review of House-Tree-Person technique. In D. J. Keyser & R. C. Sweetland (Eds.), *Test critiques,* Vol. I. (pp. 338–353). Kansas City, MO: Test Corporation of America.

Kitay, P. M. (1965). Review of Machover draw-a-person test. In O. K. Buros (Ed.). *Sixth mental measurements yearbook* (pp. 466–468). Highland Park, NJ: Gryphon Press.

Knoff, H. M., & Prout, H. T. (1985). The Kinetic Drawing System: A review and integration of the Kinentic Family and School Drawing techniques. *Psychology in the Schools, 22,* 50–59.

Koppitz, E. M. (1968). *Psychoanalytical evaluation of children's human figure drawings.* Yorktown Heights, NY: The Psychological Corporation.

Koppitz, E. M. (1984). *Psychological evaluation of human figure drawings by middle school pupils.* New York: Grune and Stratton.

Kwiatkowska, H. Y. (1971). Family art therapy and family art evaluation. *Proceedings,* 4th Annual Meeting of the American Society of Psychopathology of Expression.

Levy, F. J. (2005). *Dance movement therapy: A healing art* (2nd ed.). Reston, VA: AAHPERD.

MacGregor, J. (1989). *The discovery of the art of the insane.* Princeton, NJ: Princeton University Press.

Machover, K. (1949). *Personality projection in the drawing of the human figure.* Springfield, IL: Charles C Thomas.

Maloney, M. P., & Glasser, A. (1982). An evaluation of the clinical utility of the Draw-a-Person Test. *Journal of Clinical Psychology, 38,* 183–190.

McArthur, C. C. (1972). Review of Rorschach Test. In O. K. Buros (Ed.), *Sixth mental measurements yearbook.* Highland Park, NJ: Gryphon Press.

Meyer, G. J., & Kurtz, J. E. (2006). Advancing personality assessment terminology: Time to retire "objective" and "projective" as personality test descriptors. *Journal of Personality Assessment, 87*(3), 223–225.

Naglieri, J. A. (1988). *Draw-A-Person: A quantitative scoring system.* Pro-Ed.

Oas, P. (1984). Validity of the Draw-A-Person and Bender Gestalt tests as measures of impulsivity with adolescents. *Journal of Consulting and Clinical Psychology, 52,* 1011–1019.

Peterson, R. A. (1978). Review of Rorschach procedure. In O. Buros (Ed.), *Eighth mental measurements yearbook.* Highland Park, NJ: Gryphon Press.

Prout, H. T., & Phillips, D. D. (1974). A clinical note: The Kinetic School Drawing. *Psychology in the Schools, 11,* 303–306.

Rapaport, D., Gill, M., & Schafer, R. (1968). *Diagnostic psychological testing.* New York: International Universities Press.

Raskin, L. M., & Bloom, A. S. (1979). Kinetic family drawings by children with learning disabilities. *Journal of Pediatric Psychology, 4,* 247–251.

Robinson, W. L. (1976). The musical preferences of mental patients based on Cattell's interpretations of factors associated with certain aspects of personality. *Dissertation Abstracts International,* 149A.

Scott, L. H. (1981). Measuring intelligence with the Goodenough-Harris Drawing Test. *Psychological Bulletin, 8*(9), 483–505.

Urban, W. H. (1963). *The Draw-A-Person catalogue for interpretive analysis.* Los Angeles: Western Psychological Services.

Waldfagel, S. (1950). Review of the Machover Draw-A-Person Test. *Psychosomatic Medicine, 12,* 138–139.

Wanderer, Z. W. (1967). *The validity of diagnostic judgments based on "blind" Machover figure drawings.* Doctoral dissertation, Columbia University.

Watson, C. G. (1967). Relationship of distortion to DAP diagnostic accuracy among psychologists at three levels of sophistication. *Journal of Consulting Psychology, 31,* 142–146.

Weinberg, R. A. (1989). Review of Kinetic Drawing System for Family and School: A Handbook. In J. C. Conoley & J. J. Kramer (Eds.), *Tenth mental measurements yearbook.* Lincoln, NE: Buros Institute of Mental Measurement.

Zimmerman, J., & Garfinkle, L. (1942). Preliminary study of the art productions of the adult psychotic. *Psychiatric Quarterly, 16*(2), 313–318.

Chapter 8

BEHAVIORAL ASSESSMENT

If there were a patron saint of behaviorism, it would likely be William of Occam, the fourteenth century philosopher who spelled out the scientific doctrine that is now known as Occam's razor. This principle, also known as the Law of Parsimony, says that a simple explanation that fits the facts makes more sense than a complex one: never offer more than is necessary to explain a phenomenon.

Our minds crave explanations. Faced with insufficient data about unexplainable behavior, we try to make sense of the available bits and pieces of information by constructing elaborate plots and explanations. According to behaviorists, there are two problems with explanations of behavior that rely on hypothesized causes.

First, they introduce variables that invite the invention of still more hypotheses. So, if our strange behavior is caused by the anger of the gods, we must guess how we had offended them and then how best to placate them. If our dreams come from within ourselves, we conjecture as to whether they might be the work of a possessing demon or perhaps an unconscious mind that sends us cryptic messages about why we behave the way we do – and then dares us to make sense of these messages.

Second, hypothesized causes distract us from the behavior itself. Behaviorists believe that constructs like the unconscious, drives, needs, urges, and traits are museum pieces, relics of attempts to conjure up causes for things that aren't immediately explainable. Such constructs, they say, send us on wild-goose chases. Like the savants of the middle ages who treated mental disorders with prayer or exorcism, we treat mental health problems by dealing not with the problems themselves, but with the myths we create to explain them.

The simpler explanation, in this view, is to think of behavior as the ways we have learned to respond to circumstances and problems, rather than reflections of hypothesized innate traits or intrapsychic processes.

Many behaviorists balk at even talking about traits, or intrapsychic explanations, which Burris Frederick Skinner (1953) called "explanatory fictions" invented to explain behavior we consider deviant. Others may have no problem in talking about traits to describe habitual or characteristic ways of behaving. Behavior is flexible; individual behavior is often inconsistent and unpredictable. Not only does it vary over time, but it is usually situation-specific.

Until recently, behaviorists scoffed at attempts to assess patients through personality tests, and for the most part, they still do. They pointed out that projective tests and psychometric personality tests, in addition to seeking and measuring hypothesized traits, attempt to evaluate a client in a vacuum. The subject has been removed from the family situation, the workplace, the classroom, or the neighborhood in which the inappropriate or maladjusted behavior occurs. In such tests, says Alan Kazdin, "the tester may never observe the client's characteristic 'real-life' behaviors" (Kazdin, 1975, pp. 6, 9). As we shall see shortly, numbers of behaviorists have broadened their conceptions of behavior to include such "covert" behaviors as thoughts, sensations, perceptions, feelings and attitudes, none of which can be observed directly. As a result, many have modified their early opposition to traditional methods of assessment.

However, the basic purposes of assessment in behaviorism and in other therapies remain clearly differentiated. Behaviorists charge that the major purpose of traditional assessment is to assign labels and identify symptoms and "disorders" that go together. The resulting diagnosis provides little information beyond the symptoms that brought the client for treatment in the first place and which the therapist knew when the diagnosis was made. It provides no clue to etiology, prognosis, or treatment (Kanfer & Saslow, 1969), and it impels us to deal with the imagined cause, not with the problem behavior itself. Moreover, labels that suggest abnormality are highly subjective (Bandura, 1969; Ullmann & Krasner, 1969). The same behavior that a parent may describe as masculine and assertive may be an indication of emotional disturbance to a teacher or a guidance counselor.

Kanfer and Saslow's (1969) "functional" analysis, therefore, bypasses the traditional psychiatric label, which suggests the presence or absence of a problem. Their view is that maladaptive behavior is simply an excess or a deficit of "normal" behavior. The "obsessive-compulsive" woman who scrubs her kitchen a dozen times a day in her never-ending battle against invincible germs just has an excess of a normal desire to keep her kitchen clean.

Excesses and deficits must be identified so that treatment plans can be developed to reduce the incidence, intensity, or duration of behavioral excesses or to increase the frequency of deficits.

Behavioral assessment implicitly is concerned less with assigning a label than in considering the implications of the assessment for ways in which behaviors can be changed. Because behaviorists believe that the vast majority of behaviors are learned responses to specific types of situations, they seek to identify the situations and circumstances in which undesirable behaviors occur in order to structure relearning programs.

In recent decades, with the expansion and popularity of behavioral psychotherapeutic approaches such as Cognitive Behavioral Therapy and Dialectical Behavior Therapy, many behaviorists expanded their conceptualization of behavior to include more than just observable activity. Behavioral assessment today may consider internal behavior (such as feelings, thoughts, images, attitudes) and psycho-physiological functioning. As a result, behavioral assessment has expanded beyond reliance only on direct observation to include such previously scorned techniques as the use of self-report inventories, global ratings, and cognitive reporting (as when a client describes his or her thoughts and feelings). Some behaviorists have even developed tests to measure such personality characteristics as assertiveness and fear; what makes them "behavioral" assessments is the emphasis on the situational circumstances. To illustrate the difference, let's consider the measurement of Ted's fear. In traditional personality assessment, Ted is likely to be characterized as "fearful." His fear is considered a relatively enduring personality trait that Ted will bring to almost every situation. In behavioral assessment, it is assumed that Ted's fear is a response that he has learned from some experience or experiences and one that is evoked only under certain circumstances or in specific kinds of situations. The function of behavioral assessment, therefore, is not to identify fearfulness as an aspect of someone's personality but to identify the circumstances and situations that result in a fearful response.

IDENTIFYING TARGET BEHAVIORS

In almost any psychiatric hospital or clinic, residential setting, or special education program, staff members discuss the behavioral problems of their patients and clients. They may often agree on a description of the "problem:" Jason M. is "aggressive" and "belligerent;" Susan L. is "fearful" and "withdrawn;" Alice K. is "deficient in social skills." Or a client may tell a therapist that "I have trouble concentrating," or "I'm always angry."

To behaviorists, such traits or labels are too vague to be of much value in describing the behaviors to be changed or to suggest a course of treatment. In the case of the hospitalized patient, they are inferred from behaviors that staff members have observed. What specific behaviors led them to conclude that Susan is "withdrawn," or that Jason is "aggressive?" Did Jason strike anyone, or was his aggression limited to verbal abuse? When children "bicker," do they disagree, do they raise their voices, or do they use physical gestures or force? (Christopherson, Arnold, Hill, & Quilitch, 1972).

Moreover, these behaviors are almost always sporadic or episodic. They occur only on certain occasions or they follow a triggering event (behaviorists prefer the terms stimulus or antecedent condition). As important as identifying the behaviors that are to be changed is identifying the conditions or circumstances that precede them, accompany them, and follow them. Is Jason always aggressive? Is he aggressive only when he is with certain people, or only when someone touches his possessions, or only when he is given instructions or orders by those in authority? Is that self-described angry client really always angry – or is he or she angry only on the job, or only at home, or only with certain people or types of people?

Measurement is an important part of behavioral assessment procedures. The problem behavior must not only be identified but it must be measured to establish a baseline or operant rate. Do a child's temper tantrums really occur as frequently as parents remember and report? On the other hand, does a borderline alcoholic drink as seldom as he or she recalls?

DIRECT BEHAVIORAL ASSESSMENT

There are numbers of approaches and methods for measuring behaviors. However, all of them generally involve an examination of specific factors:

- the frequency with which a behavior occurs,
- the circumstances under which the behavior occurs,
- the things that happen before the behavior occurs (such as verbal interactions, boredom, anxiety), and
- the things that happen after the behavior occurs (such as criticism, praise, encouragement or self-satisfaction).

In addition, where it is appropriate, the intensity or the duration of the behavior is sometimes considered.

In the 1950s and 1960s, the standard approach to recording a client's or patient's behavior involved direct observation by the therapist or a surrogate, such as a parent, a teacher, or a spouse. The use of such surrogates has the advantage that such people can observe behavior in the client's natural environment, such as the home, the school, or the playground. Observation in the natural setting is preferable when the identified problem involves the kinds of behaviors that are most likely to occur in the context of the client's normal world and where they occur with some regularity. Direct observation is still the preferred approach to identifying target behaviors in cases where it is possible.

Frequency Measures

An obvious method for recording behavior is to count it. The numbers of times the behavior occurs within a specified period of time is referred to as a response rate; it is determined by counting the number of times the behavior occurs divided by the time. Obviously, it is easier to arrive at a response rate if the behaviors have a clear beginning and end and if they all last about the same amount of time (Skinner, 1966). Examples would be the number of times someone says "hello," or smokes a cigarette in the course of an hour.

Frequency can be recorded using therapist-constructed checklists or charts marked off in time intervals, such as minutes, five minutes, or half hours. A notation is made each time the behavior occurs. While the basic purpose of event recording is to count the frequency with

CLIENT: SAMUEL T.
FREQUENCY COUNT OF CIGARETTES SMOKED
DATE: 3/5

MINUTES	5	10	15	20	25	30	35	40	45	50	55	60	
9 AM - 10 AM		/		//		/				/			5
12 N - 1 PM			/			//	//			/		/	7
2 PM - 3 PM				/									1
6 PM - 7 PM					/	/		//		/		/	6
9 PM - 10 PM	/	/	/	//		//	/	/		//		/	12
												TOTAL	31

Figure 8.1. Therapist-made form for recording the frequency of a behavior within five-minute intervals for several hours of the day.

which a behavior occurs, simple coding systems can be used to indicate the intensity of the behavior: S for strong, M for moderate, W for weak.

Since a purpose of the assessment is to identify the circumstances under which the target behavior occurs, it is preferable to schedule the count at various times of day or of the week to cover a wide spectrum of times and activities.

Where frequency measures are practical, they have major advantages. They are easy and they show clearly whether the target behavior is changing.

However, frequency counts aren't very practical when the behavior involved is continuous (such as sitting immobile for a long period of time) or when each instance varies in duration (such as talking to others or having a temper tantrum). For such continuing or varied behaviors, another measurement technique must be used, such as interval recording or response duration.

Interval Recording

Interval recording is a useful way of measuring behaviors that have varying durations or that may occur sporadically, such as smiling or talking, or that don't always have a clear beginning or end, such as singing or fidgeting, or engaging in repetitious behaviors. However, the behavior itself is dichotomous: someone is talking or is not talking, so there is no question about the degree of talking. Interval recording is based on noting whether a given behavior occurs or does not occur within given blocks of time. There are several ways of determining the blocks of time. Suppose we divide a waking day into 16 hours and then observe the client for two minutes each hour. We simply record whether the behavior did or did not occur during each period. Or we can identify the block of time as one hour each day and break the hour into six ten-second intervals, alternating observation and recording for each interval. Interval recording has been used to measure such behaviors as the social responses of withdrawn children (Wahler, 1969) and the interactions of psychiatric patients (Milby, 1970).

A form of interval recording that is particularly useful for monitoring a client's progress is illustrated below. Suppose a therapist in a school for disturbed youngsters has been working with Kenneth to increase his attention span. One way to monitor change in his behavior is to record the presence or absence of attentive behavior for each minute during a class.

For each minute during which Kenneth remains seated at his desk working quietly, a check or a "plus" is marked. For each minute during which he leaves his seat or stops working, "0" or "minus" is marked. Because the purpose, in this case, is to ascertain the number of intervals in which Kenneth demonstrated this behavior rather than the specific order in which they occurred, the checks or "+"s are marked from the top down, and the "0"s from the bottom up. This coding system makes it quickly apparent whether the behavior is increasing or decreasing in each period.

The major limitation of interval recording is that, while it informs us that a behavior did or did not occur during the interval, it doesn't provide any information on the number of times the behavior occurred within that period. In the example above, we don't know how frequently Kenneth left his seat or stopped paying attention during each period. As a result, interval recording is useful primarily for recording continuing behaviors rather than fleeting ones.

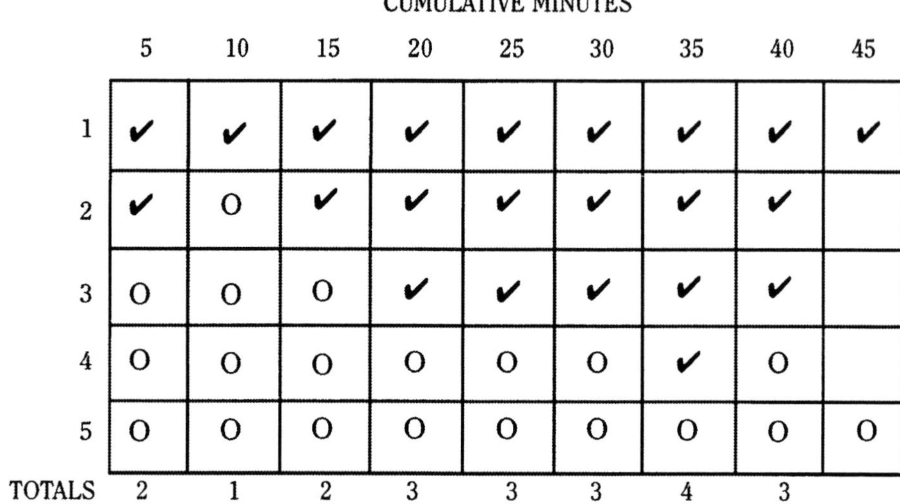

	CUMULATIVE MINUTES								
	5	10	15	20	25	30	35	40	45
1	✔	✔	✔	✔	✔	✔	✔	✔	✔
2	✔	O	✔	✔	✔	✔	✔	✔	
3	O	O	O	✔	✔	✔	✔	✔	
4	O	O	O	O	O	O	✔	O	
5	O	O	O	O	O	O	O	O	O
TOTALS	2	1	2	3	3	3	4	3	

Figure 8.2. Interval recording for monitoring change.

Duration of Response

For some treatment programs, the goal may be to increase or decrease the duration, rather than the frequency, of a behavior. Duration measures have been used to monitor the length of time a claustrophobic patient can sit in a small room (Leitenberg, Agras, Thompson, & Wright, 1986) and the time that developmentally disabled children can engage in cooperative play (Redd, 1969).

It is essential that the behavior be clearly defined, so that we can tell when it begins and ends. Does "aggressive behavior" begin when a patient glowers? When he approaches someone in an aggressive manner? When he uses aggressive language? (And just what kinds of words are to be considered "aggressive"?)

Similarly, we have to define a temper tantrum in terms of specific behaviors – whimpering, crying, screaming, kicking – and in deciding whether the periods of silence between the various behaviors are to be timed as part of the tantrum.

Self-Monitoring

A standard assessment tool is the self-monitoring record. Especially in situations in which the client has sought help in overcoming a problem and is therefore motivated to be honest in reporting, he or she may be asked to keep a detailed log or journal. Someone with a weight problem, for example, may be asked to keep a record of food intake, along with notations about time of day he or she ate, the circumstances and conditions under which the eating occurred, and perhaps the thoughts and feelings that accompanied them. A variation may call for recording what the client was doing at various times of the day, perhaps using an alarm clock set to go off at regular intervals. This experiential self-monitoring may call for recording not only behavior but additional data, such as the events that had immediately preceded the behavior, or what the client was thinking or feeling at the time.

Numbers of sophisticated self-monitoring devices have been around for many years for example mechanical counters to keep track of the number of bites someone takes while eating (Mahoney, 1974), and electronic counters to measure the numbers of times someone opens a cigarette case (Azrin & Powell, 1968). More recently, text messaging programs and mobile applications for smart phones are used to track behavior. Actigraphs, accelerometers, and global positioning systems help assess sleep patterns and when you specify locations (Muench, 2010).

Estimating Reliabilities for Direct Observation

As with any other assessment approach, there must be some consistency in measurement and/or recording, to obtain an accurate record of the client's performance. If frequency counts or estimates vary greatly from one observer to another or if there are variations in the way an observer defines the target behavior from time to time, it is difficult to identify the client's actual behavior, either to establish a baseline or to monitor change.

Frequency Counts

The reliability of observation frequency counts is determined by dividing the smaller count by the larger; if a percentage is desired, this number is multiplied by 100. Let's illustrate with the example of two parents who observe and record the number of times during a meal that a toddler spits out food. The mother counted 25 spits, the father 22. Agreement for this observation period was .88, or 88 percent.

One cautionary note: this figure does not mean that the parents agreed 88 percent of the time. Even if both parents agreed on the number of spits recorded, we can't be sure that they recorded the same incidents. So, in frequency counts, reliability refers only to agreement on the total number of behaviors, not to agreement on specific incidents. If behaviors are not carefully defined, a high percentage of agreement may mask a considerable amount of disagreement.

Interval Recording

Reliability for interval recording is calculated on the proportion of intervals in which two observers agree that a target behavior occurred. An agreement is noted if the two recorded an occurrence during the same interval.

For any interval in which one records a response and the other does not, a disagreement is noted. Intervals in which neither observer recorded a response are ignored. Reliability is computed by dividing the number of agreements by the sum of agreements and disagreements. For example, two observers may record the number of intervals during which a child was looking out a classroom window during nine five-second intervals. Both observers agreed on the occurrence of the behavior during the same five intervals but disagreed in two intervals. Reliability would be five divided by seven, or .71. It would be possible to consider the two intervals during which neither noted the behavior as agreements. Computing reliability this way would increase the figure to .78 (seven divided by nine). To maintain consistency in calculating reliability, it is conventional to restrict agreements to intervals during which one or both observers recorded the target behavior (Kazdin, 1974, p. 81). As with reliability coefficients in psychometrics, it is generally agreed that for clinical decisions an acceptable level of reliability should be .90 or above (Kazdin, p. 82).

INDIRECT AND ANALOGUE APPROACHES

Direct observation of behaviors is probably the most accurate approach to assessing the behavior of children in school or patients in a hospital, where teachers, parents, and health care workers may be trained to analyze and record behavior. However, in many circumstances, it may not always be possible or feasible to observe clients at the times or in the contexts in which the target behaviors are triggered. A number of techniques have been developed in the attempt to observe behavior that is comparable or analogous to the client's "real-world behavior."

Guided Imagery

The client is asked to imagine himself or herself in the kind of situation that may provoke an unwanted behavior: the crowded supermarket, or the cocktail party, or the office. Clients may be asked to describe their thoughts and feelings, as well as their likely behaviors.

Role Playing

Rather than describe a situation, the client may be asked to take on a role, perhaps with the therapist as the person with whom the client reports a problem, or, if a client couple is involved, the two individuals may role play. The therapist then has a behavioral sample of the problematic behavior. While role playing is becoming an increasingly important tool for identifying target behaviors, some writers have wondered whether role-played behavior elicited in the safe setting of a therapist's office is truly comparable to the actual behavior that would be evoked in real-life situations (Kolotkin & Wielkiewicz, 1984).

STANDARDIZED BEHAVIOR RATING SCALES

When behavioral assessment targets a specific behavior to be changed, there is no need for normative data. However, a number of standardized scales have been developed for syndromes, or clusters of behaviors around a central theme, like fear or anxiety. Generally, these behavior rating scales require the observer to check a box or write in a coded entry. Such scales are often used to identify groups of behaviors that are associated with a problem area, rather than the simple identification or measurement of a single behavior. While most of these behavior rating scales are completed by therapists, many such as the Beck Anxiety Inventory (1993) are designed as self-report instruments.

Standardized rating scales have been developed for the measurement of large numbers of behaviors that are associated with a response pattern. For example, the *Behavior Assessment System for Children, Second Edition* (Vannest, Reynolds, & Kamphaus, 2008) was designed for pinpointing and rating problem behaviors in children.

Because such rating scales can be used to assess quickly the behaviors of large groups of subjects, they are useful in such institutions as schools, clinics, and hospitals. However, there are several potential problems involved in using them. First, these scales tend to be less objective than are those that pinpoint specific target behaviors and are generally far more abstract and global. They involve identifying the multiple behaviors from which one may infer abstract constructs. The questions or items can rarely be constructed with the same precision that we might employ in describing a single target behavior.

As a result, we must approach behavior rating scales with the same caution that we employ when we evaluate personality tests. The authors of behavior rating scales should supply the kind of information that we would expect from the developers of any other objective test – on reliability, validity and, where it is appropriate, on standardization. The same sources we recommended earlier for locating information and reviews on tests such as the *Handbook of Psychiatric Measures* (Rush, First, & Blacker, 2007), *Mental Measurements Yearbook* online, *Tests in Print,* and *Test Critiques* can be used to locate behavior rating scales. In addition, The American Psychological Association has an excellent online guide to finding and selecting tests (http://www.apa.org/science/programs/testing/find-tests.aspx#). The Child Behavior Checklist is included as an example of a well-known behavior rating scale.

Child Behavior Checklist

The purpose of the Child Behavior Checklist (Achenbach, 1991; Achenbach & Edelbrock, 1983; Achenbach & Rescorla, 2001) is to obtain parents' reports on their children's problems and competencies. The CBCL includes a Teacher's Report Form (TRF) and a Youth Self-Report (YSR). As is to be expected, each form has a somewhat different focus, but for the most part, the CBCL and its companion forms are designed to provide standardized descriptions of behavior, rather than inferred diagnostic classifications. A similarity in items across the three checklists makes it easy to compare the lists for purposes of identifying social and emotional problems across a range of situations and perceptions.

The names of the scales (such as internalizing, externalizing, social withdrawal, depressed, schizoid, aggressive, obsessive-compulsive) suggest clinical diagnosis but, while they relate their empirically derived scales to commonly used clinical diagnoses, the authors "are very explicit that the names of the scales were selected to summarize item content of each scale, not to be used as diagnostic categories" (Christenson, 1992, p. 165).

The various scales in each of the three forms vary in clarity and practicality (Elliot, 1992, p. 166). However, the Behavior Problems Scale, the centerpiece of the TRF, is clearly focused on overt behaviors, which are rated on a three-point scale (0 = not true, 1 = sometimes true, and 2 = very true, or often true). While one reviewer found most items objective and clear, he was puzzled by ambiguities in some ("Behaves like opposite sex") that invite subjective opinions (Elliot, p. 166).

Standardization

Standardization samples were selected differently for each subtest form population – parents, teachers, and children – and for each scale as well. The standardization samples were generally of adequate size, although Hispanics, Asians, and Native-Americans are underrepresented. There are some peculiarities associated with some of the scales' norming; for example, the Behavior Problems Scale was developed on the basis of referred children, but was normed on a sample of nonreferred children.

Reliability and Validity

Each form and each scale was validated separately. Test-retest reliabilities are reasonable: mean r equals .89 for a two-week period, declining to .68 for a four-month period. The validity of the TRF, according to the authors, is based on its substantive content and the fact that its constructs are congruent with many of the problem behaviors cited in the child psychopathology literature. Its criterion validity has been based on the correlation of scores and the number of referrals that were made (Elliot, 1992, p. 167).

The CBCL is actively used and in 2001, an eight-syndrome structure model was proposed (Achenbach & Rescorla, 2001) that have been found to discriminate among groups such as children on the autism spectrum, those with attention deficit hyperactivity disorder, and typically developing children (Ooi, Rescorla, Ang, Wu, & Fung, 2011). Very interesting and useful, is that examination of the CBCL across cultures has been examined for multicultural robustness (Ivanova et al., 2007; Ooi, Rescorla, Ang, Wu, & Fung, 2010; Viola, Garrido, & Rescorla, 2011).

COGNITIVE BEHAVIORAL ASSESSMENT

Some decades ago, numbers of behaviorists, like Lazarus (1973), Bandura (1986) and Meichenbaum (1976), concluded that behaviorism was too confining if it focused exclusively on observable behaviors and ignored the cognitive and affective factors that influenced these behaviors. Among the questions cognitive behaviorists ask:

How did the client perceive the situation? What was the client thinking or feeling at the time?

Because only the client can answer such questions, a number of approaches were developed to bring these covert behaviors into the open so that they can be examined and measured. For the most part, they substitute client reports for direct observation.

Clinical Techniques for Recording Cognitions

Below are several examples of clinical techniques for recording the thoughts and feelings of clients. They tend to be relatively informal and loosely structured. Many of these parallel the techniques used in recording overt behaviors, and are used in Cognitive Behavioral Therapy, Dialectical Behavior Therapy, and other modern applications of behaviorism.

Verbalizing Thoughts

There are several variations. Clients may be instructed to verbalize their ongoing thoughts about a subject for periods of five to ten minutes, or to free associate. While it seems plausible that such verbalizations will reflect the actual thought processes of the client, the procedure has been criticized on the ground that it is artificial and that, for a variety of reasons, it produces biased samples of inner behavior.

Simulations

The therapist may create a scenario or structured situation in which the client imagines a problem situation. For example, someone who is shy or submissive may be asked to imagine himself or herself insulted by a rude waiter or ignored by a sales clerk. Conversely, the client may be asked to imagine himself or herself acting assertively in such situations and verbalizing his or her thoughts. A variation is a form of role playing in which the client is actually subjected to the stimulus that provokes the problem response. For example, someone who overreacts to criticism may be criticized by the therapist, or someone who fears cats may be confronted with one. In all of these situations, the client's thoughts and feelings are verbalized and recorded.

Thought Sampling

There are several variations of thought sampling. Clients may be instructed to keep a record not only of the target behaviors but of the thoughts that accompanied these behaviors or that were related to them and the feelings that they experienced. For example, a client may be given a beeper that goes off at varying intervals. At each beep, the client records his or her thoughts on a Thought Sampling Questionnaire (TSQ), which provides for recording such variables as vividness and controllability (Klinger, 1978).

Cognitive Behavioral Self-Reports and Rating Scales

With the expansion of the concept of behavioral assessment to include cognitions and feelings has come the increasing use of a wide variety of indirect measures. Earlier, we considered one such measure, the Beck Depression Inventory. The very fact that such instruments are sometimes designated personality tests is an indication of how far the field of behavioral assessment has expanded beyond the exclusive reliance on direct observation of overt behaviors.

In some ways, these rating scales, questionnaires and tests violate the spirit of direct behavioral approaches. From the behaviors that are reported by clients, the interpreters infer disorders (such as depression and phobias), personality patterns (such as self-efficacy or impulsivity), and skills (such as social or communication skills). Of course, the greater the leap from behavior to inference, the greater is the chance of distortion. Each step beyond the recording of the behavior itself increases the chance of faulty or biased interpretation. As a result, these indirect instruments and tests demand the same scrutiny as do more traditional measures to ascertain their validity and reliability. A wide range of specific self report measures abounds in the literature and again, we refer the reader to resources for locating these listed earlier in this chapter.

Measuring Beliefs and Expectations

To those who believe that the bulk of our behavior is shaped by social learning, an important impetus for what we do is a combination of our beliefs and our expectations. A number of cognitive behavioral measures are designed to identify and measure these beliefs and expectations.

One such measure is the Irrational Beliefs Test (IBT), to measure unreasonable beliefs that distort a subject's attitudes and behaviors (Jones, 1968). The subject is asked to indicate on a five-point scale the degree to which each of the 100 items corresponds to his or her beliefs ("I frequently worry about things over which I have no control"). Some researchers have reported a correlation between scores on the IBT with anxiety (Deffenbacher et al., 1986) and with depression (Cook & Peterson, 1986). However, as with many indirect behavioral measures, reliability figures are far more impressive than are validation data (Smith & Zurawski, 1983).

Along the same lines, one technique for cognitive behavioral measurement is based on the identification of a subject's self-statements, which reveal that individual's self-appraisal and expectations of others. Dubbed cognitive functional analysis (Meichenbaum, 1976), this approach is based on the assumption that what someone says to himself or herself in the course of daily behavior influences the way that person behaves (Meichenbaum & Turk, 1976). Meichenbaum's assessment involves identifying the client's internal dialogue prior to, during, and after behavior. The rationale behind this assessment is the hypothesis that if thoughts influence behavior, then modifying thought patterns can modify behavior.

Psychophysiological Measurement

The area of psychophysiological measurement rests on the same basic principle that underlies so much in the arts therapies: that there is an intimate relationship between body and mind, and that changes in one must involve changes in the other.

In his Fragment of an Analysis of a Case of Hysteria, Freud remarked that "He that has eyes to see and ears to hear may convince himself that no mortal can keep a secret. If his lips are silent, he chatters with his fingertips; betrayal oozes out of him at every pore" (Freud, 1924, p. 94). Since Freud's day, research findings have provided both empirical and experimental support for this connection, and the fact that this relationship exists is no longer a matter of serious debate.

However, some physiological behavior is silent, and covert, not usually open to observation by others: the tightening of our muscles when we are tense, the beating of our hearts when we are anxious, the pumping of adrenaline and other changes in hormones when we are angry or fearful. Many of these physiological responses require biological measures such as assessing blood samples for serum levels of hormones like cortisol that varies with mental and physical activity, or Dehydroepiandrosteronsulphate (DHEA-S), a hormone from the adrenal gland where high levels reflect well-being (Bojner-Horwitz, Theorell, & Anderberg, 2003). Other physiological responses may be reflected in brain activity measured by functional magnetic resonance imaging or electroencephalography (see for example, Lindenberger, Li, Gruber, & Muller, 2009).

Advances in technology such as those just mentioned have made it possible to measure many of these internal behaviors with remarkable precision. Moreover, studies have revealed relationships between some specific psychological and physiological phenomena. Over half a century ago Ax (1953) demonstrated that fear and anger, earlier assumed to trigger an undifferentiated "fight or flight" response, were associated with very different physiological responses in blood pressure and galvanic skin response. Since that time, increasingly sophisticated technology has been developed for measuring these largely unseen physiological behaviors, and over the years researchers have sought ways of using physiological indicators to probe psychological states. However, the basic question has not been yet been answered to the satisfaction of most researchers: While studies have provided evidence of general associations between physiological and psychological behaviors, are the relationships clear enough so that measurements in one area can be used to measure the dimensions of the other?

Direct Measurement

Just as the concept of behavior has been expanded to include thoughts and emotional feelings, it has been further expanded to include many internal physiological behaviors. Many of these behaviors are generally hidden even from the person experiencing them: changes in temperature, blood pressure, brain wave production, vasodilation, and peristalsis, or intestinal contractions. As a result, self-report inventories are of little value in recording or measuring them.

Indirect Measurement

The best-known application of indirect psychophysiological measurement is probably the polygraph or "lie detector." The polygraph provides a graphic record of a number of selected physiological responses – usually respiration, galvanic skin responses, and pulse rate – during a structured interview. The use of the polygraph is based on the theory that when someone lies, identifiable changes take place in his or her body.

While polygraph tests have been extensively used in industry and law, the psychometric properties of these tests raise questions about both their validity and their reliability (Kleinmuntz & Szucko, 1984; Saxe, Dougherty, & Cross, 1985). Kleinmuntz and Szucko (1987) conclude that as many as half the subjects undergoing polygraph testing may be victims of false positive findings (p. 774). Nevertheless, polygraph testing of job applicants and employees had become almost routine in many industries, particularly in retailing, by the 1980s, despite the skepticism of the American Psychological Association, most of whose members questioned the validity and reliability of the procedure. The Congressional Office of Technology Assessment found, in the late 1980s, that polygraph testing was enjoying a popularity that bid to surpass the explosion of psychological testing in the 1950s (Bales, 1989). In late 1988, in response to pressure from the APA and the American Civil Liberties Union, Congress passed the Employee Polygraph Protection Act, which virtually banned the use of polygraph tests in the screening of job applicants.

Especially in the early years of the discipline, music therapists relied a good deal on psychophysiological measurement to support their contentions that musical stimuli elicit change. In the years following World War II, music therapists reported that listening to music produced changes in blood flow and blood pressure (Sears, 1954), changes in posture (Sears, 1951), pulse rate and the general activity level of schizophrenics (Shatin, 1957; Skelly & Haslerud, 1952), and breathing (Ellis & Brighouse, 1952). For the most part, however, such psychophysiological measurement has been the subject of music therapy research rather than a practical technique for the assessment of individual patients or clients.

The correlation of physiological measurements with psychological processes holds a good deal of promise for psychodiagnosis. However, while measurement techniques have been refined, the relationships still have not emerged that provide enough precision for diagnosis or assessment of psychiatric or emotional problems, although they may be sufficient for limited use in monitoring.

PROBLEMS OF RELIABILITY AND VALIDITY IN BEHAVIORAL ASSESSMENT

It is difficult to describe the psychometric properties of behavioral assessment, mainly because there is no single approach to evaluation of behavior; in fact, the very definition of behavior has been evolving rapidly.

In addition, the discipline of psychometrics was developed on the basis of some assumptions that are often questioned by behaviorists. For example, test-retest reliability is predicated upon the assumption that traits or characteristics are relatively stable aspects of an individual's personality. Behaviorists assume that behavior is highly variable and is influenced by large numbers of environmental factors. As a result, the reliabilities that are considered important in behavioral assessment are inter-observer reliability and the internal consistency of the assessment instrument.

Similarly, it is difficult to establish validity based on normative data, because behavioral assessment assumes a wide range of individual idiosyncrasies. In this view, the function of behavioral therapy is to help individuals change specific behaviors that they or others perceive as maladjusted, regardless of how widespread (normal) those behaviors may be in society.

However true this might have been with regard to direct measurement, the older assumptions may no longer be applicable in the expanded concept of behavioral assessment. As long as behavior was carefully defined, observed, and recorded, the reliability of measurement has generally been assumed. But with the increasing use of tests and rating scales to measure unseen behaviors, many have criticized the old assumptions as unwarranted and simplistic. For example, it has been established that behavior therapists can be influenced by their expectations, their biases, and their strategies in much the same way as traditional clinicians (Cooper & Rosenthal, 1980; Rosenthal, 1966). And two critics have found that behavioral self-report procedures are as susceptible to distortion as the older paper-and-pencil personality tests (Kaplan & Sacuzzo, 1989).

In general, validation research on self-report instruments has not produced encouraging results at the same time that these instruments have proliferated. Even those that closely follow *DSM* criteria for disorders such as the Beck Depression Inventory and the Beck Anxiety have received critiques. For example, the Beck Anxiety Inventory has been challenged as a measure of panic disorder rather than general anxiety (Cox, Cohen, Direnfeld, & Swinson, 1996). For many instruments, the research that has been done has been conducted mainly on groups limited by lack of multicultural diversity. However, studies of the more popular instruments such as the Beck Depression Inventory and others continue to amass reliability and validity information for ever more diverse samples (see for example, Segal, Coolidge, Cahill, & O'Riley, 2008).

ESTABLISHING GOALS AND OBJECTIVES

> "Would you tell me, please, which way I ought to walk from here?" "That depends a good deal on where you want to get to," said the Cat. "I don't much care where," said Alice. "Then it doesn't matter which way you walk," said the Cat.
> "– so long as I get somewhere," Alice added as an explanation. "Oh, you're sure to do that," said the Cat, "if you only walk long enough."
> Lewis Carroll, Alice in Wonderland

More than any of the other forms of therapy, behavior therapy shares with education a focus on the achievement of specific goals. However, to behavioral theorists and researchers, too many educators and therapists involve themselves in activities with no idea of where they want to get to. As a result, they apply methods and techniques that they consider so intrinsically worthwhile that they must eventually lead to a worthwhile destination. But, since they don't know in advance where they want to go, they don't know if or when they've arrived.

Because behaviorists believe that changing behavior involves learning or relearning ways of dealing with situations, their methods rest ultimately on one of the theories of learning, rather than on personality theory. As a result, they make relatively little distinction between education and therapy. In fact, since the enactment of Public Law 94-142, which provided for the "mainstreaming" of children with developmental, physical, or emotional problems, increasing numbers of arts therapists have been brought into the field of special education, blurring even more the distinction between education and therapy in the care of such children. The efficacy of a teaching program or a therapeutic intervention must be evaluated in terms of what those programs set out to accomplish. James Popham, who called himself "an enlightened behaviorist," described the problems of evaluating the accomplishments of educators, and, by extension, therapists, who fail to define the ways in which their efforts should be evaluated. Those who fail to specify what they expect to accomplish, he wrote:

> have it easy when they contend that behavioral evidence is inadequate for their purposes, since it will never "capture the richness of a human being's intellectual or emotional makeup." Such educators [and therapists] never really have to put their effectiveness on the line. Since they function in ethereal realms, no one can tie them down. . . . [T]ravesties will prosper alongside . . . triumphs. We can't tell which is which. (Popham, 1977, p. 58)

In behavior therapy, assessment and treatment are intimately related in terms of objectives. The assessment identifies the behavior to be changed (the "target behavior"), while the treatment objective specifies the behavior to be demonstrated at the end of treatment.

However, it isn't enough only to specify the behavior to be changed. Getting shy, withdrawn Joan to talk more or to smile more may be of little value if Joan ends up talking to herself or chattering or smiling at funerals. We may simply have substituted one problem for another if our goal was simply to get Sam to complete his homework, and we find that he does this conscientiously when he should be paying attention in class. So the objective involves not only specifying the behavior to be changed but the conditions that we want associated with the new behavior, in order to avoid unintended consequences of treatment.

Distinguishing Between Goals and Objectives

The idea of expressing purposes and objectives in behavioral terms became popular in education during the 1960s in response to increasing demands for school "accountability."

The reformers were disturbed by discrepancies between the lofty but largely immeasurable educational goals described in school programs and course descriptions, such as "to understand," and "to appreciate." But what was actually being measured on school tests, was usually the recall of memorized information. Reformers contended that, to be meaningful and measurable, the intended consequences of instruction must be stated in terms of precise and observable, predetermined behaviors that students were expected to demonstrate at the conclusion of the instruction.

Let's clarify the distinction between goals and objectives. While the terms are sometimes used interchangeably, confusing the two can lead to problems in planning and in evaluation.

Goals

Goals relate to the purposes of the treatment or instructional endeavor. The long-term goals are the ultimate aims of a program, the basic thrust of the treatment or educational plan. In terms of the question the Cheshire Cat asked Alice, they are declarations about where you want to get to. Long-term goals are usually presented in global and even abstract terms, such as "to improve social skills" or "to reduce the patient's aggressive behavior." Short-term (or instructional) goals are usually more modest, marking mileposts along the way to the attainment of the long-term goal. These short-term goals can suggest the specific ideas, processes, and materials to be used in the treatment program, as well as the performance objectives to be used in monitoring progress. Both long-term and short-term goals are guides for planning treatment, not for evaluating it.

Some published goals are so vague and immeasurable that they offer little guidance for planning a treatment or a learning program or for knowing if or when they have been attained. Wishes to help a client "self-actualize," or "broaden his or her horizons," or "learn the reasons for his or her behavior" may be laudable, but might more accurately be termed pious hopes than attainable goals. There isn't any meaningful way of knowing when they have been achieved. On the other hand, some educators and therapists, caught up in the spirit of clarity and precision, and anxious to avoid ambiguity, go overboard in trivializing goals.

Objectives

If a goal is a destination, then objectives are the roads we take to get there. Objectives are specific behaviors or groups of behaviors that we want the client to demonstrate. They are the steps on the way to where we want to get that show progress towards the goal. The formulation of objectives directed towards the stated long-term goal involves a consideration of content validity. If the spread of objectives is too limited, it raises questions about the adequacy of the sampling of behavior and the reliability of the assessment. We would expect our list of behavioral objectives to provide a reasonable spread of sample behaviors of various types from which we can judge how successful we have been in attaining our goal. The spread may be shaped around different kinds of behavior or different levels of difficulty.

A goal of a music therapy treatment plan might be to improve the socialization skills of a patient; objectives might include having the patient greet the others in the music therapy group, play in harmony with others, and talk more with them in the course of making music. In a dance/movement therapy treatment group, the long-term goal might be to help children learn to interact with others on a body level and behavioral objectives might include the ability to control one's movement evidenced by playing "red light, green light" or "statues" that require one to move freely and then stop quickly.

The task of formulating objectives that demonstrate that a client or patient has acquired the target skill or attitude rests on three simple principles. For an observer to know that the client has attained the desired objective:

1. The task that is identified must be an observable behavior, not an "understanding" or an "appreciation" or an "attitude." Laudable as these concepts may be, they are not behaviors that can be observed or measured, and we can infer their attainment only if the client performs an appropriate task that is observable.

2. The performance objective should require that the subject perform a predetermined behavior, not, as often appears in descriptions of objectives, that he or she "will be able to perform" it. The only way the observer can know that the client is able to do it is if he or she does it.

3. The conditions under which the behavior is performed should be made clear, if the behavior is to be limited to specific situations. For example, the therapist may want to specify the situational variable, or "prompt" or "stimulus" to which the behavior is a response ("The patient will respond to a single drumbeat performed by the therapist by striking a single drumbeat in return," or "the patient will return greetings when he or she meets others").

Some behaviorists distinguish between behavioral objectives that provide general guides to treatment and performance objectives that specify the dimensions of the tasks that the patient or client will perform. To the therapist, the execution of the performance objective demonstrates that the behavioral objective has been achieved. If the objectives are distinguished in this way, a behavioral objective may be to have Ellen smile more and utter words of greeting when she encounters others, while a performance objective (or performance item) might be stated, "In at least eight out of every 10 times Ellen meets staff members or other patients in the hallways or the ward, she will greet them by saying 'Hello,' or 'Good morning,' or another socially acceptable form of greeting." While the behavioral objective may state that a subject will "be able" to do something, the performance item must specify what the subject will do and the circumstances under which it will be done.

The objectives must bear a clear relationship to the goal so that we can ascertain whether we are making progress towards our destination. Similarly, the performance item must sample directly the behaviors described in the behavioral objective. Here, as in the more traditional psychological assessment approaches, the issue of validity that some behaviorists thought they had laid to rest rises up to challenge them. Just because a patient has been encouraged to respond to a drumbeat or to sing a "hello" song may or may not suggest that he or she has improved in interpersonal skills. The problem of stating easy behavioral objectives rather than meaningful ones is a persistent one. In describing the early attempts by behavioral enthusiasts to establish behavioral objectives in education, Popham wrote:

> Most of their objectives were lucidly stated, yet dealt with pretty trivial kinds of learner outcomes. For all the good his little booklet on behavioral objectives actually accomplished, Bob Mager's 1962 publication [Preparing Instructional Objectives] contained too many clearly stated but trifling instructional objectives. And many educators, unable to separate clarity from significance, churned out a litany of objectives that far out-trifled Mager's. (Popham, 1977, p. 59)

Popham pointed out that "A really compelling advantage of behaviorally stated objectives is that they permit us to spot and dismiss truly cruddy objectives" (Popham, 1977, p. 59).

Some Problems in Measurement

The notion of behavioral objectives is closely related to another educational reform that took hold in the 1960s, that of criterion-referenced testing. Reformers criticized the traditional normative approach, in which students were evaluated in terms of how their performances compared with those of others. Normative evaluation, it was pointed out, is of limited value for diagnostic, remedial, or instructional purposes.

Criterion-referenced evaluation is based on how well a student performs a predetermined task without reference to norms. Tests and evaluation procedures may be based on a dichotomous scale (yes/no, performed/did not perform) or on a continuous scale, usually expressed in terms of the proportion of tasks performed. A student may be deemed to have demonstrated satisfactory achievement if he or she achieves the "criterion level" specified. For example, he or she might be required to spell correctly at least eight of 10 spelling words on a quiz in order to have achieved a criterion level of 80 percent – regardless of how well other students may have done.

The two approaches serve very different purposes. The continuous interval scale approach, compatible with schools' traditional practice of awarding grades, is the more commonly used approach in the specification of educational goals. As a result, it can be adopted by arts therapists who practice in school settings, usually in special education, although it may not always be appropriate, or even make sense, for the remedial or treatment program.

Let's consider an alternative approach by examining the four criteria suggested for developing behavioral objectives by the University of California Los Angeles Center for the Study of Evaluation (UCLA, 1970, pp. 3–5).

1. The objectives should be stated in a clear and unambiguous form.
2. A number of test items (tasks) should be developed for each objective, listed in an ascending order of difficulty. This practice helps the educator/therapist ascertain at what point a particular child needs help. It also provides data on which to discriminate between children who operate at different levels of competency, as a basis for making decisions about treatment plans.
3. Some items or tasks should deal with related objectives to help determine how achievement of an objective relates to other equally important objectives.
4. Scores and score interpretations should be provided for each objective. Such interpretations might include normative data, as a guide to where a particular student's score fits in terms of his or her peers.

The purported "goal" is actually an objective and the so-called objectives are actually tasks, analogous to the test items on a traditional classroom test. If these tasks were carefully developed in an ascending order of difficulty, the criterion of attainment would be the level at which a child gets stuck and cannot go on to perform the next task. Such scoring would provide a basis for determining levels of discrimination and would offer some guidance for adjusting the educational/treatment program.

SUMMARY

Behaviorism is based on the principle that aberrant or "maladapted" behavior is not a symptom or a reflection of a problem; it is the problem. Behaviorists reject intrapsychic models of psychotherapy, particularly those of psychoanalysis and of trait theory, which look for the causes of maladapted behavior in the individual's personality. They contend that most behavior is learned and is situation-specific. So, rather than identify personality traits or infer the needs, impulses, or drives that might explain the behavior, behaviorists try to identify the stimuli that seem to be associated with the behavior, in the settings in which the problem behaviors occur.

In measuring observable behaviors, the therapist attempts to identify:

- the frequency with which a behavior occurs, or its duration;
- the circumstances under which the behavior occurs;
- the things that happen before the behavior occurs; and
- the things that happen after the behavior occurs.

While early behaviorists considered only overt behavior they could observe directly, behavior therapists today have expanded the definition of behaviors to include such internal behaviors as thinking, emotions, and attitudes. What distinguishes measures of cognitive behavior from traditional personality tests is that the cognitive behavior tests seek to identify the situations in which patterns of response are evoked, rather than inferred personality traits. The development of cognitive behavioral approaches has stimulated the development of such indirect measures as cognitive self-report inventories and rating scales. In some ways, these questionnaires and tests violate the spirit of behavioral assessment. From reported behaviors, the interpreters infer disorders, personality patterns, and skills.

Because the targeted behavior is identified, measured, and then modified, it is important for behavior therapists to establish goals and objectives. Goals are usually stated in terms of long-range aims and purposes; objectives are described in terms of specific clearly defined behaviors that the client will exhibit at the conclusion of the treatment. Behavioral tasks (or performance objectives) are most useful if they are identified in hierarchical order of difficulty, to help identify the point at which the subject needs help.

REFERENCES

Achenbach, T. M. (1991). *Integrative guide for the 1991 CBCL/4-18, YSR, and TRF Profiles*. Burlington, VT: University of Vermont, Department of Psychiatry.

Achenbach, T. M., & Edelbrock, C. S. (1983). *Manual for the child behavior checklist and revised child behavior profile*. Burlington, VT: University of Vermont, Dept. of Psychiatry.

Achenbach, T. M., & Rescorla, L. A. (2001). *Manual for the ASEBA school-age forms & profiles*. Burlington: University of Vermont, Research Center for Children,Youth, and Families.

Ax, A. F. (1953). The physiological differentiation between fear and anger in humans. *Psychosomatic Medicine, 15,* 433–442.

Azrin, N. H., & Powell, J. (1968). Behavioral engineering: The reduction of smoking behavior by a conditioning apparatus and procedure. *Journal of Applied Behavior Analysis, 1,* 193–200.

Bales, J. (1989). Agency sounds alarm on work test technology. *APA Monitor, 18,* 16.

Bandura, A. (1969). *Principles of behavior modification*. New York: Holt, Rinehart and Winston.

Bandura, A. (1986). *Social foundations of thought and action: A social cognitive theory*. Englewood Cliffs, NJ: Prentice-Hall.

Beck, A. T., & Steer, R. A. (1993). *Beck Depression Inventory manual.* San Antonio, TX: Psychological Corporation, Harcourt, Brace.

Bojner-Horwitz, E., Theorell, T., & Anderberg, U. M. (2003). Dance/movement therapy and changes in stress-related hormones: A study of fibromyalgia patients with video interpretation. *The Arts in Psychotherapy, 30,* 255–264.

Christenson, S. A. (1992). Review of the Child Behavior Checklist. In J. J. Kramer & J. C. Conoley (Eds.), *Eleventh mental measurements yearbook*. Lincoln, NE: Buros Institute of Mental Measurement.

Christopherson, E. R., Arnold, C. M., Hill, D. W., & Quilitch, H. R. (1972). The home point system: Token reinforcement procedures for application by parents of children with behavior problems. *Journal of Applied Behavior Analysis, 5,* 485–497.

Cook, M. L., & Peterson, C. (1986). Depressive irrationality. *Cognitive Therapy and Research, 10,* 293–298.

Cooper, H. M., & Rosenthal, R. (1980). Statistical versus traditional procedures for summarizing research findings. *Psychological Bulletin, 87*(3), 442–449.

Cox, B. J., Cohen, E., Direnfeld, D. M., & Swinson, P. (1996). Does the Beck Anxiety Inventory measure anything beyond panic attack symptoms? *Behaviour Research and Therapy, 34,* 949–954.

Deffenbacher, J. L., Zwemer, W. A., Whisman, M. A., Hill, R. A., & Sloan, R. D. (1986). Irrational beliefs and anxiety. *Cognitive Therapy and Research, 10,* 281–292.

Elliot, S. E. (1992). Review of the Child Behavior Checklist. In J. J. Kramer & J. C. Conoley (Eds.), *Eleventh mental measurements yearbook*. Lincoln, NE: Buros Institute of Mental Measurement.

Ellis, D. S., & Brighouse, G. (1952). Effects of music on respiration and heart-rate. *American Journal of Psychology, 65,* 39–47.

Freud, S. (1924). The loss of reality in neurosis and psychosis. In J. Riviere (trans.), *Collected Papers.* New York: Basic Books. Vol. II, (pp. 277–282).

Ivanova, M.Y., Achenbach, T. M., Dumenci, L., Rescorla, L. A.,...Verhulst, F. C. (2007). Testing the 8-syndrom structure of the Child Behavior Checklist in 30 societies. *Journal of Clinical Child and Adolescent Psychology, 36*(3), 405–417, DOI: 10.1080/15374410701444363.

Jones, R. A. (1968). *A factored measure of Ellis' irrational belief system with personality and maladjustment correlates.* Unpublished doctoral dissertation, Texas Technological College.

Kanfer, F. H., & Saslow, G. (1969). Behavioral diagnosis. In C. M. Franks (Ed.), *Behavioral therapy: Appraisal and status* (pp. 417–444). New York: McGraw-Hill.

Kaplan, R. M., & Saccuzzo, D. P. (1989). *Psychological testing: Principles, applications, and issues* (2nd ed.). Pacific Grove, CA: Brooks/Cole.

Kazdin, A. E. (1974). Reactive self-monitoring: The effects of response desirability, goal setting, and feedback. *Journal of Consulting and Clinical Psychology, 42*(5), 704–716.

Kazdin, A. E. (1975). *Behavior modification in applied settings.* Homewood, IL: Dorsey.

Kleinmuntz, B., & Szucko, J. J. (1984). Lie detection in ancient and modern times: A call for contemporary scientific study. *American Psychologist, 39*(7), 766–776.

Kleinmuntz, B., & Szucko. J. J. (1987). Deception, lie detection, and the dynamics of legal decision making. (Final project report submitted on Grant NES-83-19138). Washington, DC: National Science Foundation.

Klinger, E. (1978). Modes of normal conscious flow. In K. S. Pope & J. L. Singer (Eds.), *The stream of consciousness: Scientific investigations into the flow of human experience.* New York: Plenum.

Kolotkin, R. A., & Wielkiewicz, R. M. (1984). Effects of situational demand in the role-play assessment of assertive behavior. *Journal of Behavioral Assessment, 6,* 5970.

Lazarus, A. A. (1973). Multimodal behavior therapy: Treating the BASIC ID. *Journal of Nervous and Mental Diseases, 156,* 404–411.

Leitenberg, H., Agras, W. S., Thompson, L. E., & Wright, D. E. (1968). Feedback in behavior modification: An experimental analysis in two phobic cases. *Journal of Applied Behavior Analysis, 1,* 131–137.

Lindenberger, U., Li, S., Gruber, W., & Muller, V. (2009). Brains swinging in concert: Cortical phase synchronization while playing guitar. *BMC Neuroscience, 10*(22), DOI: 10.1186/1471-2202-10-22.

Mahoney, M. J. (1974). *Cognition and behavior modification.* Cambridge: Ballinger.

Meichenbaum, D., & Turk, D. (1976). The cognitive-behavioral management of anxiety, anger, and pain. In P. Davidson (Ed.), *Management of anxiety, depression, and pain.* New York: Brunner/Mazel.

Meichenbaum, D. (1976). A cognitive behavior modification approach to assessment. In M. Hersen & A. S. Bellack (Eds.), *Behavioral assessment.* New York: Pergamon.

Milby, J. B. (1970). Modification of extreme social isolation by contingent social reinforcement. *Journal of Applied Behavior Analysis, 3,* 149–152.

Muench, F. (2010, September). Self-monitoring made easy: It's not just for engineers anymore. *Psychology Today,* Retrieved from: http://www.psychologytoday.com/blog/more-tech-support/201004/technology-and-mental-health-using-technology-improve-our-lives.

Ooi, Y. P., Rescorla, L., Ang, R. P., Wu, B., & Fung, D. S. (2011). Identification of autism spectrum disorders using the Chile Behavior Checklist in Singapore. *Journal of Autism and Developmental Disorders, 41*(9), 1147–1156, DOI: 10.1007/s10803-101-1015-x.

Popham, J. W. (1977). Behaviorism as a bugbear. *Educational Leadership, 35,* 57–62.

Redd, W. H. (1969). Effects of mixed reinforcement contingencies on adults' control of children's behavior. *Journal of Applied Behavior Analysis, 2,* 249–254.

Rosenthal, R. (1966). *Experimenter effects in behavioral research.* East Norwalk, CT: Appleton-Century-Crofts.

Rush, A. J., First, M. B., & Blacker, D. (2007). *Handbook of psychiatric measures* (2nd ed.). Washington, DC: American Psychiatric Publishing, Inc.

Saxe, L., Dougherty, D., & Cross, T. (1985). The validity of polygraph testing: Scientific analysis and public controversy. *American Psychologist, 40*(3), 355–366

Sears, W. W. (1951). *Postural response to recorded music.* Master's thesis, University of Kansas.

Sears, M. S. (1954). *A study of the vascular changes in the capillaries as affected by music.* Master's thesis, University of Kansas.

Segal, D. L., Coolidge, F. L., Cahill, B. S., & O'Riley, A. A. (2008). Psychometric properties of the Beck Depression Inventory-II (BDI-II) among community-dwelling older adults. *Behavior Modification, 32*(1), 3–20.

Shatin, L. (1957). The influence of rhythmic drumbeat stimuli upon the pulse rate and general activity of long-term schizophrenics. *Journal of Mental Science, 103,* 172–188.

Skelly, C. G., & Haslerud, G. M. (1952). Music and the general activity of apathetic schizophrenics. *Journal of Abnormal and Social Psychology, 47,* 188–192.

Skinner, B. F. (1953). *Science and human behavior.* New York: Free Press.

Skinner, B. F. (1966). What is the experimental analysis of human behavior? *Journal of Experimental Analysis of Behavior, 9,* 213–218.

Smith, T. W., & Zurawski, R. M. (1983). Assessment of irrational beliefs: The question of discriminant validity. *Journal of Clinical Psychology, 3*(9), 976–979.

Ullman, L. P., & Krasner, L. (1969). *A psychological approach to abnormal behavior.* Englewood Cliffs, NJ: Prentice-Hall.

Vannest, K. J., Reynolds, C. R., & Kamphaus, R. (2008). *BASC-2 intervention guide.* Minneapolis, MN: Pearson

Viola, L., Garrido, G., & Rescorla, L. (2011). Testing multicultural robustness of the Child Behavior Checklist in a national epidemiological sample in Uruguay. *Journal of Abnormal Child Psychology, 39*(6), 897–908 DOI: 10.1007/s10802-011-9500-z.

Wahler, R. G. (1969). Setting generality: Some specific and general effects of child behavior therapy. *Journal of Applied Behavior Analysis, 2,* 239–246.

Chapter 9

CLINICAL ASSESSMENT

We have now examined a number of approaches to evaluation. At this point, it would be tempting to ask which is best. But here we face a quandary. As in a legal contract, you can't get something of value without giving up something else of value. We can assess with a considerable degree of precision and dependability, and we can achieve a broad understanding of the complexity of a particular human being. The problem is that we can't do both simultaneously.

At the heart of the problem is what Cronbach and Gleser (1957) characterized as "the bandwidth-fidelity dilemma." In brief, the rub is this: it's possible to get a reasonably precise and reliable answer to a narrow question. But the broader the question you want answered, the less confidence you can have in the accuracy of the answer.

The "scientific" approach is based on the assumption that it is impossible to grasp the totality of someone's personality with any precision. So, just as science is divided into disciplines, each of which pursues a specialized understanding of a small segment of knowledge, this approach to personality is in terms of small chunks. By combining the answers in some meaningful way, contend the proponents of this approach, we can get an approximation of the whole.

In contrast, the "intuitive" or "impressionistic" approach is based on the assumption that any individual's personality consists of more than just a conglomerate of individual traits, or attitudes, or skills. It is not a combination of parts but the relationship between the parts that constitutes personality. The dynamics of this interaction can be grasped only through intuitive judgment.

The classical psychometric ideal is the instrument with high fidelity and low bandwidth. This is the instrument that will yield a valid and reliable response to a single question or a small group of related questions ("Is this patient suffering from bipolar disorder or from depression?"). But it will provide little information about the patient's personality structure, or value system, or any of the other information we might need to know to get a richer picture of the total person in all his or her complexity.

"At the other extreme," wrote Cronbach (1970), "the interview and the projective technique have almost unlimited bandwidth" (p. 181), but at the expense of reliability and validity. Such broadband instruments must involve a great deal of subjective clinical judgment. They will provide a rich yield of information about the idiosyncrasies of an individual, with a corresponding loss in the accuracy of our conclusions.

Therefore, no single approach to evaluation can be called "better" than another, unless we address three basic questions:

- What is our purpose in conducting this evaluation?
- Given this purpose, what questions do we need answered?
- How precise do these answers have to be?

Only after we have answered these questions can we decide which information is essential, and which we are willing to sacrifice.

THE MEANING OF CLINICAL ASSESSMENT

In its least defensible sense, clinical assessment can be described as plausible guesses based on unrepresentative samples of behavior. This kind of assessment has been described by R. R. Holt (1958) as "naive assessment" based on little more than hunch.

In its most acceptable sense, clinical assessment refers to everything the clinician does in gathering information about a client or patient and in determining the appropriate course of treatment. So "sophisticated" clinical assessment is likely to include interviews to gather information about the subject's family and personal history, likes, dislikes, and concerns; observations about the client's demeanor and behavior; data from self-reports and reports from others; measurement data, such as tests, scales, and profiles, and the examiner's intuitive impressions. If the assessor is concerned with differential diagnosis, he or she will take pains to ascertain the prevalence of the problem according to the known symptom profile. In short, clinical assessment may rely on data from any source of information that is relevant to the problem. The clinician organizes the data to create as complete a picture of the individual as possible.

Information from diverse sources may provide useful cross-references. The thrust here is on the ipsative function of assessment: the therapist has a chance to compare information about the subject from different sources to check for corroboration or for contradictions. In fact, the examiner may learn a good deal about a patient's idiosyncrasies from inconsistent evidence. In trying to reconcile apparently contradictory data, the examiner must "seek some underlying unity that resolves as many of these contradictions as possible" (Cronbach, 1970, p. 505).

CLINICAL JUDGMENT

In making decisions about which information-gathering methods to use, how to organize the data, and how to interpret them, the clinician must exercise clinical judgment to a greater or lesser degree. It is the degree of intuitive or impressionistic judgment that the clinician exercises that distinguishes between the various approaches ranging from those referred to as clinical or intuitive to those that are called statistical or actuarial.

Alternative Definitions of Intuition

Like so many of the words that are used in psychotherapy, the word intuition can mean different things to different clinicians. Most definitions of intuition will fall into one of three categories.

Intuition as Common Sense

A rule or fact that conforms with our lay or commonsense model of the world is one we can grasp intuitively without analysis. It is intuitively obvious that if there is a long line of people at the entrance to a restaurant, you'll probably have to wait to get a table. It is counterintuitive, although we are assured by authorities who should know, that the seemingly solid earth beneath our feet is not only spinning but is hurtling rapidly through space; and it violates our intuitive sense to learn that the bird at the apex of a flock of birds flying across the sky is not necessarily leading the flock in any meaningful way.

It is in this sense of the word that a test may be described as rationally or intuitively developed, and usually face-valid. It is also in this sense of the term that clinicians and researchers sometimes clash on the issue of validity. Many clinical interpretations that are based on commonsense logic cannot be verified by researchers.

Intuition as Extrasensory and Irrational

In Jungian psychology, intuition is an aspect of experience that bypasses consciousness. It is extrasensory, in that the knowledge derived goes beyond the evidence of the senses, and it is irrational (although not necessarily "unreasonable") because it does not rely on cognitive processes (Jung, 1959). It is the seer's vision, the immediate awareness of relationships, the unpredictable flash of insight or recognition that permits us to see straight through to the heart of a problem. This knowledge precedes thinking, although it may suggest a direction for thinking; it is the source of the hunch that leads to the formulation of a hypothesis.

Intuition as a Distillation of Knowledge and Experience

Operationally, cognitive psychologists describe intuition in much the same way as the Jungians. It is the "aha" effect, the ability to grasp relationships between pieces of data without going through the linear step-by-step application of analytic or structured processes.

The similarity ends here. Whereas Jung saw intuition as distinct from sensation or thinking, cognitive psychologists see it as a cognitive skill that is developed gradually through the exercise of both sensation and thinking: it represents a synthesis of knowledge, experience, and recognition, and it is really a shortcut application of learned processes. Nobel laureate Herbert Simon provided a simple example. An experienced physician looks at a spotty feverish child and quickly diagnoses measles. An inexperienced intern who looks at the same child will arrive at the same diagnosis only after methodically eliminating chicken pox, German measles, and scarlet fever. However, with repeated experience, the intern, too, will develop this specific intuitive insight and will be able to distinguish rapidly between the symptoms of each (Benderly, 1989, p. 36). In this view, the experienced doctor's expertise doesn't derive from her intuitive powers; her intuitive insight is a function of her expertise.

A rule or a procedure is said to be part of our intuitive repertory when we have internalized it. We then apply the rule or follow the procedure in our normal conduct without having to retrieve or reformulate it. The rules of grammar in our native language, for example, are part of our stock of intuitions.

There is another significant difference between the Jungian and the cognitive definitions. In the Jungian sense, intuition is a general aspect of personality; there is an intuitive "type" of person (actually, there are two: the introverted intuitive and the extroverted intuitive). In contrast, cognitive psychologists see intuitive insight as content-specific. The doctor whose diagnostic intuition is so sharp isn't likely to be equally intuitive in identifying the reason her car doesn't start or in recognizing the difference between an infant's cries of discomfort or of hunger. Similarly, the mother who has developed an intuitive sense of her baby's cries will not be able to diagnose intuitively the cause of her baby's rash and fever.

Subjectivity and Bias in Clinical Judgment

Intuitive insight will permit someone to see quickly the relationships between things. But we have seen, from the work of researchers who have conducted validation studies of projective personality tests, that it is remarkably easy to see relationships that aren't there – to fall victim to the fallacy of illusory correlation.

Jung was aware of this problem, and he wrote about the extroverted intuitive type (Jung, 1959). It is only by a form of reality testing that we can distinguish between intuitive insight and creative fantasy. In the scientific tradition, this reality testing is generally conceded to lie in the confirmatory function of research.

Clinical Accuracy

Tversky and Kahneman (1982) pointed out that the major basis for predictions about people is representativeness, a shortcut the mind takes in dealing with complicated issues. In judging the odds that a particular patient is suicidal, the mind assesses the evidence intuitively and compares it with a mental model of how a suicidal patient looks or acts. If the two sets of data match, we may conclude that the patient is suicidal, although the statistical data (base rate, for example) may suggest otherwise.

Representativeness works most of the time, but it works poorly when its conclusion is contradicted by the laws of chance or by principles of probability. It works poorly, also, when the "input data" are sketchy, unreliable or outdated. "The unwarranted confidence which is produced by a good fit between the predicted outcome and the input information," Tversky and Kahneman (1982) say, "may be called the illusion of validity. This illusion persists even when the judge is aware of the factors that limit the accuracy of his predictions" (p. 9).

Semantic Confusion. A major problem that confounds the issue of accuracy in assessment is the use of specific jargons among practitioners of the various therapies and of different theoretical schools. If a clinician uses a word that means different things to different people, Cronbach (1970) has pointed out, "he cannot hope that his interpretations will be confirmed or that they will be practically beneficial" (p. 685). Grayson and Tolman asked a number of psychologists and psychiatrists to define some words, such as bizarre and aggression. Twenty-three of the clinicians described aggression in negative terms as a personality deficiency, while 21 defined it as a personality positive. The authors wrote that, "For the most part, the lack of verbal precision seems to stem from theoretical confusion in the face of the complexity and logical inconsistency of psychological phenomena" (quoted in Cronbach, 1970, p. 685). What this means is that those who read an assessment report may interpret it in ways that are quite different from what the examiner may have intended.

Accuracy and Experience. Contrary to expectation, there seems to be very little correlation between the accuracy of an examiner, and his or her general clinical experience (Garb, 1989) or familiarity with the specific assessment procedure (Wanderer, 1967; Watson, 1967).

In the interpretation of projective tests, for example, experienced clinicians may be no better than educated laymen (Ziskin & Faust, 1988) or "naive" college students with no training in the interpretation of tests (Chapman & Chapman, 1967, 1971). Apparently, the judgments made by the experienced professionals in these studies consisted of little more than stereotyped expectations based on the same common-sense variety of intuition on which the naive subjects depended.

Accuracy and Confidence. A number of studies have found little relationship between the accuracy of a clinician's judgment and his or her confidence in that judgment (Kelly & Fiske, 1951; Oskamp, 1965). These findings parallel those of investigators who have studied eyewitness testimony. The distinguished jurist David L. Bazelon noted that several studies found "no relationship at all between [an eyewitness's] confidence and [his or her] accuracy" (1980, p. 107).

Stuart Oskamp (1965) noted that the confidence of a clinician in his or her judgment usually increases as assessment data increases. He was curious to find this increase in the confidence was justified by a corresponding increase in accuracy.

His findings were not encouraging. He found, for example, in his study of 32 judges, that when additional information was brought to their attention, their increase in accuracy was consistent with the odds of a coin toss: for about half, their accuracy increased, and for half it decreased. He found, also, that the number of changes the judges made in their judgments actually decreased as more information came to light. This finding suggested "that the judges may frequently have formed stereotyped conclusions rather firmly from the first fragmentary information and then been reluctant to change their conclusions as they received new information" (p. 265), a conclusion that is supported by reports by researchers who have observed how clinicians actually make their diagnostic judgments. In some cases, diagnoses are made very rapidly, sometimes within the first two or three minutes of an interview (Sandifer, Hordern, & Green, 1970). In such cases, the clinician often falls victim to the "primacy effect" or the "anchor" that we described in Chapter 4. He or she is likely, during an interview, to solicit expected responses in order to confirm an incorrect hypothesis. In addition, he or she is likely to exercise selective judgment in examining the results of other evidence, such as measurement scores, seizing upon those that seem to support the initial hypothesis, and discounting or minimizing those that contradict it. For those unaware of the health disparities issues in U.S. health care, it is important to note that research documents that racial and ethnic minorities are frequently misdiagnosed. For example African-Americans with affective disorders are more frequently diagnosed with schizophrenia than are white patients (Primm et al., 2010). Stereotyped conclusions in clinical decision-making have serious consequences. For clinicians in particular, there is a need not only to be aware of their biases, but also to bring unconscious, internalized biases to awareness to begin to address mental health disparities.

Experience and Confidence. While there doesn't seem to be a relationship between clinical experience and accuracy, there is apparently a relationship between the clinician's experience and his or her humility. Inexperienced clinicians have a tendency to demonstrate an unwarranted confidence in the accuracy of their assessments; more experienced clinicians tend to be no more accurate than less experienced practitioners, but they seem to be more realistic in assessing the accuracy of their judgments (Garb, 1989).

Alternatives to Clinical Judgment

Clinical intuitive accuracy can be improved only up to a point. Clinical judgment is fundamentally subjective and subject to all the quirks in heuristics and thinking that we discussed in earlier chapters. As a result, two distinct alternatives have been proposed, both resting on the same assumption: that any subjective judgment we make about another person is so hopelessly compromised and adulterated by our own mix of perceptions, beliefs, assumptions, values, and experiences as to be inherently untrustworthy.

"Scientific" critics believe that the answer lies in minimizing the subjective aspects of evaluation. This they do by attempting to create objective instruments and formulas, based on statistically sound, empirically validated procedures that can be reexamined, modified, and improved as new information is uncovered.

Another group, including many, if not most, humanists, doubts that any procedure can permit one human being to comprehend another in any meaningful way. While people can never really "know" themselves, this group contends, they know themselves better than anyone else could possibly know them, so assessment should be left to the client. In this view, the role of the therapist is to guide and facilitate the client's self-exploration by providing an atmosphere in which subjects can arrive at insights in understanding their own problems, and intuitions about possible solutions to them. At bottom, this group believes, only clients themselves can affect their own healing.

CLINICAL AND STATISTICAL APPROACHES TO ASSESSMENT

Most therapists will rely on much the same kinds of data, including personal and family histories, demographic data, scores on tests or profiles, and personal observations. The difference between "clinical" and "statistical" approaches rests mainly on the relative weight that is given to each source and the ways the data are used in arriving at a decision.

The clinical approach emphasizes the clinician's judgment, based on his or her training, knowledge, adherence to a theoretical orientation, and experience, usually expressed as his or her "intuition." Such therapists sometimes consider empirically based tests reductionist, and they may profess disdain for "cookbook" approaches, relying instead on their "gut feelings." The "actuarial" approach relies heavily on the application of rules and formulas derived from statistical correlations and empirical verification. Such clinicians, in turn, often have a profound distrust of subjective assessments.

However, many clinicians use tests but interpret them intuitively. Anne Anastasi (1961) wrote that it is common for a therapist to interpret the relationship between scores on multiple tests on the basis of an intuitive and highly subjective judgment "in terms of his own past experience with similar cases . . . or his knowledge of psychological theory and relevant published research" (pp. 177–178), rather than by using some statistical formula, such as multiple regression equations or multiple cutoff scores.

On the other hand, some therapists, wary of the influence of personal bias and misperception, will depend largely on the rules and formulas that have been derived from statistical data and that stand up against the test of empirical validation. Some "actuarial" purists will ignore any data that have not been collected according to a carefully formulated plan, and interpreted strictly by the application of established rules, in order to avoid contaminating the evidence with data that have not been standardized and programmed into the procedure.

The Search for Meaning

A major difference between intuitive approaches and actuarial approaches concerns the interpretation of assessment data.

In much of psychotherapy, there is a need to find meaning or to "interpret" observed facts. Dascal and Dascal explained the impulse to interpret. In a provocative essay entitled "The Limits of Interpretation" (1995), they described the process as a way of fulfilling the need to bring an unfamiliar fact into "the realm of the familiar," in order to make sense of it.

> Admitting meaninglessness seems to be an avowal of failure in finding meaning, failure in our interpretive efforts. . . . That is to say, we operate on a presumption that there is always some meaning to be found there. . . . Applied to human behavior, this principle reads: admit stupidity, ignorance, irrationality, incoherence, etc. – in short, meaninglessness – only if there is no way to interpret a given behavior. . . . Our relentless hunt for "meaning" is, no doubt, a significant part of our longing for a secure ground. . . where we know the rules of the game. (p. 2)

This search for meaning inheres in clinical judgment. The problem is the elusive nature of meaning. Dascal and Dascal (1995) described several models of interpretation from which the following are adapted.

Intentionality. The patient's communication or behavior is to be taken at face value. Because the rules of language limit the degree from which alternate meanings can be read into communication, the words or representations mean what they purport to mean, neither more nor less.

Pragmatic Interpretation. The therapist relies on contextual clues to ascertain the intention of the patient. An apparent insult with a smile may not be intended as an insult at all, and an apparent compliment may be a sarcastic jab. The meaning may be subject to "negotiation" between patient and therapist.

Causality. Consistent with the Freudian notion that things rarely, if ever, are what they appear to be, this model of interpretation is based on the assumption that the patient's intentions are at best rationalizations or symptoms of his or her real deep motives. In this view, only the trained expert can ferret out the unconscious mechanisms that explain the patient's behavior.

Interpretation as Meaning. In this view, no meaning is inherent in the behavior, the communication, or the work created by the patient. Just as abstract art or music may mean what the viewer or the listener reads into it, the meaning of a patient's behavior is created by the interpreter.

Meaning as Relationship. Meaning is far more than the intention of the patient or the interpretation of the therapist. It is developed from the interpersonal relationship between patient and therapist. Dascal and Dascal (1995) concluded that all models of interpretation are, at best, only partially valid and useful and that they complement each other (p. 21).

All clinical interpretations rest on a search for meaning. Examining a patient who frequently responds, "I don't know," who exhibits a restricted range of body movement, or a preference for dark colors, the intuitive clinician may ask, "Why? What does that response mean? What does such a response reveal about this patient's perception of himself or his motives?" He or she will look for a connection between the response pattern and the patient's personality or mental processes. This clinician is likely to be heavily influenced by whether the connection seems to make sense, either on a personal intuitive level or in terms of a theory of personality.

The search for meaning underlies much of both psychoanalysis and phenomenology. The major difference is that, whereas phenomenologists tend to encourage patients to find their own meanings in their behaviors, psychoanalytically inclined therapists operate on the assumption that the meaning is hidden from the patient and must be found by the therapist.

In contrast, both traditional behaviorists and statistically oriented practitioners question the need to find an elusive "meaning," to identify motives, or to "interpret" at all. Behaviorists, as we have seen, contend that it is not necessary to understand behavior in order to measure it or to change it. Clinicians using an actuarial approach are less concerned with why a patient answers, "I don't know" to so many questions, or chooses dark blue crayons, than the fact that he or she does these things. Such practitioners recognize that for many responses, we may be able to associate the response with a particular type of person, even if we can't explain why such a connection exists.

Clinical Versus Statistical Accuracy

In the 1950s, the heyday of psychological testing in this country, a major controversy raged over the relative accuracy of clinical versus statistical approaches to assessment. The most widely cited study comparing the diagnostic and predictive accuracies of the two was conducted by Paul E. Meehl in a provocative book entitled *Clinical Versus Statistical Prediction* (1954). Meehl surveyed 20 investigations involving the judgments of clinical psychologists, counselors, and psychiatrists who made predictions in a number of areas, including the anticipated responses of individuals with psychosis to therapy, and the likelihood of recidivism among inmates in correctional institutions. Meehl's survey was limited in scope. He focused primarily on the process of combining data, not differences in the kinds of data that might have been collected. Moreover, he dealt only with quantified data, such as test scores, profile scores, demographics, and scored aspects of life histories.

Meehl found (with one questionable exception involving the attempt to identify homosexuality) that when clinicians used statistical formulas, such as multiple regression equations, their predictions were consistently more accurate than those based on clinical judgment. Even in those cases in which clinicians had access to additional data that were not factored into the statistical formulas, the clinical predictions were no more accurate than were those arrived at through the application of statistical formulas.

Meehl's conclusion has generally been supported by researchers. In fact, one study (Dawes & Corrigan, 1974) found that a clinician's own decision-making processes used in a predetermined "by the book" formula yielded more accurate predictions than the same clinician's on-the-spot judgments, presumably because the formula approach minimized the influence of extraneous variables, such as the time of day, the clinician's mood or personal problems, and the impact of unpredictable and uncontrolled environmental factors.

Cronbach (1970) explained why the individual judge performs so poorly: "Almost certainly, [a judge] gives greater weight to some factors than they deserve, and changes his weights from one case to the next. The clinician might judge the same case differently on different days, whereas the formula never varies" (p. 442).

If a panel of judges were to arrive at independent intuitive conclusions, individual inconsistencies would be averaged out, and if enough judges were involved the consensus would be as valid and reliable as the formula prediction. The British have never been very keen about objective tests or formula approaches, but they developed a grading system in education that demonstrated remarkable reliability. Over a half century ago, the standard was set for the British General Certificate of Education (GCE) exam; a panel of five teachers read each essay quickly for a general impression and graded it. While there were variations in the grades assigned by individual teachers, it was found that the average grade in each panel was very similar to the average grades of other groups of five teachers asked to evaluate the same paper. This system worked for many years, to the general satisfaction of English teachers and psychologists. But paying five teachers to read each paper was expensive, and the system gradually eroded, together with the reliability level of exam grades.

Meehl (1984), trying to explain why the actuarial approach has not been more widely accepted among therapists, cited human irrationality, ignorance, claims that actuarial approaches are "dehumanizing," misunderstanding and fears of quantitative techniques, and strong theoretical biases among many therapists that impels them to reject any correlation that doesn't match their theoretical expectations.

Case for Clinical Judgment

Despite the apparently overwhelming research support for statistical approaches, there are many critics who concede that statistical data are useful in research but doubt that they provide meaningful guidance for individual assessment. While the research may describe the characteristics of the hypothetical "average" patient, critics contend, no therapist has ever encountered an "average" patient. An attempt to apply these findings to the individual patient is like sending a diagnosis to "occupant." Over a century ago, William James, the father of American psychology, pointed out that psychology can establish general rates and expectations but cannot offer biographies in advance.

In addition, the psychometric approaches to reliability and validation rest on a conception of personality that is static and that doesn't take into account individual variables or context. A client who is interviewed, probed, and tested on Wednesday is not likely to be quite the same person at his next Wednesday therapy session if during the interval his mother had died, or he had lost his job, or he had broken up with his fiancée. Identical scores on a test measuring self-esteem are not likely to have the same significance for Joan, who is bright, highly functioning, and successful in school, as it has for Theresa, who has a school history of failure and truancy.

An Overview: Comparing Clinical and Statistical Approaches

Obviously, a good case could be made for both a statistical approach to assessment and a clinical one. The actuarial approach provides uniformity and an efficiency that ranges across a wide variety of contexts;

it minimizes the subjectivity and bias of the individual clinician; and it provides a normative basis for comparing the patient with others. On the other hand, the clinical approach provides flexibility and the availability of data about the individual that may not be possible with the statistical approach. A good deal of information may come to light from unstructured clinical interviews, from case histories, and from direct observation that may not have been programmed into tests or highly structured procedures. Clinical judgment takes into account individual idiosyncrasies, special circumstances, and the context in which behavior is exhibited, and it provides for the flash of intuition that rides on an empathetic bonding with the patient. Clinical approaches offer a broadband of information at a low level of dependability and precision.

A therapist's answers to the questions we posed in the introduction to this chapter will provide a rough guide to the relative emphasis he or she might want to put on each approach. Because there are advantages and disadvantages in the use of both approaches, the most accurate assessment procedures would probably involve a combination of the two, where tests of demonstrated validity are available.

Where we need an answer to a single question, as in differential diagnosis, the statistical approach will yield more precise information. It will help prevent a misdiagnosis and a course of treatment that may be ineffective and possibly harmful.

For general screening, when there is no prior knowledge about the subject, it is likely that such tests are far more useful than are interviews or other impressionistic approaches for identifying those who should be assessed in depth and individually. Scores on standardized tests are less likely to be distorted by miscalculation of base rates than are those developed by a clinician who relies mainly on intuition. These hypotheses should then be tested against the data derived from other sources and against the therapist's recognition that the patient and the world in which he or she lives are constantly changing.

Humanist Views of Assessment

We cannot forget that for large numbers of therapists the whole notion of assessment by a clinician is irrelevant, whether it is based on statistical calculation or clinical judgment.

Nucho (1987) differentiated between two approaches to understanding the client's problem. The "nomomatic idea," which is the basis for objective testing, is the application of ideas and principles derived from either theory or empirical data. It is designed to lead to an objective understanding of the client and his or her problem. This approach is important when the therapist is expected to provide a solution to the client's problem. The other approach, Nucho proposed, the "ipsomatic" approach, uses ideas derived from the client's own life experiences and is designed to facilitate the client's own ability to deal with the problem. Whether the therapist sees the solution or not, she said, "is of lesser importance than the client's own knowledge of what he should do next" (p. 174).

The therapist's understanding of the patient, based on theory or "objective" data, Nucho (1987) contended, "may be very slanted and contaminated by the therapist' own proclivities and life experiences. This occurs because therapists feel drawn to, and tend to adopt certain theoretical positions that are congruent with their own philosophies of life, which in turn have been shaped by their own life experiences" (p. 174).

In this view, the therapist's task is largely that of a facilitator, whose task it is to help clients experience their own processes and structures, not to interpret for them. It is the client who is encouraged to develop intuitive insights. It is the client's perception and interpretation that are important.

THE UNEASY RELATIONSHIP BETWEEN CLINICIANS AND RESEARCHERS

The assessment and treatment of clients is where, in principle, there should be a convergence between the art of the sensitive and perceptive clinician who relies largely on intuition, and the research findings of the experimental investigator and the statistical analyst which will confirm or refute the intuitive judgments of the clinician.

The Enthusiastic Clinician and the Skeptical Researcher

Unfortunately, this happy marriage of the arts and sciences is rarely consummated in the arts therapies and other clinical mental health specializations (Cruz & Berrol, 2012). Research-oriented psychologists sometimes deride their clinical colleagues who, in their view, demonstrate a squishy inexactitude in their judgments. In the words of one critic, too many therapists answer largely "to their own sensibilities fluttering in the zeitgeist," and can be "unusually open to feel-good therapies of questionable legitimacy . . . [sometimes] for disorders of equally dubious validity" (Marano, 1994, p. 23). The position of the researcher is that, unless the knowledge on which intuitive judgments of clinicians is based can be confirmed by replicable, empirically verifiable research, it is difficult to differentiate between perceptive intuitive insight and self-propelled illusion.

It is true that clinicians often appear indifferent or even hostile to the research findings that raise questions about the validity of their judgments, putting more faith in their personal clinical experiences than in experimental evidence. In the face of criticism by researchers of the validity of projective assessment techniques, such as the Rorschach and figure drawing tests of personality, these tests, as Charles McArthur pointed out, "will not die" (1972, p. 442). Clinicians continue to trust in phantom evidence that they expect to see, even when that evidence is not there (see Chapter 4).

There have been numerous attempts to explain the rift between the "enthusiastic clinician" who answers to his or her own intuitive judgment and the "skeptical researcher" who rains on the parade by pointing out discrepancies between what the clinician believes and what can be confirmed through research.

McArthur (1972) suggested that researchers and clinicians operate on different sets of assumptions. At the heart of the debate may be the commitment to divergent approaches to understanding the subject: the researcher often looks for ways in which troubled people are similar, in order to identify the groups for which specific treatments are appropriate, and the clinician often looks for ways in which they are different. Interestingly the passage of time has not substantively changed this difference (Lang, Wyer, & Hynes, 2007; Orlinsky & Ronnestad, 2005; Seymour, Kinn, & Southerland, 2003).

> Psychotherapy is a focal point of the on-going debate between the operationally, empirically minded investigator and the seeker of intuitive understanding. The former often dismisses the insights of the latter as insufficiently validated or even as incapable of unambiguous validation. The latter, if he is a clinician, may fail to see how results statistically validated at the .05 level of confidence can help him deal with unique and complex troubled persons . . . whom he is trying to help. (Bergin & Strupp, 1972, p. 117)

Bergin and Strupp (1972) undertook a feasibility study exploring the potentialities for large-scale collaborative work involving both clinicians and researchers. They visited a large number of centers of research and clinical activity and interviewed key individuals, including some of the major figures in psychotherapy. To each, they sent an advance list of 18 detailed questions as stimuli for discussion. The last question was particularly relevant to this issue. Referring to a controversial theory, they noted that a sample of clinicians responded by saying, "I don't believe it." When they were shown empirical data supporting the theory "at the usual level of statistical significance," the consensus remained the same: "I still don't believe it." Bergin and Strupp wondered: "Empirical evidence confirming or disconfirming a hypothesis should make a difference in one's confidence that a given theory is true. If this does not occur, something is amiss. How can the impact of psychotherapy research be maximized?" (p. 175).

A large number of their respondents were pessimistic about the feasibility of collaboration. Lester Luborsky, who put a good deal of trust in the intuitive process, prepared a critique that he titled "Research Cannot Yet Influence Clinical Practice." In it, he wrote:

> Psychotherapists will continue to trust their clinical experience and their clinical mentors. Except for a few therapeutic innovators, the way the psychotherapist practices psychotherapy is determined by where he was trained, and, in turn, the choice of place of training probably reflects the personality of the applicant and chance life-events. (Luborsky, 1972, p. 125.)

This apparent belief that much of research is irrelevant to clinical practice seems to be shared by therapists of a variety of persuasions. Carl Rogers, for example, emphasized the importance of intuition, which he defined as cutting loose from preformed concepts and theories. "Most of my research," he told Bergin and Strupp (1972), "has been to confirm what I already felt to be true. . . . Generally, I never learned anything from research" (p. 314).

Research-oriented observers offer alternative explanations for the failure of research findings to influence clinical practice. According to one writer (Shoben, 1953), clinicians have built up a body of intuitive techniques which have been reinforced by a sense of certitude and confidence that may have little basis in actual success. Another (Luzki, 1957) suggested that clinicians may resist research findings that threaten changes in their accustomed beliefs, methods or techniques. More recently, Norcross, Beutler, and Levant (2006) wrote that the increasing requirement for evidence-based practice and accountability in modern clinical practice make demands on clinicians to base treatments on evidence.

As Cruz and Berrol (2012) pointed out:

> The frank problems in the interface between research and practice are acknowledged in most health care fields, and some authors seem hopeful that new methods can address the issue. For example, systems-based participatory research has been proposed as a means to make translational research sustainable (Schmittdiel et al., 2010) and community-based participatory methods and practice-based research networks have been proposed to be potentially helpful in bridging the researcher-clinician relationship in other areas (Macaulay & Nutting, 2006). Might these methods be useful to address the documented view by practitioners that research is somehow antithetical to the values or the artistic nature of psychotherapy (Shipton, 1996; Forrester, 1997)? The relationship of research to clinical practitioners is truly complex, but is nonetheless significant, especially as it impacts the development and growth of clinically oriented professions. . . . (p. 17)

Can the Gap Be Bridged?

One of the major issues that divide clinicians and researchers is that they often perceive propositions very differently. Clinicians tend to think in terms of assumptions, propositions that are based on theoretical tenets, or are deemed to be so self-evident that they require no validation, and even to deny evidence that contradicts commonly held beliefs. In contrast, researchers approach propositions with skepticism, as hypotheses that demand empirical support.

With respect to the arts therapies, one motivation to expand evaluation approaches to include research-validated procedures has been repeatedly noted in the literature. That motivation is that while clinicians may profess skepticism over its utility, research methodologies and research findings constitute the lingua franca, the common language of assessment. Arts therapists recognize that if they are to have credibility as professions, their practitioners must communicate with their own colleagues who may or may not share their philosophical orientations (Cruz & Hervey, 2001; Kapitan, 2010). In addition, they must communicate with those in the other mental health professions, who may not understand the basis for judgments and decisions that rest only on personal and intuitive responses.

In 1610, when Galileo demonstrated the existence of sunspots with his newly invented telescope, the most eminent astronomers of the day, committed to the Aristotelian contention that the sun consists of unblemished fire, refused even to look through the telescope. We believe that the time has come for clinicians to look through the telescope of research in order to validate their fundamental assumptions.

THE ASSESSMENT INTERVIEW

Until fairly recently, the only method for assessing clients' problems and needs was by interviewing them. In some settings, the interview is still a major source of information, and for psychiatric problems it is still probably the most important single source for the initial assessment.

Interviews may take many shapes, from those that are exclusively verbal to those that are primarily nonverbal. The purpose and the nature of the assessment interview are determined largely by the clinical setting and the perceived role of the clinician involved.

Purposes of the Assessment Interview

The interview provides a limited sample of behavior. During the interview, the examiner observes the patient's general appearance, demeanor, speech, posture and gesture patterns, to get a general preliminary impression. In the arts therapies, assessment is likely to include the way the patient approaches the media, the tools, or the activity. For example, an art therapist would be interested not only in the product, such as the drawing that the patient produces, but in the process involved, or the way the patient handles the materials, chooses the colors, and reacts to the work. The therapist would be alert to any comments that the patient makes both during the course of producing the drawing and about the drawing after it has been finished. A music therapy assessment, wrote Wilson (1990), "offers the opportunity to observe the client's response to auditory, yet nonverbal stimuli;" for example, "auditory perception and memory may be tested through singing a song. Verbal and nonverbal responses to a musical selection may reveal either healthy or incongruent social and emotional patterns of behavior" (p. 130).

The second major function is to gather information about the patient's history, problems, and concerns. Third, because the interview is the first significant communication between client and therapist, it offers a unique opportunity to define the client-therapist relationship and to establish the rapport that is so important in establishing an accurate evaluation and that enhances the likelihood of effective treatment. For the therapist in private practice who works one-to- one with a client, the interview represents an opportunity to establish a "therapeutic contract" in which expectations and goals may be negotiated and agreed upon.

It would be a mistake to think of the assessment interview as a mere ice-breaking conversation or activity. No matter how unstructured the style of interviewing, the interview is purposeful. It is designed to gather specific information that may not be available through other means, to develop an understanding of the problem, to suggest direction for the treatment program, and to define the relationship between the patient and the therapist.

Structure of the Interview

Interviews and assessment activities may be structured or unstructured, free-ranging or highly directive. Each format offers advantages and disadvantages. The unstructured interview offers flexibility and an opportunity to observe how patients organize their responses, nonverbal and/or verbal. The ways in which the responses are organized are deemed to reveal a good deal about the patient's underlying perceptual principles. The major criticism of unstructured interviews is that they tend to be deficient in validity and reliability. For example, the patient's "natural imagery" might be interpreted quite differently by different art therapists.

As a result, spurred by increasing sophistication about the need for an increased range of assessment approaches, and by criticism about the poor reliabilities of psychiatric diagnosis, there has been an increasing emphasis on the use of patterned semi- structured and of highly structured interviews in psychiatric evaluation. One example of this trend is the Structured Clinical Interview for DSM-IV Axis I Disorders (SCID-I; First, Spitzer, & Williams, 1995).

Semi-structured interviews are generally guided to cover certain predetermined areas. The therapist may use a checklist during the course of an interview to be sure that all the pertinent elements have been covered. The format, however, usually permits the client to organize his or her responses freely within loose confines, a feature that may not be part of structured approaches. Highly structured interviews are usually carefully directed, and many used in psychiatric settings are keyed to the diagnostic categories of the DSM such as the SCID-I.

In addition to having somewhat improved psychometric qualities, these structured and semi-structured interviews may be administered, in larger institutions, by staff members who need not be as highly trained (or as well paid) as therapists. Structured interviews may be considered an attempt to bridge the gap between the intuitive and the statistical approaches to assessment. Even those who prefer an unstructured interview approach may use such structured devices as intake forms to be filled out by the patient, providing elements of family history and personal data.

While structured and semi-structured approaches have greater validity and reliability than unstructured interviews, they are less sensitive to nuances, personal idiosyncrasies, and other aspects of assessment that may be important in interpreting test scores or other data. Moreover, the more highly structured techniques provide less opportunity for establishing rapport with a patient.

A combination of approaches was suggested by Maloney and Ward (1976), who thought that beginning with open-ended questions (such as, "Tell me about yourself") would permit the therapist to observe how the patient perceived the problem, organized the response, and expressed himself or herself. This format also may elicit from patients information that might not normally come out in the course of a preprogrammed interview. The therapist would subsequently use more directed and structured questions to cover areas that had been missed, to clarify, or to resolve inconsistencies, and to test his or her intuitive judgment.

SUMMARY

Clinical judgment is based, fundamentally, on the intuitive sense of the practitioner. Intuition itself is a somewhat ambiguous term because it is used to mean several different things, although all the meanings refer to an immediate recognition of a problem or a situation. On a "rational" level, it may mean a commonsense understanding of a phenomenon. In Jungian terms, it may mean an extrasensory apprehension of relationships. To the cognitive psychologist, it means a shortcut leap across intermediate steps of analysis, based largely on training and experience.

Although it is generally acknowledged that intuitive insights are inherently subjective, it is impossible to eliminate intuition entirely from the process of evaluation. However, two groups of critics have concluded that clinical judgment is so hopelessly compromised by personal perceptions, values and biases as to be of little value in the evaluation process. This conclusion has led many to propose that personal subjectivity be minimized by relying as much as possible on empirically validated and relatively impersonal "objective" statistical approaches. Others are dubious that any method of evaluation can permit any human to know or comprehend another. These critics have proposed that the task of the therapist should be that of a facilitator, who can only help establish an environment in which clients and patients can come to a broader recognition of their personalities, their strengths, and their susceptibilities, and arrive at a resolution of their own problems.

The interview is probably the most important single source of information on which most global assessments are based. There are three major purposes for the interview.

- It provides a limited sample of the client's behavior.
- It is a vehicle for gathering pertinent data on personal and family history.
- It defines the therapist-client relationship. In private practice, it may lay the basis for establishing the "therapeutic contract."

There are two poles in interview styles: the unstructured, or free-ranging interview, and the highly structured and directive interview. Many, if not most, interviews fall somewhere between these two types; they may be loosely structured or semi-structured. The unstructured approach offers an opportunity for patients to project and to reveal their perceptual and organizational structures. The major criticism of unstructured or loosely structured interviews is that they are deficient in validity and reliability.

Highly structured approaches are sometimes difficult to distinguish from tests, with which they are often confused. Structured interviews involve efforts to standardize the administration of the procedure so that subjects can be compared. However, like tests, they may sacrifice sensitivity to nuances and personal idiosyncrasies. Numbers of semi-structured procedures have been developed in an attempt to keep some of the flexibility of the unstructured interview while gaining some of the psychometric strengths of the structured procedures. Especially in institutions, combinations of structured and unstructured approaches may be used.

REFERENCES

Anastasi, A. (1961). *Psychological testing* (2nd ed.). New York: Macmillan.

Bazelon, D. L. (1980). Eyewitless news. *Psychology Today, 13*(10), 102–107.

Benderly, B. L. (1989, September). Everyday intuition. *Psychology Today,* 35–40.

Bergin, A. E., & Strupp, H. H. (1972). *Changing frontiers in the science of psychotherapy.* Chicago and New York: Aldine-Atherton.

Chapman, L. J., & Chapman, J. P. (1967). Genesis of popular but erroneous psychodiagnostic observations. *Journal of Abnormal Psychology, 72,* 193–204.

Cronbach, L. J. (1970). *Essentials of psychological testing* (3rd ed.). New York: Harper and Row.

Cronbach, L. J., & Gleser, G. C. (1957). *Psychological tests and personnel decisions.* Urbana, IL: University of Illinois Press.

Cruz, R. F., & Berrol, C. F. (2012). What does research have to do with it? In R. Cruz and C. Berrol (Eds.), *Dance/movement therapists in action* (2nd ed.). (pp. 12–22). Springfield, IL: Charles C Thomas.

Cruz, R. F., & Hervey, L. W. (2001). The American Dance Therapy Association research survey. *American Journal of Dance Therapy, 23*(2), 89–118.

Dascal, M., & Dascal, V. (1995). The limits of interpretation. In J. Rozenberg (Ed.), *Sense and nonsense in psychotherapy.* Jerusalem: Magnes Press.

Dawes, R. M., & Corrigan, B. (1974). Linear models in decision making. *Psychological Bulletin, 8,* 95–106.

First, M. B., Spitzer, R. L., & Williams J. B. W., et al. (1995). *Structured clinical interview for DSM-IV user's guide and interview research version.* New York: Biometrics Research Department, New York Psychiatric Institute.

Garb, H. N. (1989). Clinical judgment, clinical training, and the professional experience. *Psychological Bulletin, 105,* 387–396.

Jung, C. G. (1959). *Psychological types.* London: Routledge and Kegan Paul.

Kapitan, L. (2010). *Introduction to art therapy research.* New York: Routledge.

Kelly, E. L., & Fiske, D. W. (1951). *The prediction of performance in clinical psychology.* Ann Arbor, MI: University of Michigan Press.

Lang, E. E., Wyer, P. C., & Haynes, R. B. (2007). Knowledge translation: Closing the evidence-to-practice gap. *Annals of Emergency Medicine, 49*(3), 355–363.

Luborsky, L. B. (1972). Research cannot yet influence clinical practice. In A. E. Bergin & H. H. Strupp (Eds.), *Changing frontiers in the science of psychotherapy.* Chicago and New York: Aldine-Atherton.

Luzki, M. B. (1957). *Interdisciplinary team research: Methods and problems.* New York: New York University Press.

Maloney, M. P., & Ward, M. P. (1976). *Psychological assessment: A cognitive approach.* New York: Oxford University Press.

Marano, H. E. (1994). Wave of the future. *Psychology Today, 27*(4), 22–25.

McArthur, C. C. (1972). Review of Rorschach Test. In O. K. Buros (Ed.), *Sixth mental measurements yearbook.* Highland Park, NJ: Gryphon Press.

Meehl, P. E. (1954). *Clinical versus statistical prediction: A theoretical analysis and a review of the evidence.* Minneapolis, MN: University of Minnesota Press.

Meehl, P. E. (1984). Clinical and statistical prediction: A retrospective and would-be integrative view. In R. K. Blashfield (Chair), *Clinical versus statistical prediction.* A symposium at the 92nd Annual Meeting of the American Psychological Association, Toronto, Canada.

Norcross, J. C., Beutler, L. E., & Levant, R. F. (Eds.). (2006). *Evidence-based practices in mental health: Debate and dialogue on the fundamental questions.* Washington, DC: American Psychological Association.

Nucho, A. O. (1987). *The psychocybernetic model of art therapy.* Springfield, IL: Charles C Thomas.

Orlinsky, D., & Ronnestad, M. (2005) *How psychotherapists develop: A study of therapeutic work and professional growth.* Washington: American Psychological Association.

Oskamp, S. (1965). Overconfidence in case-study judgments. *Journal of Consulting Psychology, 2*(9), 261–265.

Primm, A.B., Vasquez, M., Mays, R., Sammons-Posey, D., McKnight-Eily, L., Presley-Cantrell, L. . . . Perry, G. (2010). The role of public health in addressing racial and ethnic disparities in mental health and mental illness. *Preventing Chronic Disease: Public Health Research, Practice, and Policy,* 7(1), A20.

Sandifer, M. G., Harden, A., & Green, L. M. (1970). The psychiatric interview: The impact of the first three minutes. *American Journal of Psychiatry, 126,* 968–973.

Seymour, B., Kinn, S., & Sutherland, N. (2003). Valuing both critical and creative thinking in clinical practice: Narrowing the research-practice gap? *Journal of Advanced Nursing, 42*(3), 288–296.

Shoben, E. J. (1953). Some observations on psychotherapy and the learning process. In O. H. Mowrer (Ed.), *Psychotherapy: Theory and research.* New York: Basic Books.

Tversky, A., & Kahneman, D. (1982). Causal schemes in judgments under uncertainty. In D. Kahneman, P. Slovic, & A. Tversky (Eds.), *Judgment under uncertainty: Heuristics and biases.* (pp. 87–128). Cambridge: University of Cambridge Press.

Wanderer, Z. W. (1967). *The validity of diagnostic judgments based on "blind" Machover figure drawings.* Doctoral dissertation, Columbia University.

Watson, C. G. (1967). Relationship of distortion to DAP diagnostic accuracy among psychologists at three levels of sophistication. *Journal of Consulting Psychology, 31,* 142–146.

Wilson, B. L. (1990). Music therapy in hospital and community programs. In R. F. Unkefer (Ed.), *Music therapy in the treatment of adults with mental disorders*. New York: Schirmer.

Ziskin, J., & Faust, D. (1988). *Coping with psychiatric and psychological testimony* (3rd ed.). Marina del Rey, CA: Law and Psychology Press.

Chapter 10

ISSUES IN ARTS THERAPIES EVALUATION

The fundamental principles that we have discussed up to this point apply to all the fields of mental health and education. However, there are numbers of issues that are unique to the arts therapies. One central issue is that of identity, and whether one views one's practice as psychotherapy. An additional issue is extent to which the arts therapist aligns or locates his or her practice with regard to the medical model found in many treatment settings. Allen (1992) referred to the alignment with the medical model prevalent in mental health as "clinification." Issues of state licensing requirements for most arts therapists serve to underscore that alignment for many practitioners. For the individual arts therapist, his or her response to these issues weighs heavily in determining how he or she shapes and implements an evaluation program.

WHY ARTS-BASED ASSESSMENT?

All arts therapies, to some extent, represent a triangulated relationship between the art form, the creative process, and psychological theory. Arts therapists often use many of the assessment procedures and tests that have been developed in other health, mental health, and education disciplines. If they work in the field of mental health, therapists are likely to use approaches that have been devised by psychologists or to rely on assessments and labels created by psychiatrists. If they work in special education or in developmental remediation, they will often use tests designed by educators or psychologists.

However, many in the field believe that there is a need for arts therapists to develop their own, mainly nonverbal, assessment approaches. In the 1970s, some therapists contended that until the arts therapies developed their own bodies of knowledge and their own independent assessment procedures based on this knowledge, they could not lay claim to autonomy as independent professions and would remain the handmaidens of psychotherapy (Cohen, Averbach, & Katz, 1978). But the realities of broad changes in health care and mental health care systems specifically since the 1970s seem to have focused most arts therapists on job and licensure issues at the expense of the need to claim independence. Also of interest is that counseling and psychology have appropriated some of the techniques that arts therapists pioneered (Gladding, 2005; Degges-White & Davis, 2011).

In virtually all of the arts therapies, attempts have been made to develop assessment and evaluation procedures that are unique. Chapters 11, 12, and 13 deal in depth with these modality-specific assessment and evaluation procedures. Generally, there are five areas in which arts therapies practitioners have sought to establish approaches and procedures that may be used to supplement (or in some cases to supplant) the traditional psychological or psychiatric approaches.

Differential Diagnosis. There are many situations in which traditional verbal or behavioral procedures are not feasible. A patient may be unable to communicate verbally or may feel threatened or overwhelmed by traditional verbal tests. Or he or she may, consciously or otherwise, censor communication or otherwise fail to disclose vital information when the communication is solely in words. In the arts therapies, the art forms used offer alternative representations of the human experience.

Personality Assessment. There are some situations in which nonverbal procedures may be better than verbal ones in assessing personality or affect or even cognition. While he was most comfortable with "the talking cure," commented that his patients frequently said that they could draw an image, but that they were unable to describe it in words (Freud, 1933, p.10), and he noted that even though we can control and censor our words, our bodies betray our innermost thoughts. "Betrayal," he wrote, "oozes out [of the body] at every pore" (Freud, 1924, p. 94).

Assignment to Therapy. Once a client presents for therapy and a diagnosis has been made, therapists need some method for ascertaining whether a patient or client is a suitable candidate for a particular arts therapy group or individual treatment, or for deciding which of several possible arts therapies is most appropriate.

Data for Developing an Individual Treatment Plan. It is essential not only to know a patient's preferences, interests, and previous experience with the art modality but also his or her specific problems, deficiencies, or dysfunction in relation to the specific modality in order to establish treatment goals and to plan a meaningful individual plan of treatment in that modality.

Monitoring Progress. Unless a baseline has been established from which to estimate change, there is no way of knowing whether there has been improvement or how well the treatment program is working for an individual.

PERSPECTIVES

When you look into a mirror, according to a saying sometimes attributed to George Bernard Shaw, you can see your face; when you look at art, you can see your soul. We would extrapolate that when you produce art, regardless of its form, you can do more than see your soul; you reveal it. Arts therapists are interested in getting to their clients' internal structuring systems (if not necessarily their souls) through art.

While there is general agreement that the arts reach into the depths of their clients, two camps have been identified among arts therapists regarding the function of art production. Not all of the arts therapies are divided between the camps. Particularly in art therapy and music therapy practitioners have expressed differences. One opinion is that expression in the art form is communication through which clients reveal material that serves as the focus of therapy. The other opinion holds that simply engaging in the creative process of art production permits a client or patient to deal with a new circumstance that can provide alternative ways of coping with problems. These two opinions are usually referred to in the art and music therapy literatures as "art in therapy" and "art as therapy." Interestingly, discussions of these two camps are all but missing in the dance/movement therapy literature. Practitioners in dance/movement therapy seem to merge the two approaches viewing the art forms as aesthetic containers for client material that allow the safe, symbolic communication of otherwise unsafe material. The dance and movement process that brings this about is the creative imperative of the therapist.

While it is true that all arts therapy approaches incorporate varying degrees of both expressive communication and creativity, for assessment and evaluation the distinction of what the particular therapist emphasizes has an impact. The arts therapist can focus on the expressive or on the creative, or even on both. However, the terms are not interchangeable; each carries clear implications for evaluation.

Margaret Naumburg, a Freudian-oriented art therapist, articulated the position of those who see the value of art therapy in enhancing communication between patient and therapist. "Whether messages are understood by others or not, for the disturbed patient they are attempts to communicate" (Naumburg, 1966, p. 45). Naumburg observed that although Freud had noted that the unconscious speaks in images, he didn't follow the suggestion of his patients that they be permitted to draw their dreams rather than tell them (Naumburg, 1966, p. 2). In contrast with Jung, who encouraged art as a valuable device with which to capture dream-images (Jung, 1965), Freud insisted that his patients verbalize their dreams (Ghadirian, 1974). Yet, many observers believe that there are significant differences between verbal and visual communication. Gregory Bateson (1973) wrote that:

> . . . our iconic communication serves functions totally different from those of language and, indeed, performs functions which verbal language is unsuited to perform. (p. 388)

Many childhood memories, for example, may be accessible only through remembered images, but can't be remembered in language that was not available to the child at that stage of development. Moreover, the images that emerge through drawing (Horowitz, 1971), music, or movement are far more ambiguous than verbal descriptions and are thus far less likely to be censored, suppressed or intellectualized.

To Naumburg and to those who accept her position, the most important single function of a patient's art production is as a vehicle for enriched communication between patient and therapist. The images produced, she wrote, "constitute symbolic speech" (Naumburg, 1958, p. 561). The use of visual images permits direct expression of dreams and fantasies; it minimizes self-censorship; it provides for the preservation of the communication; and it encourages the resolution of transference by permitting the patient to help in interpreting the product more readily than in a verbal translation. Some practitioners are skeptical about claims that the art process itself has any special healing value, contending that most responses to visual art and most spontaneous production of art are associative – Freud's own personal response to art (Halsey, 1977), rather than aesthetic. These practitioners may even evoke support for this idea by citing well-known artists who were known to have severe and persistent mental illnesses that were not obviously relieved by their art making. For example, the art of Van Gogh is cited as revealing his increasing mental disturbance. Art production, to such therapists, is one of several tools employed in the service of psychotherapy. For such therapists, evaluation is based primarily on the content, rather than the form, of artwork. Both content and form are usually interpreted in terms of projection.

Other arts therapists, in contrast, believe that the art process itself can be healing. The most clearly developed theoretical position for this view also derives from Freudian theory. The idea of creativity as healing borrows heavily from the construct of "sublimation," in which sexual energy and aggressive drives are transformed into socially accepted forms. Although the supporting arguments for art as therapy may vary, Freudians and Jungians can be found in alliance with humanists on this issue.

Like Naumburg, Edith Kramer based her views on Freudian theory, but she arrived at a very different view of the role of art in the healing process. Kramer wrote (1971): "When visual symbols are used mainly to supplement the spoken word in the interchange between therapist and patient, as in the art therapy of practitioners such as Margaret Naumburg, the creative act is of secondary importance and usually remains abortive" (p. 25). In contrast, Kramer described her approach as "art as therapy"; she believed that the healing potentialities of art therapy reside in "the psychological processes that are activated in creative work" (p. 25).

Kramer contended that the creative act itself, not the communication, is the contribution of art therapy. It is precisely the act of creating that provides the healing force by offering an opportunity for the patient to work out "equivalents" and analogues for daily life experiences. The function of producing art as therapy is to "create a symbolic living, which allows experimentation with ideas and feelings" (1971, p. 219). In this view, the creative act is an act of sublimation – of channeling, reducing and transforming potentially destructive or antisocial energies. It is an act of personality integration, in which the patient can try new ways of coping with changing realities. As a result, the artistic coherence of the work produced is a sign of successful sublimation. The quality of the work "becomes a measure (though not the only measure) of therapeutic success" (1971, p. 223).

In recent decades, training programs for the arts therapies increasingly provide curricula that prepare students for state licensing requirements usually related to counseling. Licensing carries a financial benefit for the arts therapist by allowing for third-party billing for services delivered in private practice or in clinic and organizational settings. Tracking licensing regulations in states across the U.S. has become a major focus for government affairs representatives in the American Art Therapy Association, the American Music Therapy Association, and the American Dance Therapy Association over the past 20 years. Efforts to write arts therapists into state regulations and into proposed regulations for arts therapists working with the medically ill are ongoing by arts therapies associations in the U.S. (Goodill, personal communication, October, 2011). Possibly due in part to this change in education standards and important licensing accessibility for graduates, many (but not all) arts therapies clinicians today identify as psychotherapists or counselors who are arts therapists.

PROFESSIONAL IDENTITY AND LEVELS OF ASSESSMENT

It is difficult to accurately characterize the many ways in which practice settings have changed for arts therapists due to managed care in the U.S. and overall changes in the ways that health care, mental health settings and even educational settings have been affected. Many arts therapists now hold job titles in which their specialization is not reflected at all. However, the ways in which arts therapists assess their clients and evaluate their own creative arts therapy treatments remain based largely on two factors. The first is their professional identity: how they define their own work; this, in turn, is influenced by such factors as their theoretical orientation, their training, their licenses, and their view of clinical practice as primarily scientific or artistic. The second is defined by institutional administrators, licensing agencies, insurance companies, and their organizations' certification boards. Some arts therapists work in settings, for example, private practice or clinical settings where billing for insurance coverage or even Medicare proscribes how treatment is described and tracked. Others may work in inpatient settings where the length of hospitalization averages between five and seven days, and thus must adapt treatment and evaluation of treatment to this constraint. Nevertheless, three general areas that are usually still of interest for assessment are described below.

Assessment of Psychosocial Abilities

Many of the problems that bring individuals to the therapist for treatment manifest themselves in interpersonal or social situations within the family, at work, or in the community. The improvement of socialization skills may be an important primary goal of treatment, if it is believed that the lack of such skills is at the root of the problem. On the other hand, it may be a secondary goal, based on the principle that whatever gains are derived from treatment are likely to be eroded unless the client has the support of his or her family and associates. As a practical guide to the specifics of treatment planning, an assessment of the client's functioning on the social level may indicate the most appropriate form of treatment designed to promote these skills.

Assessment of Pertinent Abilities, Interests, and Preferences

A basic premise in the arts therapies is that the therapist must meet the client at the client's level of comfort. In planning the specifics of treatment, it is important to identify clients' abilities, interests, and preferences. There are many ways to gather such information. The therapist may use self-report questionnaires, or may observe how long a client works at certain tasks, or chooses certain materials, or responds to certain stimuli. Sometimes, the simplest and most effective method is simply to ask the patient about leisure activities, preferences, or previous training or experience.

Assessment of Life Experiences, Capacities, and Deficiencies

This area of assessment can refer either to the presenting problems of the patient in broad or specific terms, and capacities and deficiencies revealed may be related to the treatment modality. For example, a patient's problems can be described in terms of the general symptoms that led to the referral to treatment, or in terms of abilities or strengths the patient possesses that can be used in treatment.

In a psychiatric admission, the institutional intake assessment team may use both broad and targeted assessments to determine the admission criteria of danger to self or other that determines whether admission is medically necessary. Once the patient is admitted, the arts therapist likely bypasses the broader areas of personality assessment or illness taxonomy and focuses specifically on the behavioral manifestations of the disorder, usually in terms of what they observe relevant to the arts modality. In other practice settings, as in inpatient psychiatry as it currently exists, arts therapists may frequently engage in assessment as a dual function of treatment. The pressure to move quickly with limited numbers of sessions allotted for those in private practice, hospital, and other settings frequently makes lengthy assessment processes impossible.

CATEGORIES OF ASSESSMENT PROCEDURES

Isenberg-Grzeda (1988) identified five parameters used to define music therapy assessment instruments in the music therapy literature: client population, area of functioning/condition, theory/model, technique, and response to the institution. These categories are still useful in conceptualizing assessment procedures and protocols and can be applied to the other arts therapies.

Client Population

Some instruments are designed specifically to assess the status of specific target populations, such as psychiatric patients in hospitals or developmentally disabled adults or children with autism. Such assessments may be the basis for differential diagnosis; many are designed to assess levels of functioning for clients in such target populations, such as motor functioning, communication skills, cognitive functioning, and social-emotional development. For example, Kalish-Weiss's (1988) body movement scale is part of the Behavior Rating Instrument for Autistic and Other Atypical Children (BRIAAC) to ascertain the degree of body movement dysfunction among autistic children and Michel and Rohrbacher's (1982) Music Therapy Assessment Profile for Severely/Profoundly Handicapped Persons, focuses on such areas as motor functioning, communication skills, cognitive functioning, and social-emotional development.

Area of Functioning

Some assessment instruments may be used across the board to identify or to assess problems and dysfunctions in patients regardless of the patient populations to which they may belong. Such instruments may include tests of cognition or emotional level, such as Rider's (1978, 1981) Musical Perception Test of Cognitive Development, and the Goodenough-Harris drawing tests (Harris, 1963a, 1963b). They include, also, tests of physiological functioning, such as Sutton's (1984) Music Therapy Physiological Measures Test.

Theory/Model

Often, the therapist's personal belief system or the prevailing institutional philosophy is likely to guide treatment. For assessment findings to be useful in a theory-based treatment program, they must be derived from evaluation techniques that are consistent with the underlying theory. In each of the arts therapies, there are assessment instruments that have been constructed in conformity with specific theoretical constructs and assumptions. Some of these assessments are detailed in Chapters 11, 12, and 13.

Technique

Obviously, the arts therapies are focused on the use of techniques that involve specific art forms, either in terms of response or of production. However, in some situations particular techniques are deemed so generally useful that they are employed as a sort of all-purpose instrument for assessment. In music therapy, for example, improvisational music is sometimes used as an assessment tool for a wide variety of target client groups and for a wide variety of disorders and problems. Such techniques may be tied to a specific theory as in the case of the improvisational scales created by Nordoff and Robbins (1977). On the other hand, some may draw from a variety of theoretical formulations and approaches. Bruscia's (1987) Improvisation Assessment Profiles (IAPs) are described explicitly as atheoretical. They can be interpreted using different theories and for a wide variety of target populations. Specific techniques are often used in both visual art and dance/movement assessment. Just as music therapists may use improvisational music as a diagnostic tool, art therapists and dance/movement therapists may visual art created or movement in the same way.

CAUTIONS IN RELYING ON EXTERNAL ASSESSMENTS

In many instances, arts therapists may rely on assessment reports by others. In hospitals and mental health centers, for example, therapists often accept at face value the psychiatric label that has been assigned by a psychiatrist. The diagnosis can be accompanied by a diagnostic report that spells out the patient's needs and a recommendation for treatment goals. Other areas in which arts therapists must rely, at least in part, on evaluations that are done by others, are in the diagnosis of learning disability, attention deficit disorder, neurological damage, developmental disability, and numerous other physical or mental problems.

Whenever arts therapists must rely on an assessment or a diagnosis that is made by others, they should be careful not to rely too uncritically on the expert judgment of the referring examiner. Arts therapists should make every effort to become familiar with the psychometric properties of the assessment instruments used by those who refer patients or clients. The most obvious way is to ask the assessor for data from the test manual. The other, and probably the more preferable, is for the arts therapist to check directly by referring to such standard sources as reviews in the professional literature in the areas of the problem and in such standard references as *Test Critiques* or the *Mental Measurements Yearbooks.* The arts therapist should be skeptical about interpretations by outside examiners without acquiring some knowledge of the test or procedure used.

PSYCHOPHARMACOLOGY AND ARTS THERAPY ASSESSMENT

There have been many changes in mental health practices over time and several very notable changes took place in the previous century that still impact mental health care today. In the 1950s, neuroleptic medications were introduced and provided the first true psychopharmacological intervention. While this change is the focus of this section, three other changes bear mention first for their impact.

In 1963, the Federal Community Mental Health Centers Act was passed. This legislation was an attempt to emphasize community-based, outpatient care as a preferable alternative to institutionalization. Its impact was life changing for patients who had lived for years in psychiatric hospitals, and it spurred thinking and ideas about de-institutionalization and living with mental illness outside the hospital. In 1973, The Health Maintenance Organization (HMO) Act was passed which is surprising to many people since its effects did not fully begin to be felt until the 1990s. Regardless of how we think of this legislation and its repercussions now, initially it was intended positively to control health care costs. In 1989, a lawsuit, *Arnold v. Sarn,* established a precedent for the right of individuals with mental illnesses to be treated in the least restrictive environment. While many people diagnosed with mental illnesses had begun living in their communities and attending outpatient treatment after the 1963 legislation, the *Arnold v. Sarn* ruling made it illegal to treat individuals in ways that were unnecessarily restrictive. Many arts therapists were affected by these changes in both positive and negative ways. For example, arts therapies were a natural for providing community-based outpatient care, and many jobs were created. Then in the mid to late 1990s, health maintenance organizations ended many of these jobs in efforts to cut costs, and arts therapists moved into a range of other job titles that remained.

The neuroleptic medications introduced in the 1950s produced changes in the symptoms of patients with severe forms of mental illnesses and began to produce changes in thinking about the basis of mental disorders. In effect, this change established the neurological basis for understanding mental disorders and advanced the understanding of neurotransmitters (Cruz, 1995). A host of other psychopharmacologic agents followed, and today it is generally thought that psychiatric medications work by targeting these neurotransmitters: (a) monamines (dopamine, norepenephrine, serotonin), (b) GABA (gamma-aminobytric acid), and (c) opioid peptides. Neurotransmitters are chemicals that relay, amplify, and modulate electrical signals between neurons and other cells. They work in two ways – either by helping initiate a nerve impulse or discouraging (inhibiting) a nerve impulse. Neurotransmitters are processed in the brain – either by being taken in and used (uptake or reuptake) or they are digested by enzymes.

Psychotropic medications can be categorized into five basic groups, antidepressants, anxiolytics, antipsychotics, mood stabilizers, and opioid blockers (Cruz, 2007). We associate these groups of drugs with these neurotransmitters:

1. Antidepressants (serotinin & norepinephrine)
2. Anxiolytics (GABA)
3. Antipsychotics (dopamine & serotonin)
4. Mood stabilizers (lithium [not a neurotransmitter])
5. Opioid blockers (GABA & dopamine)

All psychopharmacology is aimed at controlling problematic symptoms of illness and in general psychoactive drugs affect symptoms resulting from either high or low neurotransmitter activity. Most psychoactive drugs have a range of side effects, for example tricyclic and tetracyclic antidepressants can cause dry mouth, blurred vision, constipation, and confusion among other things. Selective serotonin reuptake inhibitors (SSRIs), another class of antidepressants, can initially cause nausea, headaches, and insomnia. A more complete list of common medications is located in Appendix A.

Of specific interest to creative arts therapists, some side effects are cognitive. For example, all antipsychotics except Zyprexa and Risperdal (trade names for olanzapine and risperidone, respectively) can slow thinking and cause lethargy (i.e., physical performance) and cause some sedation. Antidepressants such as Sinequan (doxepin), Serzone (nefazodone), and Remeron (mirtazapine) can cause sedation. The mood stabilizer, valproate can cause sedation, and lithium, another mood stabilizer, can cause patients to "feel out of it." So patients who have had psychotic symptoms, some treated for depression, anxiety, and some with bipolar disorder might be treated with these agents and experience these effects (Cruz, 2007).

Arts therapists should pay attention and notice if patients seem extremely lethargic, and take seriously clients' reports of possible medication side effects. These need to be reported to the appropriate treating psychiatrist or other treating physician. In addition, arts therapists can notice if there are any drastic changes in patients' energy level or functioning and again take concerns to the prescribing physician. Finally, if sessions must be scheduled just after psychiatric medications are taken (e.g., early in the morning after a breakfast dose or after a lunchtime dose), the therapist can use relaxation, guided imagery, or other low key – low demand techniques.

An important caveat is that the intended effects of many psychoactive drugs need time to build up in the individual's system. For example, it takes seven to 14 days for the therapeutic effects of tricyclic antidepressants to become apparent, and it is not always possible to ascertain the degree to which a patient's behavior reflects his or her underlying problem rather than the effects of the medicine. If the therapist is knowledgeable about possible side effects, he or she will not mistake them for symptoms and will take them into account in planning a treatment program.

SUMMARY

In both psychiatric and educational settings, many arts therapists either use traditional psychological assessment instruments and psychodiagnostic tests or rely on assessment reports prepared by others who use such procedures.

However, there is a growing body of arts-based evaluation procedures. There are five major applications of arts-based evaluation: for differential diagnosis, for personality assessment, to determine a client's suitability for a particular activity or group, as a basis for designing an individual arts therapy treatment program, and to establish a baseline from which to measure or monitor progress.

The role of arts-based evaluation is closely associated with the conceptualization of the role of the arts therapies. In some of the arts therapies, there are two fundamental views of the role of the arts modality. One holds that the arts are useful mainly as sources of information for use in psychotherapy, sometimes referred to as the "arts-in-therapy" position. In this view, the process in which the patient creates and responds to an art form is revealing. However, the art activity itself is not thought to have sufficient healing properties used on its own; it requires the presence and essential component of the therapist.

The "arts-as-therapy" camp, on the other hand, holds that the creative process itself is healing. It provides the opportunity for the client to sublimate, or channel and transform potentially aggressive or destructive impulses; to use the creative process as a way of experimenting with "life equivalents"; and to try out new ways of coping with changing realities.

In actual practice, many arts therapists likely place themselves somewhere on the continuum between these two positions. The therapist's place on this continuum is determined in large part by the professional identity that is assumed by (or assigned to) the practitioner and by the institutional demands of hospitals, clinics, community centers, certification and registry boards, and state licensing agencies.

The arts therapies practitioners work in a wide variety of settings, and sometimes depending on the setting any assessment beyond that of general interests and abilities is largely irrelevant, as treatment is purposefully planned in light of patients' problems and insurance timeframes. As a result, assessments and evaluations are usually limited to those that relate to the process and the product of the patient's involvement. It is frequently assumed that change via participating in an arts therapy will lead to personal insights and will transfer automatically to other areas of the client's life.

However, increasing numbers of therapists have expressed skepticism that there is an automatic transfer from the way in which the patient comes to perform the activity and the way he or she behaves in other areas of life. As a result, arts psychotherapists tend to use the arts experience as a stimulus to initiate mainly verbal exploration of emotional responses. The purpose of such exploration is generally to probe for deeper or "unconscious" sources for the responses.

Both those who identify their work as arts-as-therapy and those who see themselves as arts psychotherapists may rely on assessments conducted by outside specialists, such as psychiatrists, neuropsychologists, speech/language pathologists, audiologists, and others who are trained to conduct specialized assessments. In planning their treatment programs on the basis of such external assessments, arts therapists are cautioned to exercise the same caution in evaluating the tests and procedures that are used that they would exercise in their own choice of approaches.

APPENDIX A

Common Psychoactive Medications

Antidepressants

Generic Name (trade name)	*Usual Daily Dosage (mg)*	*Side effects*
Tricyclics & Tetracyclics		
Amitriptyline (Elavil, Endep)	100-300	Anticholinergic (dry mouth,
Clomipramine (Anafranil)	100-250	blurred vision, constipation,
Doxepin (Sinequan)	100-300	urinary retention, tachycardia,
Imipramine (Tofranil)	100-300	possible confusion)
Trimipramine (Surmontil)	100-300	Orthostasis
Desipramine (Norpramin)	100-300	Effects on cardiac condition
Nortriptyline (Pamelor, Aventyl)	50-200	Lethal in overdose
Protriptyline (Vivactil)	15-60	Periodontal disease
Amoxapine (Asendin)	100-400	
Maprotiline (Ludiomil)	100-225	
Selective Serotonin Reuptake Inhibitors (SSRIs)		
Citalopram (Celexa)	20-60	
Fluoxetine (Prozac)	20-60	Initial: nausea, loose bowel
Fluvoxamine (Luvox)	50-300	movements, headache, insomnia
Paroxetine (Paxil)	20-60	
Sertaline (Zoloft)	50-200	
Dopamine-Norepinephrine Reuptake Inhibitors		
Bupropion (Wellbutrin IR)	300	Initial: nausea, headache, insomnia,
Bupropion SR (Wellbutrin SR, Zyban)	300	anxiety/agitation, seizure risk
Serotonin-Norepinephrine Reuptake Inhibitors		
Venlafaxine (Effexor)	75-225	Similar to SSRIs (see above)
Venlafaxine XR (Effexor XR)	75-225	Dose-dependent hypertension
Duloxetine (Cymbalta)	20-40	n/a
Serotonin Modulators		
Nefazodone (Serzone)	150-300	Initial: nausea, dizziness, confusion
Trazadone (Desyrel)	75-300	Initial: sedation, priapism, dizziness, orthostasis
Norepinephrine-serotonin modulator		
Mirtazapine (Remeron)	15-45	Anticholinergic, orthostasis, hypertension, edema, agranulocytosis, liver dysfunction
Monoamine Oxidase (MAO) Inhibitors		
Phenelzine (Nardil)	15-90	Orthostatic hypotension, insomnia,
Tranylcypromine (Parnate)	30-60	edema, not for patients with CHF, potentially life-threatening drug interactions, dietary restictions

Table Note: SR – slow release; XR – extended release; MAO is a brain protein that breaks down norepinephrine, serotonin, and dopamine the brain's three neurotransmitters (called monoamines).

Antipsychotics

Generic Name (trade name)	*Usual Daily Dosage (mg)*	*Characteristics/Side effects*
Conventional Antipsychotics		
Phenothiazines		These agents are "high-affinity antagonists of dopamine D2 receptors in the brain and are effective against psychotic symptoms but have high rates of neurologic side effects, such as extrapyramidal signs and tardive dyskinesia," (Lieberman et al., 2005). Also causes hyperprolactinemia (breast lactation) and amenorrhea in women
Chlorpromazine (Thorazine)	300-600	
Perphenazine (Trilafon)	2-64	
Piperidines		
Thioridazine (Mellaril)	300-600	
Mesoridazine (Serentil)	150-300	
Pimozide (Orap)	2-6	
Thioxanthenes		
Thiothixene (Navane)	15-30	
Butyrophenones		
Haloperidol (Haldol)	5-15	
Dibenzoxazepines		
Loxapine (Loxitane)	45-90	
Molindone (Moban)	30-60	
Atypical Antipsychotics		
Clozapine (Clozaril)	250-500	These agents are greater in their "affinity for other neuroreceptors, including those for serotonin and norepinephrine," (Lieberman et al., 2005). However, they induce weight gain, alter glucose and lipid metabolism, and are much more costly. Reduce negative symptoms (emotional blunting)
Risperidone (Risperdal; Consta)	4-6	
Olanzapine (Zyprexa; Zydus)	10-20 (Risperdal)	
Quetiapine (Seroquel)	300-600 (Zyprexa)	
Ziprasidone (Geodon)	80-160	

The most common indications for use of antipsychotics are in treatment of acute psychosis and maintaining remission of psychotic symptoms in patients with schizophrenia. A study comparing the effectiveness of conventional and atypical antipsychotics in the treatment of patients with chronic schizophrenia found 74% of patients discontinued the medication before 18 months. Olanzapine was the most effective in terms of rate of discontinuation but was associated with greater weight gain and increases in glucose and lipid metabolism. The efficacy of perphenazine was similar to quetiapine, risperidone, and ziprasidone. Lieberman, Stroup, McEvoy, Swartz, Rosenhech, Perkins, et al., (2005). Effectiveness of antipsychotics drugs in patients with chronic schizophrenia. *New England Journal of Medicine, 353*(12), 1209–1223.

Common Mood Stabilizers

Generic Name (trade name)	*Starting Dosage (mg)*	*Contraindications*
Lithium Lithium Carbonate (Eskalith, Lithonate, Lithotabs) Extended Release (Eskalith CR) (Lithobid)	 300 bid (twice a day) 450 300	 Unstable renal function; can cause tremors that are commonly treated with Propranolol (Enderol) a Beta blocker in bipolar patients
Valproate Divalproex sodium (Depakote) Valproic Acid (Depakene) Divalproex ER	 250 tid (three times a day)	 Hepatic dysfunction
Lamotrigine (Lamietal)*	25	Can cause red, raised rash
Carbamazepine (Tegretol)*	200mg tablet bid (twice a day)	May exacerbate seizures, can cause rashes

Note: mood stabilizers are defined as agents that have "efficacy in treatment of acute manic and depressive symptoms and in prophylaxis of manic and depressive symptoms in bipolar disorder" [see Bauer & Mitchner, 2004). What is a "Mood Stabilizer"? An evidence-based response. *American Journal of Psychiatry, 161,* 3–18. p. 3]

*Lamotrigine is currently under investigation for its mood stabilizing properties. Carbamazepine, previously considered a mood stabilizer, has been found to have few mood stabilizing properties.

Treatments for Addictions

Individuals with opioid or alcohol addictions are commonly treated with the following drugs:

Methadone – opioid
Buprenorphine (Tengesic, Subutex) – opioid
Naltrexone (Revia) – opioid or alcohol
Acamprosate (Campral) – alcohol

Common Anxiolytic and Hypnotic Medications

Generic Name (trade name)	*Usual Daily Dosage (mg)*	*Side effects*
Benzodiazepines		
Alprazolam (Xanax) Chlordiazepoxide (Librium) Clonazepam (Klonapin) Clorazepate (Tranxene) Diazepam (Valium) Lorazepam (Ativan) Oxazepam (Serax)	1-4 15-100 1-4 15-60 4-40 1-6 30-120	Habit forming – popularly sold on the street; most habit forming: Xanex, Klonapin, Valium; least habit forming: Librium.
Nonbenzodiazepines		
Buspirone (BuSpar)	30-60	Not habit forming, but only has modest effects and thus not used much.

Anxiolytics are used to treat disorders where anxiety is an important component including, generalized anxiety disorder, obsessive-compulsive disorder, panic disorder, performance anxiety, and social phobia. Generalized anxiety disorder is commonly treated with low dose venlafaxine (Effexor) or duloxetine (Cymbalta).

Treatments for Insomnia

Medications commonly used to treat insomnia include:

Temazepam (Restoril)
Trazedone (Desyrel) – is not addictive but can cause nightmares and priapism
Zolpidem (Ambien)

Treatments for Children

Very few drugs have been tested for use with children. Recently the FDA has put out warnings due to an increased use of antidepressants (SSRIs) in children that have been associated with severe suicidality. Currently, Wellbutrin and Prozac have not shown to be as associated with this risk in children as other antidepressants.

Children with attention deficit hyperactivity disorder (ADHD) are frequently prescribed methylphenidate (Ritalin), atomoxetine (Strattera), and modafinil (Provigil). Atomoxetine is a non-stimulant.

REFERENCES

Allen, P. (1992). Artist-in-residence: An alternative to "clinification" for art therapists. *Art Therapy: Journal of the American Art Therapy Association, 9*(1), 22–29.

Bruscia, K. E. (1988). Standards for clinical assessment in the arts therapies. *Arts in Psychotherapy, 15,* 5–10.

Cohen, G., Averbach, J., & Katz, E. (1978). Music therapy assessment of the developmentally disabled child. *Journal of Music Therapy, 15*(2), 86–99.

Cruz, R. F. (1995). An empirical investigation of the Movement Psychodiagnostic Inventory. *Dissertation Abstracts International: Section B: The Sciences & Engineering Vol. 57*(2-B), August, 1996, 1495.

Cruz, R. (2007, November). Psychopharmacology. Symposium conducted at Lesley University, Cambridge, MA.

Degges-White, S., & Davis, N. I. (Eds.). (2011). *Integrating the expressive arts into counseling practice: Theory-based interventions.* New York: Springer.

Freud, S. (1924). The loss of reality in neurosis and psychosis. In J. Riviere (trans.), *Collected papers.* Vol. II, 277–282. New York: Basic Books.

Freud, S. (1933). *New introductory lectures on psychoanalysis.* (J. Strachey, trans. and Ed.) New York: Norton, 1966.

Ghadirian, A. M. (1974). Artistic expression of psychopathology through the media of art therapy. *Confinia Psychiat, 17,* 162–170.

Gladding, S. (2005) *Counseling as an art: The creative arts in counseling* (3rd ed.). Alexandria, VA: American Counseling Association.

Halsey, B. (1977). Freud on the nature of art. *American Journal of Art Therapy, 16,* 99–101.

Harris, D. B. (1963a). *Children's drawings as measures of intellectual maturity: A revision and extension of the Goodenough Draw-A-Man Test.* Cleveland, OH: The Psychological Corporation.

Harris, D. B. (1963b). *Goodenough-Harris Drawing Test: Manual.* Cleveland, OH: The Psychological Corporation.

Horowitz, M. J. (1971). The use of graphic images in psychotherapy. *American Journal of Art Therapy, 10,* 156.

Isenberg-Grzeda, C. (1988). Music therapy assessment: A reflection of professional identity. *Journal of Music Therapy, 25*(3), 156–169.

Kalish-Weiss, B. I. (1988). Born blind and visually handicapped infants: Movement psychotherapy and assessment. *The Arts in Psychotherapy, 15,* 101–108.

Kramer, E. (1971). *Art as therapy with children.* New York: Schocken.

Michel, D., & Rohrbacher, M. (1982). *The music therapy assessment profile for severely/profoundly handicapped persons.* Research Draft III. Unpublished manuscript, Texas Women's University.

Naumburg, M. (1958). Case illustration: Art therapy with a seventeen year old girl. In E. F. Hammer (Ed.), *The clinical application of projective drawings* (pp. 511–517). Springfield, IL: Charles C Thomas.

Naumburg, M. (1966). *Dynamically oriented art therapy: Its principles and practices.* New York: Grune and Stratton.

Nordoff, P., & Robbins, C. (1977). *Creative music therapy.* New York: John Day.

Rider, M. (1978). *The development of the musical-perception assessment of cognitive ability.* Unpublished master's thesis. Dallas, TX: Southern Methodist University.

Rider, M. (1981). The assessment of cognitive functioning level through musical perception. *Journal of Music Therapy, 18,* 110–119.

Sutton, K. (1984). The development and implementation of a music therapy physiological measures test. *Journal of Music Therapy, 21,* 160–169.

Chapter 11

ART THERAPY ASSESSMENT AND EVALUATION

DONNA BETTS

In Bernard and Elaine Feders' original 1998 edition of this book, Chapter 11 was entitled "Visual Art Therapy." In re-reading this text, it became readily apparent that although the realm of art therapy assessment has made strides over the past 15 years, some of the same issues addressed by the Feders pervade. The Feders' contribution to evaluation in the creative arts therapies has a significant place in our history. Many of the points articulated in their book are very relevant today, while providing an historical perspective of accomplishments in assessment, and where we next need to focus our clinical and research energies to continually improve this realm of practice.

The Feders (1998) set out to provide an introductory handbook and text in assessment and evaluation in the "emerging arts therapies" (p. v). They did not intend to provide formulas or recipes. Rather, they wanted to ". . . help therapists to relate their evaluation program to their goals, to identify what they are interested in evaluating and to design the kind of evaluation program that can do what the therapist wants it to do" (p. x). Their intended audience was students and clinicians, with a focus on methodological and theoretical approaches. For clinicians, the intent was to provide ". . . guidelines for developing and implementing evaluation programs" (p. v). The present chapter also addresses these audiences, but includes implications for educators and researchers as well.

For purposes of simplification, when "Feder and Feder" or "the Feders" are referred to and cited in this chapter, it indicates reference to their original 1998 publication, upon which the present chapter is based.

The Art and Science of Evaluation

"The art and science of evaluation . . . ," the title and philosophical thread of the Feders' book, is woven throughout this chapter. They astutely anchored the book's contents in the mainstream thinking about the inter-relationship between art and science, and by extension, between the "creative and scientific approaches to evaluation" (p. v), asserting that the two are intertwined. ". . . We believe that the argument over whether art therapy is an art or a science is not only fruitless but counterproductive; it can only perpetuate divisions in a field in which both artistic creativity and scientific validation are necessary" (p. vii). They also asserted, as have other arts therapies researchers since 1998, that we need to systematically demonstrate the efficacy of our work if it is to be meaningful. In the art therapy literature, Linda Gantt's article *A Discussion of Art Therapy as a Science* (1998) and Frances Kaplan's (2000) book, *Art, Science and Art Therapy: Repainting the Picture,* are just two examples addressing the need to apply the scientific method to our research.

Despite the number of research-related, peer-reviewed articles published to date (too numerous to include here), the Feders' (1998) finding still bears some relevance: "at present, there is paucity of materials that correlate the theory and practice of the arts therapies with generally accepted procedures in evaluation" (p. v). Thus, it is clearer than ever that we need to embrace the whole spectrum of the creative (traditionally arts-based and qualitative) approaches to evaluation and research, as well as the scientific (quantitative). In the original edition of this book, the authors astutely stated, "We must be careful to avoid viewing quantitative and qualitative evaluation as antagonistic." The Feders cited support for this statement with a quote by Assistant Surgeon General Gary Noble (1991): "The best way to plan for evaluation is to establish programs that incorporate specific, measurable goals. Quantitative evaluation can then tell us *what* effect we are having (how much, where, who, when); qualitative evaluation can tell us *why* the program is effective or why there is a problem. Both are equally important" (p. 2; in Feder & Feder, p. 18). This stance supports recent work that calls for a mixed-methods or integrated approach to assessment (Betts, 2012a).

The Feders acknowledged that there may never be a resolution between the qualitative and quantitative divergences, but asserted that they should be understood. This chapter is written from the standpoint of an art therapist clinician, educator and researcher, who is not only comfortable embracing both the creative and scientific, but who recognizes the necessity to do so, for the benefit of the people whom we serve. "Without science, therapy can degenerate to the practice of superstitious ritual, in which each practitioner owes allegiance only to his or her personal myth of existence. Without art, it can lose the very humanity it seeks to examine (p. ix)." This is an important consideration, because too many art therapists are dismissive of the value of the scientific method. Responsible practice necessitates comfort with both art and science, and this author asserts it is the duty of educators and supervisors to impart this to their students. Furthermore, perpetuation of a fabricated split between a qualitative, humanistic "sitting beside" approach to assessment versus the quantitative promotion of "a more distant calculation," as designated by Gilroy, Tipple, and Brown (2012), is nonproductive.

Feder and Feder observed that ". . . few arts therapies programs offer instruction either in research or in evaluation" (p. xi). This has since changed. For one, American Art Therapy Association (AATA) approved programs require content in both research and assessment.

The Feders cited the "the uneasy relationship between the therapist as artist and the therapist as scientist" as a theme throughout their book (p. ix). For example:

> The relationship between art and science in the modern practice of psychotherapy is a restless and disturbed one. With the increasing specialization of occupation, artist and scientist frequently speak in different tongues and have difficulty understanding each other. From what should be a harmonious chorus often comes a disturbing and dissonant cacophony. (p. 8)

While expressing support the Feders' stance, this author disagrees with their assertion that the art versus science debate will "never be resolved" (p. ix). This chapter will explain the ways in which, over the past 15 years, this relationship has eased, making today's atmosphere more conducive to a comfortable interplay across the art and science spectrum.

In the past decade or so, two approaches to education in the United States have emerged, further drawing attention to the importance of integrating disciplines in the successful education of students. First, the STEM approach set the foundation for STEAM in education. STEM is an acronym for Science, Technology, Engineering, and Mathematics. This program was initiated by Judith Ramaley, the former director of the National Science Foundation's education and human-resources division. A meta-disciplinary approach to education, STEM was established in 2001 to revolutionize the teaching of math and science by incorporating aspects of technology and engineering into the curriculum (DRPF Consults, 2012). An important area for education policy focus and development, STEM was integrated into many higher education institutions and scientific communities soon after its inception (TIES, 2012).

Georgette Yakman, an educator with a PhD in Curriculum and Instruction, took the STEM approach a step further, to integrate the arts, in her STEAM program. Established in 2006, STEAM ("STΣ@M") represents "Science & Technology interpreted through Engineering & the Arts, all based in Mathematical elements" (STEAM EDU, 2012). It is an educational model of how traditional academic subjects can be structured into a framework by which to plan integrative curricula. "When planning integrative curriculum, one field may be the dominant base discipline or all may be planned to be more equally represented" (Wells, 2006, in Yakman, 2008).

Other evidence of the integration of the arts and sciences at the federal level within the United States includes the National Academy of Sciences-sponsored free events. In Washington, D.C., for instance, these events are known as the Art Science Evening Rendezvous (DASER), a monthly discussion forum on art and science projects. Speakers present work that integrates art and science.

In the field of art therapy, Betts, Gantt, and Lorance (2011) have brought these realms together with the International Art Therapy Research Database (IATRD; www.arttherapyresearch.com). The IATRD is a service provided to the art therapy community, sponsored by the George Washington University, as a tool to inform practice and facilitate research. As originally conceived by Linda Gantt, PhD, ATR-BC in 1986, the IATRD is intended to provide a resource of artwork done by members of particular social, national and/or diagnostic groups, supplemented with de-identified demographic and diagnostic data, and comments from clients and art therapists. As approved researchers continue to add their GW Institutional Review Board-approved art therapy assessment data to the IATRD, the database will expand and researchers, clinicians, educators and students will benefit from being able to access thousands of artworks and corresponding data.

HISTORY OF ASSESSMENT IN ART THERAPY

Early Foundations

As previously discussed by Betts (2006, pp. 426–427), psychologists, psychiatrists, anthropologists, and educators have used artwork in evaluation, therapy, and research for over 100 years (MacGregor, 1989). During the 20th century, several psychological projective tests were developed. However, ". . . the research on projective drawings has yielded mixed results" (Gantt & Tabone, 1998, p. 8). The tools that have been called into question include Rorschach's inkblot projective test (1921), the Goodenough-Harris Draw-A-Man Test (Harris & Roberts, 1972), the House-Tree-Person (HTP) Test (Buck, 1948), and the Thematic Apperception Test (TAT) (Murray, 1943) (Betts, 2006, pp. 426–427). During the 1970s and 1980s, the use of these projective tools declined due to decreased belief in psychoanalytic theory, greater emphasis on situational determinants of behavior, questions regarding the cost-effectiveness of these tools, and poor reviews of their validity (Groth-Marnat, 1990). Although projective tests are still popular among psychologists, several authors have questioned their scientific value, pointing to questionable research findings (Chapman & Chapman, 1967; Dawson, 1984; Kahill, 1984; Klopfer & Taulbee, 1976; Roback, 1968; Russell-Lacy, Robinson, Benson & Cranage, 1979; Suinn & Oskamp, 1969; Swensen, 1968; Wadeson & Carpenter, 1976). For a detailed review of this literature, see Betts (2005), pp. 16–20. For a detailed review of projective drawing techniques used with children, including Human Figure Drawing; Frank Drawing Completion test; HTP; Kinetic Family Drawing; Free Drawing; Draw A Person; Modified DAP/Draw a Man Test; Loney Draw a Car Test; A Favorite Kind of Day (FKOD); Kinetic School Drawing; Draw-a-Story; and, the Silver Drawing Test (SDT), see Neale & Rosal (1993).

Further Understandings of Art Interpretation

The Feders described isomorphism, a concept integral to art interpretation and assessment, as the idea that content manifest in our thoughts, perceptions, and behaviors is reflected in the artwork we make. Although this principle may be espoused by art therapists, we may not agree on how it applies in artwork interpretation. Three general ways to correlate art products with personality, pathology, and development in the process of art interpretation were cited by the Feders as: the dictionary approach; quantification of formal elements; and the phenomenologic approach. In recent years, the formal elements and phenomenologic approaches have emerged in the literature as the preferred methods of assessment interpretation (Betts, 2012a).

The dictionary approach is based on the concept of isomorphy, and refers to outdated applications of Freudian principles of dream interpretation to drawings. Symbols identified in drawings were thought to reveal the client's unknown or repressed concerns, impulses, and desires. The Feders looked to Freud and Jung to address this topic. They wisely concluded that the analysis of symbols in artwork is an inadequate procedure, and that ". . . the interpretation of symbols in artwork is generally considered part of a clinical assessment, rather than an aspect of testing" (p. 263). As such, symbol interpretation can be used as a therapeutic tool (to prompt a discussion, for instance), as opposed to assignment of a diagnosis. Feder and Feder cited Tessa Dalley (1984) as describing British art therapists' belief that ". . . art therapists cannot and should not attempt to 'read' or interpret a patient's artwork, since the only person qualified to interpret accurately is the patient who produced the work. The therapist may 'speculate, suggest, and connect aspects of the picture, but this occurs within the therapeutic relationship in an environment of trust, openness, and safety' (p. xxiv)." This is also true of American art therapists. Today, most art therapists are savvy about this issue. In a recent British publication (Gilroy, Tipple, & Brown, 2012), which brought American and British art therapists together to explore the current status of assessment on both sides of the Atlantic, this truth is echoed.

The underlying principle of quantification of formal elements is actuarial, and the method requires little interpretation. Elements such as a drawing's composition, the use of color and space, and overall coherence, can implicate presence or absence of diagnostic indicators.

This concept is later elucidated at length.

The phenomenologic approach takes into account behavioral aspects of the assessment session, such as the client's behavior and verbal expression during art-making, the artwork itself. Within this framework, the client is typically invited by the therapist to guide in interpreting these behavioral elements. Citing the work of Janie Rhyne (personal communication, 1995), the Feders provided an instance of the potential for problems in interpretation of artwork. Discussing the case of "Billy," Rhyne reported advising an art therapy student to ". . . use your experience as a creator and perceiver of forms. Look for overall qualities in all three of Billy's drawings, seeing them as part of a whole series . . ." (p. 264). Despite her wise counsel, the student misinterpreted Billy's HTP drawings, with disastrous results. Rhyne contended that when encouraged by the therapist, the client can ". . . recognize the dynamics of structure in the artwork as manifestations of behavioral patterns and as evidence of present concerns" (p. 265). The art therapy student's lack of knowledge and experience in this regard likely explains her misinterpretation of the drawings. This example underscores the importance of considering a client's perceptions of his or her own artwork and process, as well as the client's comments and behaviors during the session, and thus supports the necessity of an integrated approach to the assessment and evaluation process.

Recent Developments and Current Status

Metzl (2008) conducted a systematic analysis of methodologies used in research published in *Art Therapy: Journal of AATA* between 1987 and 2004. In the literature she reviewed on assessment research, Metzl found that "the interest in art therapy assessment measures has slightly decreased over time and focus on specific tools shifted" (p. 68). Specifically, she identified an increase in Person Picking an Apple from a Tree and Formal Elements of Art Therapy Scale research, and a comparative decline in the number of Diagnostic Drawing Series and mandala studies published in the AATA journal. Another shift that was identified involves the increased use of triangulation of methods, replacing the use of singular art therapy assessments as established, independent research measures. Such triangulation, or integration of multiple sources of data, is explored forthwith.

A FOUNDATION FOR INTEGRATION OF APPROACHES

Having established a need for qualitative and quantitative approaches to assessment, two means to provide a more strengths-based, thorough evaluation of clients are proposed: the use of assessment batteries, and integration of multiple data sources.

Assessment Batteries

In their "primer" *A Clinical Guide to Writing Assessments, Diagnosis, and Treatment,* Horovitz and Eksten (2009) provide a valuable guide for writing clinical reports based on results derived from a variety of assessments conducted with a client, and integrating these with treatment goals, objectives, summaries, and termination reports. This comprehensive evaluation process results in a broad and fair review of a patient's presenting problem, and serves to increase the accuracy of the treatment plan.

Assessment batteries in art therapy are evaluation procedures that include more than one directive, providing the client with a series of tasks, ideally completed during one session (so as to hold variables like time of day, patient mood, etc., as constant as possible). Some of the better known batteries in art therapy include the Art Therapy Projective Imagery Assessment (AT-PIA; Raymond, Bernier, Rauch, Stovall, Deaver, & Sanderson, 2010); the Kramer (Kramer & Schehr, 1983), and the Levick Emotional and Cognitive Art Therapy Assessment (Levick, 1983). These are described later in more detail. While batteries are time consuming to administer, they do provide a more just and well-rounded picture of the client, and therefore provide valuable information to aid in the clinical process.

Integration of Multiple Data Sources

The Feders looked to Wadeson (1980) to address the issue of whether artwork alone is sufficient for assessing a patient. Wadeson's vast clinical experience at the National Institutes of Health was cited as a source of her wisdom on this issue:

> While Wadeson found some general tendencies among the drawings produced by patients in some groups, she found so much variability

> within groups and so much overlap between groups that she concluded that distinctions based on art alone were impossible to make. (pp. 188–198)

The Feders justifiably expressed their skepticism of clinical judgments based on artwork alone, as "single diagnostic procedures of any kind are seldom accurate" (p. 277). Quantification of a drawing can be part of an assessment process, but only one part, and the results should be integrated with a variety of other sources of information about the client. This conclusion is supported in the current literature (Betts, 2012a; Groth-Marnat, 2003). Psychologists, art therapists and other mental health professionals are knowledgeable about the importance of data triangulation and integration.

Betts (2006) and others have articulated the debate about art therapy assessments. There are art therapists who don't like scoring artwork, because they find it to be dehumanizing and devaluing of the art product and the artist who made it. On the other hand, there are art therapists who acknowledge this problem with quantification of imagery. However, they choose to pursue tabulation of formal elements, recognizing the need to apply the scientific approach so that others (clinicians, journals, funding agencies, etc.) take us more seriously. Rather than taking sides on this issue, several art therapists have embraced the need for both approaches to artwork, and they espouse the triangulation/integration of data approach.

A modern way to consider this issue is found in Betts (2012a). By studying the literature on positive psychological assessment, and collaborating with colleagues who use this approach in treatment, Betts established positive art therapy assessment. Positive psychology assessment involves integration of multiple sources of data gathered about a client into the psychological report, combining qualitative and quantitative data sources such as referral questions, records, interviews, observations, and results of psychological tests. Test results are minimized, and meaningful descriptions about the client and how the information derived from the assessment relates to his or her life are maximized (Groth-Marnat, 2009).

In addition to data integration, positive psychologists have additional recommendations for improving the assessment process: being cautious about test selection (Snyder, Ritschel, Rand, & Berg, 2006); incorporating 'inside' and environmental assets and weaknesses in the clinic interview process; working collaboratively with the client (Snyder et al., 2006; Bornstein, 2009); focusing on the client-therapist relationship (Dudley, 2004); and including strengths and hope in client reports (Snyder et al., 2006). Art therapists who espouse these approaches to assessment value that the client's integrity is maintained through the assessment process, while certain scientific methods are also upheld.

Sub-branches of positive psychological assessment, Therapeutic Assessment and Collaborative Assessment, are two contemporary methods that creative arts therapists need to be aware of. Therapeutic assessment is an approach that considers both the assessor's and the client's influence on the outcome of a psychological test (Bornstein, 2009). It emphasizes a collaborative approach to assessment that "can have a positive impact on patient insight, adjustment, and therapeutic engagement" (p. 6). Psychological testing is approached as a way to help clients better understand themselves, find solutions to their problems, and facilitate positive changes (Finn, 2009). Therapeutic Assessment encompasses techniques of Collaborative Assessment (Fischer, 2001), a technique based in humanistic and human-science psychology. The Collaborative Assessment approach minimizes the power differential between the assessor and client in a team approach to understanding the client's problems and implementing more functional ways of thinking and being. Since the quality of the client-therapist relationship affects the success of an intervention, assessment techniques that will foster this relationship are advantageous (Martin, Garske, & Davis, 2000). In the art therapy literature, Cohen and Cox's (1995) *Integrative Method* places importance on integrating multiple data sources to supplement formal evaluation of artwork, to gain a more accurate and cohesive impression of the client. Dudley (2004) underscored the impact of the client-therapist relationship in the assessment process and de-emphasized the traditional "fact-finding" approach. Rather, she indicated that the initial meeting with a client presents an opportunity to observe the "unfolding" of a relationship between the therapist, the client, and the art product (p. 19).

THE DOMAINS OF ART THERAPY ASSESSMENTS

There is not one assessment that is best for all populations across all settings. Assessments must be used for specific reasons. In fact, the most important factor in selecting an assessment should be based upon the instrument's usefulness in addressing the referral question (Groth-Marnat, 2009).

Different sources describe domains somewhat variously. In considering the Feders' original domains (psychodiagnosis and personality assessment; family and couple drawing assessments; and cognitive and developmental evaluation), and seeking updated information, it is helpful to look to Groth-Marnat's classification system (2009), and that of the Buros Institute of Mental Measurements. Buros has worked for more than 70 years to serve the public interest and advance the field of measurement (Buros, n.d). It is a respected database of information about commercially published tests that promotes meaningful and appropriate test selection, utilization, and practice, and is included as a resource on the American Psychological Association's website. Based on these three reliable sources, it is still relevant to categorize some of our assessments in the Feders' original domains, but to also consider the broader applications of some of these tools. Thus, the domains are discussed as follows: (1) Psychodiagnosis and personality assessment; (2) Assessment of relationship dynamics; (3) Cognitive/Neuropsychological and developmental evaluation; and (4) Tools and techniques to address other realms of treatment. Each domain and its designated assessment tools are listed in Table 1. These four domains reflect a shift in the purpose and applications of art therapy assessments since 1998. This is in keeping with Groth-Marnat's (2009) observation that traditional assessment methods have decreased due to an expansion in the definition of assessment, and because of psychologists' overall increased involvement in other activities, as well as Metzl's (2008) finding that triangulation of methods is on the rise.

Table 11.1
Art Therapy Assessments & Corresponding Rating Systems
(NB: Not an exhaustive list)

Art Therapy Assessment Instruments	*Corresponding Rating System (Used in Art Therapy)*
Psychodiagnosis and Personality Assessment	
Diagnostic Drawing Series (DDS) (Cohen, Hammer, & Singer, 1988)	Drawing Analysis Form; Content Checklist (Cohen, 1985; 1994; 2012)
Person Picking an Apple from a Tree (PPAT) (Gantt, 1990)	Formal Elements Art Therapy Scale (FEATS) (Gantt & Tabone, 1998)
Ulman Personality Assessment Procedure (UPAP) (Ulman, 1965)	A checklist

Table 11.1 *(Continued)*
Art Therapy Assessments & Corresponding Rating Systems
(NB: Not an exhaustive list)

Art Therapy Assessment Instruments	*Corresponding Rating System (Used in Art Therapy)*
Assessment of Relationship Dynamics	
Bird's Nest Drawing (BND) (Kaiser, 1993)	Manual for Kaiser's Bird's Nest Drawing Checklist (Kaiser, 2009)
Kinetic Family Drawings (Holt & Kaiser, 2001)	FADS training manual
The Kwiatkowska System (Kwiatkowska, 1978)	Scoring system
Landgarten's Family Art Psychotherapy Assessment (Landgarten, 1987)	17 observational points; interactional information
Art Therapy Evaluation for Couples (Wadeson, 1980)	
Cognitive/Neuropsychological and Developmental Evaluation	
Cognitive Art Therapy Assessment (CATA) (Horovitz-Darby, 1988).	Observational guidelines
Face Stimulus Assessment (FSA) (Betts, 2003)	FSA Rating Manual, 1st Edition (Betts, 2010)
Human Figure Drawing (HFD) (Deaver, 2009; Golomb, 1974; Harris, 1963; Koppitz, 1968; Naglieri, 1988)	Five modified FEATS scales (Deaver, 2009)
The Kramer Art Therapy Evaluation (Kramer & Schehr, 1983)	Observational considerations
Levick Emotional and Cognitive Art Therapy Assessment (LECATA) (Levick, 2001)	Scoring manual
House-Tree-Person (HTP) (Buck, 1948; Lopez & Carolan, 2001)	51 formal element indicators (Lopez & Carolan, 2001)
Silver Drawing Test (SDT) (Silver, 1976)	Scoring manual
Tools and Techniques to Address Other Realms of Treatment	
Arrington Visual Preference Test (AVPT) (Arrington, 1986)	Interpretation manual
Art Therapy-Projective Imagery Assessment (AT-PIA) (Raymond, Bernier, Rauch, Stovall, Deaver, & Sanderson, 2010)	Interpretation manual
Belief Art Therapy Assessment (BATA) (Horovitz, 2002)	
Bridge Drawing (Hays & Lyons, 1981)	The Bridge Drawing Rating Manual 2nd Edition (Martin & Betts, 2012)
The Brief Art Therapy Screening Evaluation (BATSE; Gerber, 1996).	
Expressive Therapies Continuum (ETC) (Kagin & Lusebrink, 1978; Lusebrink, 2010)	
Favorite Kind of Day (Manning Rauch, 1987)	Aggression Depicted in the AFKD Rating Instrument (three-item checklist)
Mandala drawing technique (Elkis-Abuhoff, Gaydos, Goldblatt, Chen & Rose, 2009)	Formal elements (color checklist, etc.)
Mandala Assessment Research Instrument (MARI) Card Test (Kellogg, 2002)	Interpretation manual
Pictured Feelings Instrument: A nonverbal vocabulary of feelings (Stone, 2004)	Rating Manual
Road Drawings (Hanes, 1995)	

Domain 1: Psychodiagnosis and Personality Assessment

Shortly following publication of the Feders' 1998 book, Cox, Agell, Cohen, & Gantt's (2000) article *Are you assessing what I am assessing? Let's take a look!* was published in the *American Journal of Art Therapy*. This article is a fascinating read for anyone interested in art therapy assessment. It was a follow-up to two panel presentations at American Art Therapy Association conferences in 1998 and 1999. The objectives of the presentations were to ". . . appreciate the similarities, differences, and unique qualities among three formal art therapy assessments for adults: the Ulman Personality Assessment Procedure (UPAP), the Diagnostic Drawing Series (DDS), and the Person Picking an Apple from a Tree Drawing (PPAT)." These three assessments are subsequently described.

Personality Assessment Procedures. Rather than identifying a diagnostic category to which a patient belongs, the Ulman Personality Assessment Procedure (UPAP; Ulman, 1965) was intended to focus on understanding the dynamics of the patient (Feder & Feder, 1998). Art therapy pioneer Elinor Ulman developed this four-picture series that requires the client to use 18" x 24" grey bogus paper and a set of 12 Nupastels. The consecutive art tasks include: (1) a picture of anything; (2) a kinesthetic drawing (detailed guidelines are provided for this task); (3) a scribble picture; (4) choice of a picture of anything, or another scribble picture. Gladys Agell, former Editor of the *American Journal of Art Therapy,* helped to popularize the UPAP. Rating guidelines are provided, but there is no scoring guide. Application of established rating scales such as those derived from the DDS or FEATS (subsequently discussed) to scoring UPAP drawings would be an interesting contribution to the literature.

Attempts to Standardize Art Therapy Diagnosis. The Feders listed three guiding principles that should be applied when conducting research, when using artwork to diagnose a patient, or to monitor change and progress: normative data should be available to provide a baseline comparison; the administration and scoring procedures should be standardized; and the emphasis should be on form, not content, so as to enable quantification of scoring. These principles are underscored in an important article by Linda Gantt (2004), *The Case for Formal Art Therapy Assessments.* Although these principles are especially important for researchers and diagnosticians, they also bear some relevance for clinicians:

> Change will occur whether a patient is in therapy or not. The central issues are to recognize and identify the nature of change, and to know with some assurance the degree to which such change is the result of therapy, and not coincidental with it. (Feder & Feder, 1998, p. x)

In addition, information mediating variables should also be gathered, including the participant's cultural background, art experience, and perceived art skill. These principles are rooted in two of the most prominent diagnostic procedures used in art therapy: the Person Picking an Apple from a Tree (PPAT; Gantt, 1990) and its corresponding rating system,, the Formal Elements Art Therapy Scale: The Rating Manual (FEATS; Gantt, 1990; Gantt & Tabone, 1998); and the Diagnostic Drawing Series (DDS; Mills, Cohen, & Meneses, 1993; Cohen, Mills, & Kijak, 1994).

The Person Picking an Apple from a Tree (PPAT). The Person Picking an Apple from a Tree (PPAT; Gantt, 1990) assessment was used by Gantt and Tabone (1998) in their attempts to develop the standardized rating procedure, the Formal Elements Art Therapy Scale: The Rating Manual (FEATS). A more in-depth discussion of the FEATS, including a complete literature review of studies that have used or adapted the FEATS, is included in Betts (2012b).

The strength of the PPAT is its utility as a brief art therapy assessment for evaluation of a client's clinical state and his or her response to treatment (Gantt & Tabone, 1998). The FEATS is a rating method that employs interval measurement scales to enable scoring of 14 graphic equivalents of psychiatric symptoms (Figure 11.1), as well as a Content Tally Sheet comprised of dichotomous and categorical scales to collect data on frequency of content found in artwork, such as details of clothing, color use, etc.

Responding to Gantt's (2001) call for more normative research, Bucciarelli (2011) conducted a PPAT study with a sample of 100 nonclient university students. Results confirmed Gantt's (1993) anticipated outcome that the FEATS scores of normative, baseline PPATs would:

> . . . have colors appropriate to the subject matter, would be logical, have a well-integrated composition, show at least the developmental features common to adolescent drawings, have a reasonable amount of detail, color and energy, depict a fairly realistic person, and show a practical way of getting the apple out of the tree. (p. 72)

Bucciarelli's study confirmed many of Gantt's assumptions about nonclient PPATs. The Developmental Level scale was one exception to

Picture #: ________________

Rater: ________________

FORMAL ELEMENTS ART THERAPY SCALE (FEATS)©
RATING SHEET

Linda Gantt, Ph.D., ATR-BC & Carmello Tabone, M.A., ATR

The FEATS uses scales that measure **more or less** of the particular variable. Look at the degree to which a picture fits the particular scale by comparing the picture you are rating with the examples in the illustrated rating manual. **You may mark between the numbers on the scales.** Approach the picture as if you did not know what it was supposed to be. Can you recognize individual items? If you have a picture that is hard to rate, do your best to compare it to the illustrations and the written descriptions. Do not worry whether your rating is the same as another rater's. Concentrate on giving your first impression to the variable being measured.

#1 - Prominence of Color

Color used for outlining only	0 | 1 | 2 | 3 | 4 | 5	Color used to fill all available space

#2 - Color Fit

Colors not related to task	0 | 1 | 2 | 3 | 4 | 5	**Colors related to task**

#3 - Implied energy

No energy	0 | 1 | 2 | 3 | 4 | 5	Excessive energy

#4 - Space

Less than 25% of space used	0 | 1 | 2 | 3 | 4 | 5	100% of space used

#5 - Integration

Not at all integrated	0 | 1 | 2 | 3 | 4 | 5	Fully integrated

#6 - Logic

Entire picture is bizarre or illogical	0 | 1 | 2 | 3 | 4 | 5	Picture is logical

From: L. Gantt & C. Tabone, 1998, *The Formal Elements Art Therapy Scale: The Rating Manual,* Morgantown, WV: Gargoyle Press. Copyright © 1998 Linda Gantt.

Figure 11.1. The Formal Elements Art Therapy Scale (FEATS)© Rating Sheet. Reproduced with permission.

Figure 11.1.–*Continued*

#7 - Realism

Not realistic (cannot tell what was drawn)	0	1	2	3	4	5	Quite realistic

#8 - Problem-solving

No evidence of problem-solving	0	1	2	3	4	5	Reasonable solution to picking apple

#9 - Developmental Level

Two-year-old level	0	1	2	3	4	5	Adult level

#10 - Details of Objects and Environment

No details or environment	0	1	2	3	4	5	Full environment, abundant details

#11 - Line Quality

Broken, "damaged" lines	0	1	2	3	4	5	Fluid, flowing lines

#12 - Person

No person depicted	0	1	2	3	4	5	Realistic person

#13 - Rotation

Pronounced rotation	0	1	2	3	4	5	Trees & people, upright, no rotation

#14 - Perseveration

Severe	0	1	2	3	4	5	None

From: L. Gantt & C. Tabone, 1998, *The Formal Elements Art Therapy Scale: The Rating Manual,* Morgantown, WV: Gargoyle Press.

this, and the study also found that variables including participants' mood, gender, race, and artistic experience were mediating factors in the study results, and warrant further exploration.

Munley (2002) compared the PPATs of five boys between the ages of six and 11 with attention deficit hyperactivity disorder (ADHD) to an age-matched group of five normative boys. Results showed that the drawings of the boys with ADHD had lower scores on three FEATS scales: the Color Prominence scale, the Details of Objects and Environment scale, "reduced control" in Line Quality compared to the control group (p. 74). Although these findings are interesting, they cannot be generalized due to the small sample size of the study.

Rockwell and Dunham (2006) compared the FEATS scores of PPAT drawings administered to a control group of 20 normative adults, and an experimental group of 20 adults with Substance Use Disorder who were either on parole or probation, and had been court ordered to receive counseling. Subjects were closely matched on age, gender, race, socioeconomic status, and education level. Results indicated that three FEATS scales accurately distinguished the two groups: The experimental group scores were lower than the control group scores on the Developmental Level, Realism, and Person scales.

In a study of health risk behaviors, Conrad, Hunter, and Krieshok (2011) collected data from 193 students at a traditional high school and a therapeutic high school. Participants completed the Behavioral Assessment System for Children, Second Edition (BASC-2) measure and two drawings: (1) their perfect romantic date, and (2) a place where they might be exposed to alcohol or drugs. The study sought to explore the psychometric properties and underlying factor structure of the FEATS when used to score the two drawings, and to test the ability of FEATS composite scale scores ". . . to accurately identify adolescents at-risk for emotional and behavioral disturbance as indicated by scores on the self-report BASC-2" (p. 345). Although an exploratory factor analysis supported the use of three reliable FEATS composite scales, the scales were unable to detect between-group differences in students scoring At-Risk on BASC-2 composite scales. These results suggest the need for future research to adequately determine the ability of the FEATS composite scales scores to accurately identify socio-emotional disturbance in adolescents when using drawing techniques such as the two derived for this study.

The Diagnostic Drawing Series (DDS). The Diagnostic Drawing Series (DDS) is a three-picture art interview developed in 1982 by art therapists Barry M. Cohen and Barbara Lesowitz (Cohen, Mills, & Kijak 1994). The materials, administration, collection, and rating of the DDS are standardized, and guidelines are specified in the DDS Handbook (Cohen, 1985). The DDS is comprised of three drawing tasks to be completed on 18" x 24", 60 lb, white sulphite drawing paper with a 12-pack of unwrapped square chalk pastels. When collected for research, a maximum of 15 minutes is allowed for the creation of each picture. However, the full series is usually completed in 20 minutes. The directions for completing a DDS are given one at a time, as each drawing is completed. They are: (1) make a picture using these materials; (2) draw a picture of a tree; and (3) make a picture of how you're feeling, using lines, shapes, and colors. These directions have been translated into Arabic, Dutch, French, German, Japanese, Latvian, and Spanish.

The DDS Rating Guide (Cohen, 1985/1994/2012) and Drawing Analysis Form provide illustrated and clearly defined criteria that address the structure, not the content, of the drawings, influenced by the "form as content" approach of art therapist and psychologist Janie Rhyne. The DDS, designed for use with people 13 years of age and older, was the first art-based assessment to be systematically correlated with the classification system of the *Diagnostic and Statistical Manual of Mental Disorder* (DSM) in the field of art therapy. The Feders wrote in 1998, "the DDS would appear to be a good source of presumptive evidence to be weighed along with other data, either to formulate a diagnostic hypothesis or to corroborate a psychiatric diagnosis" (p. 276), and that has been borne out in the consistency of more than 65 DDS-related studies.

One of the most recognized and widely taught of all art therapy assessments, the DDS entered the published literature in 1985, when it was profiled in the American Psychological Association's newsletter, *Monitor,* and the handbook was made available (Turkington, 1985). The DDS boasts the most concentrated research in the field of art therapy, worldwide. This includes normative studies of 46 *DSM* diagnostic groups, non-*DSM* groups, replications of earlier normative studies, as well as outcome studies. In addition to establishing graphic profile norms for a variety of psychiatric diagnoses through statistical research, the DDS is the first art-based assessment to study the "normal" (non-clinical) adult population, providing empirical data on how adults draw. These efforts to establish norms, and amalgamate the collective results, are a major value of the DDS, according to the Feders.

Over a period of 30 years, much of the research, training, and archiving of DDS projects has been performed by Barry M. Cohen and Anne Mills, director of the DDS Archive. According to them, the strengths of the DDS include its multi-drawing format accomplished with materials and tasks that provide a broad range of graphic expression; compatibility with diverse theoretical approaches; cross-cultural neutrality; Joint Commission recognition; and established reliability and validity as a research instrument. Many art therapists mistakenly think of the DDS only as a tool for assessment and research, but it was also designed to be used by art therapists in their daily clinical work.

The Diagnostic Drawing Series was first published in Holland in 1986 (Cohen, 1986), and continues to be taught and studied in The Netherlands by a network of clinicians, educators, and researchers. The current Dutch national multidisciplinary guidelines for mental health diagnosis and treatment specify that the DDS be used "as an important contribution to the diagnosis of . . . depression, as well as to the multidisciplinary team, as well as for an independent practice/office." Similar specifications are published for diagnosis and treatment of adult patients with a personality disorder (Trimbos Instituut, 2009).

In 1998, Feder and Feder found that the "greatest value" of the DDS "resides in its promise to build a data base for further research" (p. 276). DDS data are continually donated from around the world, and maintained in the DDS Archive in Alexandria, Virginia and are available as a resource for art therapy researchers. After 30 years of use, the DDS Rating Guide and Drawing Analysis Form have recently been revised (Figure 11.2). The current versions of the FEATS and DDS systems, both updated and improved, are reprinted or excerpted here with permission from the respective authors. Thanks to three decades of technological advances, an interactive rating website is under construction, which will aid in the building of a larger database. The first machine learning analysis of DDS data is also underway, building on a successful 1987 expert systems trial using the DDS (Cohen & DeLeo, 1987). Its primary goal is to create an algorithm that will enable trained clinicians rating DDSs online to receive a differential diagnosis report.

Detailed information about the DDS is available in a number of publications, but the definitive resources for information and references to all DDS studies, as well as directions for ordering the DDS ePacket, is

DIAGNOSTIC DRAWING SERIES
Drawing Analysis Form II (DAF2)
©1985/2012 Barry M. Cohen
(Revised 2012 by Barry M. Cohen, ATR-BC and Kathryn Johnson, PhD, ATR)

MARK ONLY ONE ITEM PER CATEGORY FOR EACH PICTURE

Facility/Researcher #			
Subject number			
Rater			
Age			
Gender			
Ethnicity			
Diagnosis			

CATEGORIES	Pic 1 — Free Picture	Pic 2 — Tree Picture	Pic 3 — Feeling Picture
Color	Mono 2-3 4+ Blank	Mono 2-3 4+ Blank	Mono 2-3 4+ Blank
Idiosyncratic Color	No Yes	No Yes	No Yes
Blending	No Yes Overlapping	No Yes Overlapping	No Yes Overlapping
Elements	Line Shape Mix Blank	Line Shape Mix Blank	Line Shape Mix Blank
Line Length	Short Broken Long Blank	Short Broken Long Blank	Short Broken Long Blank
Integration	Disintegr Integr Impov Blank	Disintegr Integr Impov Blank	Disintegr Integr Impov Blank
Tree	Unrecog Chaotic Falling apart None	Unrecog Chaotic Falling apart None	Unrecog Chaotic Falling apart None
Depiction	Abstraction Representation Blank	Abstraction Representation Blank	Abstraction Representation Blank
Edges	Angular Curvilinear Mix Blank	Angular Curvilinear Mix Blank	Angular Curvilinear Mix Blank
Image	Single Multiple Unrelated Blank	Single Multiple Unrelated Blank	Single Multiple Unrelated Blank

	Picture 1	Picture 2	Picture 3
Color type: Mono Two-three Four or more	=m= =t= =f=	=m= =t= =f=	=m= =t= =f=
Blending: No Yes	=n= =y=	=n= =y=	=n= =y=
Idiosyncratic color: No Yes	=n= =y=	=n= =y=	=n= =y=
Line/shape: Line Shape Mix	=l= =s= =m=	=l= =s= =m=	=l= =s= =m=
Integration: Disintegrated Integrated Impov.	=d= =i= =m=	=d= =i= =m=	=d= =i= =m=
{Abstraction: Geometric Biomorphic Mix	=g= =b= =m=	=g= =b= =m=	=g= =b= =m=
{Representational: Angular Curvilinear Mix	=a= =c= =m=	=a= =c= =m=	=a= =c= =m=
Image: Single Multiple Blank	=s= =m= =b=	=s= =m= =b=	=s= =m= =b=

Figure 11.2. Excerpts from the DDS Drawing Analysis Forms (top: 1985; bottom: 2012). Reproduced with permission.

available at: http://ww.diagnosticdrawingseries.com/. There is also a website about the DDS in The Netherlands, which can be accessed at http://www.dedds.nl/index.html.

More on Rating Systems. Betts (2006) outlined important information about scoring systems for art-based data. A rating instrument is "... a scoring procedure that enables the examiner to quantify, evaluate, and interpret ... behavior or work samples" (p. 25). Some art therapy assessments are equipped with a standardized scoring procedure, typically comprised of scales used to determine the extent to which an element is present in a drawing (such as amount of color used in the picture), such as those described with the FEATS and DDS rating systems. The purpose of these scales is to present a variable or formal element with a corresponding scale of categories, and assessors are asked to decide which category most accurately approximates their judgment (Wiersma, 2000). Rating instruments vary in the types of scales that they use for scoring. There are generally four types of scales, each of which has a different degree of refinement in quantifying test variables: nominal (binary/categorical/dichotomous), ordinal, interval (Likert), and ratio (Aiken, 1997). There are varying opinions as to which of these four scales is superior for assessment scoring purposes (Tables 11.2 & 11.3). Betts (2006) addressed this question at length, and concluded that "... the choice should be specific to the instrument's purpose" (p. 425):

> There is no conclusive evidence for using Likert-type versus binary-choice items in rating instruments. The format that best represents the underlying construct you are trying to measure should guide the selection of format. One must define the purpose of the scale, weigh the pros and cons of various format options – including score interpretation – and make the best choice while being aware of the limitations of score interpretation due to format. Both methods – and points of view – have value as long as we realize their limitations as well. (B. Biskin, personal communication, February 22, 2005)

Although there are benefits and drawbacks to the various rating scale formats, some research discussed seems to favor the use of nominal/categorical scales as opposed to ordinal. Feder and Feder explained that the continuous scales of the FEATS are more useful than numeric/dichotomous scales for observing change in patients because

Table 11.2
Features of Rating Scales

Characteristics	*Nominal & Ordinal*	*Interval & Ratio*
Rating time	Shorter	Longer
Inter-rater reliability	Higher (due to more consistency in responses)	Lower (more variability in scores due to more specificity in scales)
Amount of data gleaned	Less (eg., presence or absence of Idiosyncratic Color)	More (5 interval Color Fit scale plus true zero)
Comparison of data in terms of direction or magnitude	Not possible	Possible

Table 11.3
Differences Between Measurement Variables: Implications for Statistical Analysis Procedures

OK to compute. . . .	*Nominal*	*Ordinal*	*Interval*	*Ratio*
Frequency distribution	Yes	Yes	Yes	Yes
Median and percentiles	No	Yes	Yes	Yes
Add or subtract	No	No	Yes	Yes
Mean, standard deviation, standard error of the mean	No	No	Yes	Yes
Ratio, or coefficient of variation	No	No	No	Yes

http://www.graphpad.com/faq/viewfaq.cfm?faq=1089

it is more sensitive to such shifts. However, some researchers have found it to be more difficult to achieve high inter-rater reliability with continuous scales, citing dichotomous and ordinal scales as more efficient in this area.

In addition to the formal elements rating scales, some art therapy assessments also include content checklists (Betts, 2006). These are usually comprised of categorical items that can be checked off as either present or not present in a drawing. For example, the DDS includes a content checklist in its rating system, and the FEATS incorporates a Content Tally Sheet. The rater is required to place a checkmark for all items they see in the picture they are rating, such as, in the case of the PPAT, the number of apples in the image. A checklist can provide useful supplemental information about a drawing.

Other more recent developments in rating artwork include computer programs that are designed to assist in rating formal elements in a manner more efficient than human scoring. Seong-in Kim in South Korea and his colleagues have published prolifically on this topic, too numerous to include here, but the reader is directed to his most recent publication (Kim, Han, Kim, & Oh, 2011). American art therapist Donald Mattson has done similar work (see Mattson, 2012).

The FEATS and the DDS rating systems were both instrumental in establishing the springboard upon which art therapists could look at drawings more systematically, in the contexts of diagnosis and/or research. This is evidenced in the literature published since 1998, especially as pertaining to the Bridge Drawing. This tool was developed by Hays and Lyons (1981) as an art task which directs the client to "draw a bridge going from some place to some place." Hays and Lyons elected to work with a normative adolescent population because this stage of life is typically a tumultuous period, and the Bridge Drawing is conducive to exploration of transitions, including the past, present, and future. The integrated rating system of Bridge Drawing research was explored in a study by Teneycke, Hoshino, and Sharpe (2009). This team investigated artwork characteristics in Bridge Drawings to analyze differences between in-patients ($n = 34$), out-patients ($n = 26$) and a comparison group comprised of mental health workers ($n = 29$). They developed a rating system for the drawings by combining selected rating variable categories from the Diagnostic Drawing Series (DDS) Drawing Analysis Form, the Formal Elements Art Therapy Scale (FEATS) Rating Manual, and from the 12 original Bridge Drawing variables used for interpretation of the drawings. Statistically significant differences between the patients with psychosis and the comparison group were found for: direction of travel, placement of future, prominence of color, use of monochrome, number of colors used, accuracy of color and use of the colors: yellow, green, blue, purple, and brown. These results confirmed that formal element variables in artwork may indicate the presence of psychosis.

In their study of health risk behaviors, Conrad, Hunter, and Krieshok (2011) also found relevance in comparing the Diagnostic Drawing Series (DDS; Cohen, 1985) categorical rating variables to the FEATS scales. These authors attempted a promising task of dichotomizing some of the FEATS scales in their study, having determined that the DDS has acceptable levels of inter-rater reliability using categorical items (Mills, Cohen, & Meneses, 1993), and that several DDS studies have supported its use in distinguishing between-group differences (Cohen, Hammer, & Singer, 1988; Leavitt, 1988; Morris, 1995; Neale, 1994). However, they also found evidence to support the use of continuous rating scales such as the FEATS. Conrad, Hunter, and Krieshok (2011) concluded that the literature on rating systems in art therapy is inconclusive, and that further investigation of formal elements appears to be a promising area.

Based on the previous literature, such as the Teneycke, Hoshino, and Sharpe (2009) study, as well as ongoing research (Councill & Martin, 2012), Martin and Betts (2012) are developing a rating manual for the Bridge Drawing. The manual is currently in its 2nd edition. Several art therapists have done promising work combining the FEATS and DDS rating systems.

Domain 2: Assessment of Relationship Dynamics

Art therapists have distinct tools for examining couples, family, and group dynamics. Four examples of familiar tools are described here, beginning with an overview of the Bird's Nest Drawing (BND; Kaiser, 1996).

Bird's Nest Drawing. Art therapist Donna Kaiser (1996) used the Bird's Nest Drawing in individual and family art evaluation sessions "to enhance therapeutic understanding of existing attachment patterns" (p. 340). Kaiser developed therapeutic interventions based on the nest symbol, and used these in individual, couples, family, and group art therapy to introduce attachment concepts. She found that this process was conducive to increasing her clients' understanding of relationship and intimacy issues, often resulting in their increased self-awareness and insight, promoting healthy attachments and the strengthening of connections to others. Inspired by research on family drawings, The BND is "grounded in attachment theory and seeks to access a person's internal representation of self and other" (Kaiser & Deaver, 2009, p. 26). As such, this assessment can provide clinically useful information about a client's attachment security, which influences the development of the therapeutic relationship and has implications for treatment planning.

Kaiser and Deaver (2009) published a salient review of BND research. They examined and summarized the contributions of five BND studies: Kaiser's (1996) investigation of 41 mothers and their BNDs to examine indications of attachment theory; Overbeck's (2002) study of 32 high-risk pregnant women's BNDs; Hyler's (2002) examination of 49 children's BNDs (ages 9–11) as representations of attachment; Francis, Kaiser and Deaver's (2003) study of attachment security representations in the BNDs of clients with substance abuse disorders ($n = 43$) to determine whether they would depict BNDs differently than patients in a comparison group who had no known substance abuse disorders ($n = 27$); and Trewartha's (2004) exploration of the attachment strategies of 14 adolescents in foster care. Among other conclusions, Kaiser and Deaver (2009) found that these five studies provided valuable data for art therapists to aid in their clinical assessment of attachment. Kaiser (2009) regularly updates the BND Manual and rating scales based on newly accumulated research data and as informed by clinical observations.

Family Art Therapy Assessment

Similar to techniques used in group therapies, family art therapy assessment protocols provide a way in which to determine family dynamics, not to assess personality or diagnose patients per se. Family drawings provide the foundation for discussion of family relationships, and the outcomes include integrated results derived from the drawings themselves as well as the individual family members' interpretations of their drawings, the behavioral interactions of the family members as they created joint drawings, and their perceptions of each members' assumed roles during the procedure.

Hanna Yaxa Kwiatkowska and Helen Landgarten were cited by the Feders as the main developers of assessment systems for families, and today these two systems appear to have retained their prominence.

The Kwiatkowska System. Among other accolades, Hanna Yaxa Kwiatkowska (1910–1980) pioneered clinical work in family art therapy and introduced art therapy in the research program at the National Institute of Mental Health. She developed the Family Art Evaluation (FAE), which typically consists of a single meeting with all available nuclear family members (Kwiatkowska, 1978). The average time needed for the evaluation session is one and one-half to two hours, but this is flexible. Only semihard square-edged pastels are used for the FAE. Some of the procedures are similar Ulman's UPAP assessment. The FAE includes six successive activities: (1) a free picture (no subject is assigned); (2) a picture of your family; (3) an abstract family portrait; (4) a picture started with the help of a scribble; (5) a joint family scribble; and (6) a free picture.

In an effort to create this standardized tool, Kwiatkowska developed a scoring system. However, as with other assessments, and as discussed by the Feders, art therapists seem to have adopted and adapted the technique but have tended to neglect the scoring procedure, using it essentially as a structured clinical interview.

Landgarten's Family Art Task. Helen Landgarten (1921–2011) was an art psychotherapy clinician at the Thalians Community Mental Health Center-Cedars-Sinai Hospital, Los Angeles, and Chair of the Loyola Marymount University art therapy department until 1988. She developed a tool known as the "Family Art Task" or "Family Art Diagnostic" (Landgarten, 1987). To assess the family system, the participants are invited to engage in three art tasks: (1) team art that is made in silence;

(2) the entire family working together, maintaining the nonverbal stance; and (3) the entire family creating a single piece of artwork, with permission to speak to each other. The Feders cited Landgarten's assessment as a "structured clinical evaluation" (1998, p. 279). They explained: "While Landgarten called the exercise a 'standardized method' of assessment (1987, p. 14), she apparently referred only to the structure of the procedure, since there are no norms involved and the interpretations are qualitative and intuitive." As has been established in this chapter, however, there is clinical utility in such evaluation procedures. With application of 17 observational points, Landgarten's tasks provide the therapist with direct interactional information about the family dynamics.

Assessment of Couples

Wadeson (1980) employed three techniques to assess ". . . the complex intermeshing of expectations and interactions arising out of perceptions of self, spouse, and the marital relationship" (p. 285). Established materials for this evaluation procedure include 18" x 24" paper and thick pastels in a wide variety of colors. Couples are asked to complete a Joint Picture, an Abstract of the Marital Relationship, and a Self-Portrait Given to Spouse. The art therapist then facilitates a discussion of the artwork and process with the couple, encouraging them to ". . . reflect upon their feelings while making the pictures and their associations while looking at them" (p. 285). Although no published research has been located on this approach to couples assessment, some qualitative papers have demonstrated promising outcomes for applications of Wadeson's techniques, such as Snir and Hazut's (2012) study of couple patterns reflected in joint paintings.

Domain 3: Cognitive/Neuropsychological and Developmental Evaluation

The Feders astutely included a section on "Cognitive and Developmental Evaluation," to distinguish these types of evaluations from others covered in this chapter. Although there is a wide overlap between these realms of assessment, procedures designed to address cognitive skills or intelligence are usually categorized separately from those that are known as developmental evaluations. A developmental evaluation is one that generally issues a global judgment about clients with a cognitive, emotional, and/or physical developmental delay.

According to the Feders, another approach to developmental art therapy assessment is based on the observations of Erikson and Piaget. With a focus on determining developmental levels for educational planning purposes, these assessments seek to derive more behaviorally-based manifestations of developmental stages as opposed to constructs such as intelligence.

Four cognitive and developmental tools are discussed below: The Silver Drawing Test of Cognitive Skills and Adjustment (SDT; Silver, 1976); the Face Stimulus Assessment (FSA; Betts, 2003); Human Figure Drawings (HFDs; Deaver, 2009; Golomb, 1974; Harris, 1963; Koppitz, 1968; Naglieri, 1988); and the Levick Cognitive and Emotional Art Therapy Assessment (LECATA; Levick, 1983). Two other developmental tools are also summarized.

The Silver Drawing Test of Cognitive Skills and Adjustment (SDT; Silver, 1976). Crehan (1992, in Feder & Feder, 1998) found that the SDT had mixed to low concurrent validity, suggesting that the tool may be measuring a construct other than that which it is intended to measure. Crehan also determined that the norms were based on small, convenience samples, and that descriptions of the data collection methods were not described. Since 1998, the peer-reviewed literature has included a few additional articles on Rawley Silver's assessments. In 2003, Silver published a paper summarizing cultural differences and similarities in responses to the Silver Drawing Test in the USA, Brazil, Russia, Estonia, Thailand, and Australia. In 2009, an article authored by Silver on her work in identifying children and adolescents with depression presented a review of the Stimulus Drawing Task and Draw A Story Research. This summary of the literature determined that drawing responses that are strongly negative (receiving of a score of one out of a total possible five points) on the Emotional Content and the Self-Image scales can aid in early identification of children and adolescents who may be at risk for depression.

The Face Stimulus Assessment. The FSA (Betts, 2003) was created to determine the abilities of children with communication disorders and developmental disabilities, including autism, to help establish treatment goals and determine client progress. Betts recognized a need to incorporate methods that would elicit clients' strengths through art, and found support for her ideas in Silver (1976) and Stamatelos and Mott

(1985). Silver (1976) noted that even if a client's capacity for language was severely impaired, his or her ability to symbolize might be intact nonetheless, since higher-level cortical functioning can advance even without language. Stamatelos and Mott (1985) addressed the creative potential of clients with developmental delay, and asserted that the use of symbolic processes and abstract thought occur in these individuals. Over the course of four years, Betts developed the three-picture drawing series that comprises the FSA. The first image presents the client with a standardized stimulus image of a face on 8½" x 11" white paper; the second presents the outline of the face and neck only; and the third, a blank piece of paper. The regular set of Crayola markers and a set of the Crayola Multicultural markers are provided to the client, who is invited to "use the markers and this piece of paper" (Betts, 2003, p. 81). Betts (2003, 2009, 2012c) and others (Hamilton, 2008; Hu et al., 2012; Robb, 2002; Soon Ran Kim, 2010) have explored the use of the FSA, and more research is underway.

Soon Ran Kim (2010) conducted the largest scale FSA study to date. In order to develop and validate an evaluation method for the FSA, 921 potential participants were identified from the elementary school system in South Korea, and 296 nonnormative and 240 normative student drawings were analyzed. The nonnormative sample was comprised of 144 students with a developmental disorder and 152 with a hearing impairment. Results showed that the FSA evaluation method developed in this study was able to discriminate between the normative and nonnormative groups. The author concluded that the FSA evaluation method she employed demonstrated success in evaluating the cognitive abilities of the children with developmental disabilities and hearing impairment. Further research will contribute to the FSA's validity and reliability in determining client cognitive abilities and developmental levels. The FSA packet (Betts, 2010) is available from the author (http://www.art-therapy.us/FSA.htm).

The Levick Emotional and Cognitive Art Therapy Assessment (LECATA; Levick, 1983). If conceived of as a standardized test rather than a structured clinical interview, the Feders claimed that there were not sufficient empirical data supporting the LECATA as an evaluation procedure. The Feders further indicated that Levick faced a "formidable task" in finding a substantial enough population with which to attempt validation (1998, p. 282). Levick (2009) met this challenge, and, as discussed in Betts (2011, p. 147), amalgamated her collective normative results in a volume that reflects steps taken toward the arduous goal of establishing modern-day norms for childhood developmental indicators in artwork.

The LECATA (Levick, 1983) is a criterion-referenced test that compares chronological age to performance on five standardized art tasks: (a) a free art task and story about it, (b) a drawing of the self, (c) a scribble using one color and a picture created from the scribble, (d) a place where one would like to be (for children 3–5 years old) or a place that is important (for children 6–11 years old and older), and (e) a family, which taken together are intended to provide information about an individual's cognitive and emotional abilities.

As described in Betts (2011, p. 148), cognition and emotion are broad domains that are difficult to define and measure, and may be confounded by cultural differences. Levick (2009) justified application of these two domains by referring to the "considerable data collected to support the reliability of the criteria for cognitive indicators and the defense mechanisms of the ego as manifested in drawings" (p. 26), but such data are not directly cited. Additional justification for use of the cognition and emotion domains is provided by Sholevar (1984), who reviewed Levick's use of these theories as the basis for the LECATA. Sholevar wrote that connecting ego defense mechanisms to stages of development is challenging because "there is great difference in the literature as to which defense mechanism belongs to which stage" (p. 45), but also that identifying the defense mechanisms enables profitable understanding of art products. Despite this support for the application of cognitive indicators and the defense mechanisms of the ego in the LECATA, peer-reviewed research of these constructs would improve this assessment's validity.

The Kramer Art Therapy Evaluation. The primary purpose of "The Kramer" (Kramer & Schehr, 1983) is to provide information about the child client's developmental level, although, based on the detailed outline of observational considerations, the evaluation is also very applicable for treatment planning. The child is directed in a series of three open-ended tasks, using pencils and markers, then paint, and finally, clay. Following administration, the art therapist should engage the client in a discussion about the art and the process. Observational considerations include character of the art works, the child's attitudes during the session, and other pertinent information including whether any learning took place, whether the child would be a good candidate for art therapy services, etc.

Human Figure Drawings. HFDs (Deaver, 2009; Golomb, 1974; Harris, 1963; Koppitz, 1968; Naglieri, 1988) were discussed in the 1998 version of this book, in Chapter 7, *Projective Approaches in Assessment.* HFDs have been highly criticized in the psychology literature, as is discussed at length in Betts (2006) and Groth-Marnat (2009). The criticisms derive largely from the outdated dictionary approach to interpretation. Despite these criticisms, however, many clinicians still use these tools, and some interesting research has been published in the art therapy literature, assigning scores based on formal elements in the artwork, as opposed to symbol interpretation.

Deaver (2009) undertook an impressive effort to establish and expand the research on normative children's drawings in the United States using the HFD. In her 2009 study, Deaver studied the HFDs of 316 fourth graders (mean age 9.69 years) and 151 second graders (mean age 7.56 years). The drawings were scored with five scales modified from the FEATS (Gantt & Tabone, 1998): Scale I (Prominence of Color); Scale II (Color Fit); Scale III (Space); Scale IV (Developmental Level); and Scale V (Details of Objects and Environment).

Deaver's application of the FEATS scales to rate HFDs is an important departure from the traditional methods of scoring these drawings:

> Koppitz and Naglieri, as well as many other researchers, focused solely on measuring the presence or absence of specific aspects of the drawn human figure, such as arms, hair, nose, and so forth (Groth-Marnat, 1999), and did not attempt to measure formal artistic elements of the drawings such as color or the amount of space the drawing occupies on the paper. (Deaver, 2009, p. 5)

Data for Deaver's study were analyzed according to the variables of gender, age, ethnicity, and mean scores on each of the five scales, yielding some interesting findings. As would be expected, second graders used significantly more color and space in their drawings, typical of younger children's use of bold color and less refined motor skills. Regarding the Details of Objects and Environment scale, it was formerly thought that as children age and become increasingly aware of their surroundings their drawings reflect more details (Lowenfeld & Brittain, 1987; Naglieri, 1988). However, contrary to this belief, Deaver found that the second grade children's drawings had a significantly higher mean score ($M = 3.08$, $SD = 1.24$) on this scale than the fourth graders ($M = 2.37$, $SD = 1.32$) ($t = 5.6$, $p < .01$). On the Developmental Level scale, fourth graders scored significantly higher ($M = 3.25$, $SD = 0.66$) than second graders ($M = 3.00$, $SD = 0.59$) ($t = 4.0$, $p < .01$), which corresponds with Lowenfeld's stages of artistic development. Gender differences were only significantly different on the Color Fit scale, reflecting girls' more realistic use of color than boys. Ethnicity did not demonstrate any significant main effect (all p values $> .01$).

Packman, Beck, VanZutphen, Long, and Spengler (2003) used the HFD to measure siblings' emotional distress toward bone marrow transplants. Qualitative and quantitative findings were derived from the HFDs of 42 participants, ages six to 18 years, including data from case vignettes of four siblings. The art therapists who scored the drawings using Koppitz's objective criteria also provided qualitative comments on the HFDs when they noted certain features of the drawing that might not have been detected by Koppitz's system. Among the siblings, feelings of isolation, anger, depression, anxiety, and low self-esteem emerged as major themes.

Hagood (2003) conducted a longitudinal of the Naglieri Draw-a-Person Test (DAP; Naglieri, 1988), a measurement of normal drawing development in children, for its appropriateness for use by art therapists. Participants included 34 primary school children, ages 5 to 10. A total of 306 man, woman, and self drawings were collected over a one-year period, in three phases. Three age groups were composed as follows: Primary One (ages 5 to 6, $n = 12$), Primary Three (ages 7 to 8, $n = 10$), and Primary Five (ages 9 to 10, $n = 12$). Hagood maintained the use of Naglieri's original scoring system. Scores increased by age and over time, as predicted by the investigator. No significant gender differences were found. The Naglieri DAP was deemed to be a useful tool for art therapists in the assessment of cognitive development as well as for research purposes.

Other Developmental Tools. The Feders mentioned a few variations of developmental art therapy evaluations, such as Aach-Feldman and Kunkle-Miller's (1987) system, which uses a Piagetian model to focus on sensorimotor and preoperational developmental stages. These refer ". . . to the client's choice of media, activity, and theme as well as the content of the drawing. The therapist gathers information about the client's level of skill and organization, response to media properties, and his or her capacity to express affect" (p. 283). Williams and Wood (1977) discussed a tool in their book about developmental art therapy, also cited by the Feders. The Williams and Wood tool is a developmental rating scale for children with emotional, intellectual and physical impairments to aid as a guide in planning an individualized educational program.

Domain 4: Tools and Techniques to Address Other Realms of Treatment

Assessments and techniques that don't fit neatly into one of the aforementioned domains are included here. These tools and methods can be used for treatment planning, to address the presenting problem, goals of therapy, and other aspects of the clinical process. Formal and informal (nonstandardized) tools, including portfolio review, are considered part of this domain. To validate these tools and approaches, a review of the Feders' three guiding principles is in order: normative data should be available to provide a baseline comparison; the administration and scoring procedures should be standardized; and the emphasis should be on form, not content, so as to enable quantification of scoring. Even if not used for formal research for assessments and techniques used for clinical purposes, these guidelines provide the clinician with ways to validate their conclusions. As the Feders pointed out, some art therapists are not interested in diagnosis, and feel disinclined to use scoring systems. Some assessments and procedures are then often used as semi-structured clinical interviews or techniques for stimulating conversation, with modifications to the tools' administration and the interpretation. In such instances, the tests are no longer used as diagnostic or personality tests.

The Expressive Therapies Continuum. Lusebrink (2010) cited The Expressive Therapies Continuum (ETC) as "a theoretical model for art-based assessments and applications of media in art therapy" (p. 168). The three levels of the ETC (Kinesthetic/Sensory, Perceptual/Affective, and Cognitive/Symbolic) seem to parallel different brain structures and functions that process affective and visual information. As such, the ETC can be used as a framework for aiding the art therapist in determining how a client processes information. In treatment, transitions within and between the ETC levels can be monitored. Lusebrink advocated for application of the ETC as a means to enhance art therapy interventions and contribute to research on art therapy and the brain.

The Bridge Drawing. Originally intended as a "projective technique for assessment in art therapy," The Bridge Drawing (Hays & Lyons,

1981) is a good example of a technique which has lacked in standardization of materials and a consistent rating system, but which has been used by art therapy clinicians as a tool helpful in treatment planning and measuring client progress in treatment. The various applications of the Bridge Drawing have included: to determine the features of drawings of normative adolescents experiencing difficult change (Hays & Lyons, 1981); to explore adolescents' transitions between childhood and adulthood, their independence and identity (Stepney, 2001); to examine resiliency in homeless youth (Prescott, Sekendur, Bailey, & Hoshino, 2008); to determine formal elements of bridge drawings in patients with psychosis (Teneycke, Hoshino, & Sharpe, 2009); to examine the weekly progress of clients with eating disorders and assess readiness for termination (Betts, 2008); to explore the transitions, strength of support systems, threats experienced, and potential suicidal ideation of incarcerated women who have experienced the death of a loved one (Ferszt, Hayes, DeFedele, & Horn, 2004); and, to determine suicide risk among adult psychiatric patients (Martin, Betts, Warson, & Lorance, 2012). Use of the Martin and Betts (2012) Bridge Drawing Rating Manual (2nd Edition) in future research, and standardization of the Bridge Drawing's administration (consistent use of art materials, etc.), will contribute to validation of the instrument.

Other tools and techniques to address other realms of treatment used by art therapists are numerous, and some of these are included in Table 11.1.

CONCLUSION

In 1998, Bernard and Elaine Feder inquired, "How do you know what's working?" As responsible practitioners, we should continue to ask ourselves this significant question. Embracing the art and science of evaluation in our respective arts therapies professions is a means to achieve this. Further development of the International Art Therapy Research Database (IATRD; www.arttherapyresearch.com) is one way art therapists can engage in research of a scale larger than previously possible.

Regardless of where one practices creative arts therapies evaluation procedures, we have a duty to improve our methods through sound research. As discussed in this chapter, in different parts of the world, societal issues such as health care have impacted the development and use of assessments in art therapy. However, as this chapter has established, one has only to return to the Feders' wisdom, and consider developments over the past 15 years, ". . . the argument over whether art therapy is an art or a science is not only fruitless but counterproductive; it can only perpetuate divisions in a field in which both artistic creativity and scientific validation are necessary" (1998, p. vii). It is not a matter of "sitting beside" versus "a more distant calculation," both approaches will continue to be integrated and embraced for the furtherance of the creative arts therapies and the benefit of the public whom we serve. As the current approaches discussed in this chapter reflect, art and science coexist, and future work will continue to propel the fields forward.

Author's Note: Information about art therapy assessments is available at: http://www.art-therapy.us/assessment.htm.

REFERENCES

Aach-Feldman, S., & Kunke-Miller, C. (1987). A developmental approach to art therapy. In J. A. Rubin (Ed.), *Approaches to art therapy* (pp. 251–274). New York: Brunner/Mazel.

AERA (American Educational Research Association), APA (American Psychological Association) & NCME (National Council on Measurement in Education). (1999). *Standards for educational and psychological testing.* Washington, DC: American Educational Research Association.

Aiken, L. R. (1997). *Psychological testing and assessment* (9th ed.). Boston: Allyn & Bacon.

Arrington, D. (1986). *The Arrington Visual Preference Test (AVPT) and Manual.* Belmont, CA: Abbeygate Press.

Betts, D. J. (2003). Developing a projective drawing test: Experiences with the Face Stimulus Assessment (FSA). *Art Therapy: Journal of the American Art Therapy Association, 20*(2), 77–82.

Betts, D. J. (2005). *A systematic analysis of art therapy assessment and rating instrument literature.* Doctoral dissertation, Florida State University, Tallahassee. Published online at http://www.art-therapy.us/assessment.htm.

Betts, D. J. (2006). Art therapy assessments and rating instruments: Do they measure up? *The Arts in Psychotherapy: An International Journal, 33*(5), 371–472.

Betts, D. J. (2008). Art therapy approaches to working with people who have eating disorders. In S. Brooke (Ed.), *The creative therapies and eating disorders.* Springfield, IL: Charles C Thomas.

Betts, D. J. (2009). Introduction to the Face Stimulus Assessment (FSA). In E. G. Horovitz & S. Eksten (Eds.), *The art therapists' primer: A clinical guide to writing assessments, diagnosis, and treatment.* Springfield, IL: Charles C Thomas.

Betts, D. (2010). *The Face Stimulus Assessment (FSA) E-packet.* Self-published manual, Department of Art Therapy, George Washington University, Washington, DC.

Betts, D. J. (2011). Review of the book *Levick Emotional and Cognitive Art Therapy Assessment: A Normative study,* by M. F. Levick. *Art Therapy: Journal of the American Art Therapy Association, 28*(3), 147–148.

Betts, D. J. (2012a). Positive art therapy assessment: Looking towards positive psychology for new directions in the art therapy evaluation process. In A. Gilroy, R. Tipple & C. Brown (Eds.), *Assessment in art therapy* (pp. 203–218). New York: Routledge.

Betts, D. J. (2012b). Art therapy assessments: A general and historical overview. In M. L. Rosal & D. Gussak (Eds.), *The Wiley-Blackwell handbook of art therapy.* Manuscript accepted for publication.

Betts, D. J. (2012c). A fair assessment: Art therapy approaches in the evaluation of diverse populations. In P. Howie, S. Prasad & J. Kristel (Eds.), *Using art therapy with diverse populations: Crossing cultures and abilities.* London: Jessica Kingsley. Manuscript in preparation.

Betts, D. J., Gantt, L., & Lorance, J. (2011, July). *The International Art Therapy Research Database: Introducing an innovative and essential resource.* Paper presented at the 42nd Annual AATA conference, Washington, DC.

Bornstein, R. F. (2002). A process dissociation approach to objective – projective test score interrelationships. *Journal of Personality Assessment, 78*(1), 47–68.

Bornstein, R. F. (2009). Heisenberg, Kandinsky, and the heteromethod convergence problem: Lessons from within and beyond psychology. *Journal of Personality Assessment, 91*(1), 1–8.

Bucciarelli, A. (2011). A normative study of the Person Picking an Apple from a Tree (PPAT) assessment. *Art Therapy: Journal of the American Art Therapy Association, 28*(1), 31–36.

Buck, J. N. (1948). The H-T-P technique, a qualitative and quantitative scoring manual. *Journal of Clinical Psychology Monograph Supplement, 4,* 1–120.

Buros (n.d.). *The Buros Institute of Mental Measurements: About.* http://buros.unl.edu/buros/jsp/search.jsp.

Chapman, L. J., & Chapman, J. P. (1967). Genesis of popular but erroneous psychodiagnostic observations. *Journal of Abnormal Psychology, 72*(3), 193–204.

Cohen, B. M. (Ed.). (1985). *The diagnostic drawing series handbook.* Self-published manual, Alexandria, VA.

Cohen, B. M. (Ed.). (1985; 1994; 2012). *The diagnostic drawing series rating guide.* Self-published manual, Alexandria, VA.

Cohen, B. M. (1986). Een nieuwe tekentest [A new diagnostic test – Dutch]. Psychologie, Amsterdam, April.

Cohen, B. M., & Cox, C.T. (1995). *Telling without talking: Art as a window into the world of multiple personality.* New York: W.W. Norton.

Cohen, B., & DeLeo, J. (1987, November). *Teaching computers to diagnose? Computer generated learning and Diagnostic Drawings Series research.* Poster session presented at the 18th annual meeting of the American Art Therapy Association, Miami, FL.

Cohen, B. M., Hammer, J. S., & Singer, S. (1988). The Diagnostic Drawing Series: A systematic approach to art therapy evaluation and research. *The Arts in Psychotherapy, 15*(1), 11–21.

Cohen, B. M., Mills, A., & Kijak, K. (1994). An introduction to the Diagnostic Drawing Series: A standardized tool for diagnostic and clinical use. *Art Therapy, 11*(2), 105–110.

Conrad, S. M., Hunter, H. L., & Krieshok, T. S. (2011). An exploration of the formal elements in adolescents' drawings: General screening for socio-emotional concerns. *The Arts in Psychotherapy: An International Journal, 38,* 340–349.

Councill, T., & Martin, K. (2012, July). *Assessment research in pediatric oncology: Making the Bridge Drawing measurable.* Paper presented at the 43rd Annual AATA conference, Savannah, GA.

Cox, C. T., Agell, G., Cohen, B. M., & Gantt, L. (2000). Are you assessing what I am assessing? Let's take a look! *American Journal of Art Therapy, 39,* 48–67.

Crehan, K. D. (1992). Review of Silver Drawing Test of Cognitive Skills and Adjustment. In J. J. Kramer & J. C. Conoley (Eds.), *Eleventh mental measurements yearbook.* Lincoln, NE: Buros Institute of Mental Measurement.

Dalley, T. (Ed.). (1984). *Art as therapy.* London, England: Tavistock.

Dawson, C. F. S. (1984). *A study of selected style and content variables in the drawings of depressed and nondepressed adults.* Unpublished dissertation, University of North Dakota, Grand Forks, ND.

Deaver, S. P. (2009). A normative study of children's drawings: Preliminary research findings. *Art Therapy: Journal of the American Art Therapy Association, 26*(1), 4–11.

DRPF Consults. (2012). Retrieved from http://drpfconsults.com/understanding-the-basics-of-stem-education/.

Dudley, J. (2004). Art psychotherapy and the use of psychiatric diagnosis. *Inscape, 9*(1), 14–25.

Elkis-Abuhoff, D., Gaydos, M., Goldblatt, R., Chen, M., & Rose, S. (2009). Mandala drawings as an assessment tool for women with breast cancer. *The Arts in Psychotherapy: An International Journal, 36,* 231–238.

Feder, B., & Feder, E. (1998). *The art and science of evaluation in the arts therapies: How do you know what's working?* Springfield, IL: Charles C Thomas.

Ferszt, G. G., Hayes, P. M., DeFedele, S., & Horn, L. (2004). Art therapy with incarcerated women who have experienced the death of a loved one. *Art Therapy: Journal of the American Art Therapy Association, 21*(4), 191–199.

Finn, S. E. (2009). *How is Therapeutic Assessment different from other types of psychological assessment?* Retrieved April 5, 2010, from http://therapeuticassessment.com/about.html.

Fischer, C. T. (2001). Collaborative exploration as an approach to personality assessment. In K. J. Schneider, J. F. T. Bugenthal & J. F. Pierson (Eds.), *The handbook of humanistic psychology: Leading edges in theory, research and practice.* Thousand Oaks, CA: Sage.

Francis, D., Kaiser, D., & Deaver, S. P. (2003). Representations of attachment security in the Bird's Nest Drawings of clients with substance abuse Disorders. *Art Therapy: Journal of the American Art Therapy Association, 20*(3), 125–137.

Gantt, L. M. (1986). Systematic investigation of art works: Some research models drawn from neighboring fields. *American Journal of Art Therapy, 24*(4), 111–118.

Gantt, L. M. (1990). *A validity study of the Formal Elements Art Therapy Scale (FEATS) for diagnostic information in patients' drawings.* Unpublished doctoral dissertation, University of Pittsburgh, Pittsburgh, PA.

Gantt, L. M. (1993). Correlation of psychiatric diagnosis and formal elements in artwork. In F. J. Bejjani (Ed.), *Current research in arts medicine: A compendium of the MedArt International 1992 World Congress on Arts and Medicine* (pp. 69–74). Pennington, NJ: A Cappella Books.

Gantt, L. M. (1998). A discussion of art therapy as a science. *Art Therapy: Journal of the American Art Therapy Association, 15*(1), 3–12.

Gantt, L. M. (2001). The Formal Elements Art Therapy Scale: A measurement system for global variables in art. *Art Therapy: Journal of the American Art Therapy Association, 18*(1), 50–55.

Gantt, L., & Tabone, C. (1998). *The Formal Elements Art Therapy Scale: The Rating Manual.* Morgantown, WV: Gargoyle Press.

Gantt, L. M. (2004). The case for formal art therapy assessments. *Art Therapy: Journal of the American Art Therapy Association, 21*(1), 18–29.

Gerber, N. (1996). The Brief Art Therapy Screening Evaluation (BATSE). Unpublished manual, PhD Program in Creative Arts Therapies, Drexel University, Philadelphia, PA.

Gilroy, A., Tipple, R., & Brown, C. (Eds.). (2012). *Assessment in art therapy.* New York: Routledge.

Goodenough, F. (1926). *Measurement of intelligence by drawings.* New York: World Book.

Golomb, C. (1974). *Young children's sculpture and drawing.* Cambridge, MA: Harvard University Press.

Groth-Marnat, G. (1990; 1999; 2003; 2009). *Handbook of psychological assessment* (2nd, 3rd, 4th & 5th editions.). New York: John Wiley & Sons.

Hagood, M. M. (2003). The use of the Naglieri Draw-a-Person Test of Cognitive Development: A study with clinical and research implications for art therapists working with children. *Art Therapy: Journal of the American Art Therapy Association, 20*(2), 67–76.

Hamilton, M. (2008). *Developing a standardized rating system for the Face Stimulus Assessment (FSA) using 12 scales adapted from the Formal Elements Art Therapy Scale (FEATS)* (Unpublished master's thesis). Avila University, Kansas City, MO.

Hanes, M. J. (1995). Utilizing road drawings as a therapeutic metaphor in art therapy. *American Journal of Art Therapy, 34*(1), 19–23.

Harris, D. (1963). *Children's drawings as measures of intellectual maturity.* New York: Harcourt, Brace & World.

Harris, D. B., & Roberts, J. (1972). Intellectual maturity of children: Demographic and socioeconomic factors. *Vital & Health Statistics, Series 2,* 1–74.

Hays, R. E., & Lyons, S. J. (1981). The Bridge Drawing: A projective technique for assessment in art therapy. *Arts in Psychotherapy, 8*(3-sup-4), 207–217.

Holt, E. S., & Kaiser, D. H. (2001): Indicators of familial alcoholism in children's Kinetic Family Drawings. *Art Therapy: Journal of the American Art Therapy Association, 18*(2), 89–95.

Horovitz-Darby, E. G. (1988). Art therapy assessment of a minimally language skilled deaf child. Proceedings from the 1988 University of California's Center on Deafness Conference: *Mental Health Assessment of Deaf Clients: Special Conditions,* Little Rock, AR: ADARA.

Horovitz, E. G. (2002). *Spiritual art therapy: An alternate path* (2nd ed.). Springfield, IL: Charles C Thomas.

Horovitz, E. G., & Eksten, S. (Eds.). (2009). *The art therapists' primer: A clinical guide to writing assessments, diagnosis, and treatment.* Springfield, IL: Charles C Thomas.

Hu, V., Betts, D., Jenkins, R., Lieberman, D., Potolicchio, S., Subiaul, F., Choi, J., & Kelly, B. (2012). *Identifying and assessing "biological phenotypes" of autistic individuals based on medication responsiveness for "reverse pharmacogenomics" analyses.* Manuscript in preparation.

Hyler, C. (2002). *Children's drawings as representations of attachment.* Unpublished master's thesis, Eastern Virginia Medical School, Norfolk, VA.

Kahill, S. (1984). Human figure drawing in adults: An update of the empirical evidence, 1967–1982. *Canadian Psychology, 25*(4), 269–292.

Kaiser, D. (1996). Indications of attachment security in a drawing task. *The Arts in Psychotherapy: An International Journal, 23*(4), 333-340.

Kaiser, D. H. (2009). *Manual for Kaiser's Bird's Nest Drawing Checklist.* Self-published manual, Creative Arts Therapies Department, Drexel University, Philadelphia, PA.

Kaiser, D. H., & Deaver, S. P. (2009). Assessing attachment with the Bird's Nest Drawing: A review of the research. *Art Therapy: Journal of the American Art Therapy Association, 26*(1), 26–33.

Kaplan, F. (2000). *Art, science and art therapy: Repainting the picture.* Philadelphia: Jessica Kingsley.

Kellogg, J. (2002). *Mandala: Path of beauty* (3rd ed.). Belleair, FL: ATMA, Inc.

Kim, S., Han, J., Kim, Y., & Oh, Y. (2011). A computer art therapy system for Kinetic Family Drawings (CATS_FKD). *The Arts in Psychotherapy, an International Journal, 38*(1), 17–28.

Kim, S. R. [Soon Ran] (2010). *A study on development of FSA evaluation standard and its validation* (Unpublished doctoral dissertation). Yeungnam University, Daegu, South Korea.

Klopfer, W. G., & Taulbee, E. S. (1976). Projective tests. *Annual Review of Psychology, 27*(54), 3–567.

Koppitz, E. M. (1968). *Psychological evaluation of children's human figure drawings.* New York: Grune and Stratton.

Kramer, E., & Schehr, J. (1983). An art therapy evaluation session for children. *American Journal of Art Therapy, 23,* 3–11.

Kwiatkowska, H. Y. (1978). *Family therapy and evaluation through art.* Springfield, IL: Charles C Thomas.

Landgarten, H. B. (1987). *Family art psychotherapy: A clinical guide and casebook.* New York: Brunner/Mazel, Inc.

Leavitt, C. G. (1988). *A validity study of the Diagnostic Drawing Series used for Assessing depression in children and adolescents.* Doctoral dissertation, California School of Professional Psychology, Los Angeles, CA.

Levick, M. F. (1983). *They could not talk and so they drew: Children's styles of coping and thinking.* Springfield, IL: Charles C Thomas.

Levick, M. F. (2009). *Levick Emotional and Cognitive Art Therapy Assessment: A normative study.* Bloomington, IN: AuthorHouse.

Lopez, J. R., & Carolan, R. (2001). House-Tree-Person drawings and sex offenders: A pilot study. *Art Therapy: Journal of the American Art Therapy Association, 18*(3), 158–165.

Lowenfeld, V., & Brittain, W. L. (1987). *Creative and mental growth* (8th ed.). New York: Collier Macmillan.

Lusebrink, V. B. (2010). Assessment and therapeutic application of the Expressive Therapies Continuum: Implications for brain structures and functions. *Art Therapy: Journal of the American Art Therapy Association, 27*(4), 168–177.

MacGregor, J. M. (1989). *The discovery of the art of the insane.* Princeton, NJ: Princeton University Press.

Manning, T. M. (1987). Aggression depicted in abused children's drawings. *The Arts in Psychotherapy: An International Journal, 14,* 15–24.

Martin, D. J., Garske, J. P., & Davis, M. K. (2000). Relation of the therapeutic alliance with outcome and other variables: A meta-analytic review. *Journal of Consulting and Clinical Psychology, 68*(3), 438–450.

Martin, K., & Betts, D. J. (2012). *The Bridge Drawing Rating Manual* (2nd ed.). Art Therapy Program, The George Washington University, Washington, DC.

Martin, K., Betts, D. J., Warson, E., & Lorance, J. (2012). *The Bridge Drawing: An evaluation tool for suicide risk among adult psychiatric patients.* Manuscript in preparation.

Mattson, D. C. (2012). An introduction to the computerized assessment of art-based instruments. *Art Therapy: Journal of the American Art Therapy Association, 29*(1), 27–32.

Metzl, E. S. (2008). Systematic analysis of art therapy research published in Art Therapy: Journal of AATA between 1987 and 2004. *The Arts in Psychotherapy: An International Journal, 35,* 60–73.

Mills, A., Cohen, B., & Meneses, J. Z. (1993). Reliability and validity tests of the Diagnostic Drawing Series. *The Arts in Psychotherapy: An International Journal, 20,* 83–88.

Morris, M. B. (1995). The Diagnostic Drawing Series and the Tree Rating Scale: An isomorphic representation of multiple personality disorder, major depression, and schizophrenia populations. *Art Therapy: Journal of the American Art Therapy Association, 12,* 118–128.

Munley, M. (2002). Comparing the PPAT drawings of boys with AD/HD and age-matched controls using the Formal Elements Art Therapy Scale. *Art Therapy: Journal of the American Art Therapy Association, 19*(2), 69–76.

Murray, H. A. (1943). *Thematic Apperception Test.* Cambridge, MA: Harvard University Press.

Naglieri, J. (1988). *Draw A Person: A quantitative scoring system.* San Antonio, TX: The Psychological Corporation.

Neale, E. L. (1994). The Children's Diagnostic Drawing Series. *Art Therapy: Journal of the American Art Therapy Association, 11,* 119–126.

Neale, E., & Rosal, M. L. (1993). What can art therapists learn from the research on projective drawing techniques for children? A review of the literature. *The Arts in Psychotherapy: An International Journal, 20,* 37–49.

Noble, G. R. (1991, February). Director's update. *CDC HIV/AIDS Newsletter.*

Overbeck, L. (2002). *A pilot study of pregnant women's drawings.* Unpublished master's thesis, Eastern Virginia Medical School, Norfolk, VA.

Packman, W. L., Beck V. L., VanZutphen, K. H., Long, J. K., & Spengler, G. (2003). The Human Figure Drawing with donor and nondonor siblings of pediatric bone marrow transplant patients. *Art Therapy: Journal of the American Art Therapy Association, 20*(2), 83–91.

Prescott, M. V., Sekendur, B., Bailey, B., & Hoshino, J. (2008). Art making as a component and facilitator of resiliency with homeless youth. *Art Therapy: Journal of the American Art Therapy Association, 25*(4), 156–163.

Raymond, L., Bernier, M., Rauch, T., Stovall, K., Deaver, S., & Sanderson, T. (2010). *The Art Therapy-Projective Imagery Assessment* (rev. ed.). Unpublished manual, Graduate Art Therapy and Counseling Program, Eastern Virginia Medical School, Norfolk, VA.

Roback, H. B. (1968). Human figure drawings: Their utility in the clinical psychologist's armamentarium for personality assessment. *Psychological Bulletin, 70*(1), 1–19.

Robb, M. (2002). Beyond the orphanages: Art therapy with Russian children. *Art Therapy: Journal of the American Art Therapy Association, 19*(4), 146–150.

Rockwell, P., & Dunham, M. (2006). The utility of the Formal Elements Art Therapy Scale in assessment for substance use disorder. *Art Therapy: Journal of the American Art Therapy Association, 23*(3), 104–111.

Rorschach, H. (1921). *Psychodiagnostics: A diagnostic test based on perception.* Oxford, England: Grune & Stratton.

Russell-Lacy, S., Robinson, V., Benson, J., & Cranage, J. (1979). An experimental study of pictures produced by acute schizophrenic subjects. *British Journal of Psychiatry, 134,* 195–200.

Silver, R. A. (1976). Using art to evaluate and develop cognitive skills. *American Journal of Art Therapy, 16,* 11–19.

Silver, R. (2003). Cultural differences and similarities in responses to the Silver Drawing Test in the USA, Brazil, Russia, Estonia, Thailand, and Australia. *Art Therapy: Journal of the American Art Therapy Association, 20*(1), 16–20.

Silver, R. (2009): Identifying children and adolescents with depression: Review of the Stimulus Drawing Task and Draw A Story research. *Art Therapy: Journal of the American Art Therapy Association, 26*(4), 174–180.

Snir, S., & Hazut, T. (2012). Observing the relationship: Couple patterns reflected in joint paintings. *The Arts in Psychotherapy: An International Journal, 39,* 11–18.

Snyder, C. R., Ritschel, L. A., Rand, K. L., & Berg, C. J. (2006). Balancing psychological assessments: Including strengths and hope in client reports. *Journal of Clinical Psychology, 62*(1), 33–46.

Stepney, S. A. (2001). *Art therapy with students at risk.* Springfield, IL: Charles C Thomas.

Stamatelos, T., & Mott, D. W. (1985). Creative potential among persons labeled developmentally delayed. *The Arts in Psychotherapy: An International Journal, 12,* 101–113.

STEAM EDU (2012). Retrieved from http://www.steamedu.com/.

Stone, B. A. (2004). *Pictured Feelings Instrument, A Nonverbal Vocabulary of Feelings.* Melbourne, AU: Australian Council for Educational Research (ACER).

Suinn, R. M., & Oskamp, S. (1969). *The predictive validity of projective measures: A fifteen-year evaluative review of research.* Springfield, IL: Charles C Thomas.

Swensen, C. H. (1968). Empirical evaluations of human figure drawings: 1957–1966. *Psychological Bulletin, 70*(1), 20–44.

Teneycke, T. L., Hoshino, J., & Sharpe, D. (2009). The Bridge Drawing: An exploration of psychosis. *The Arts in Psychotherapy: An International Journal, 36,* 297–303.

TIES (2012). Retrieved from http://www.tiesteach.org/stem-education.aspx.

Trewartha, S. (2004). *Attachment strategies of adolescents in foster care: Indicators and implications.* Unpublished master's thesis, Eastern Virginia Medical School, Norfolk, VA.

Trimbos Instituut (Netherlands Institute of Mental Health and Addiction) (2009). DDS. Richtlijnherziening van de Multidisciplinaire richtlijn DEPRESSIE (eerste revisie) (Diagnostic Guidelines for Depression) (p. 144). Retrieved from http://www.cbo.nl/thema/Richtlijnen/Overzicht-richtlijnen/Richtlijnen-A-t-m-D/?p=402.

Turkington, C. (1985). Therapist seeks correlation between diagnosis, drawings. *APA Monitor, 16*(4), 34–36.

Ulman, E. (1965). A new use of art in psychiatric diagnosis. *Bulletin of Art Therapy, 4,* 91–116.

Wadeson, H. (1980). *Art psychotherapy.* New York: John Wiley & Sons.

Wadeson, H., & Carpenter, W. (1976). A comparative study of art expression of schizophrenic, unipolar depressive, and bipolar manic-depressive patients. *Journal of Nervous and Mental Disease, 162*(5), 334–344.

Wells, J. G. (2006). *VT STEM Curriculum Class.* In M. O. Class (Ed.). Blacksburg, VA.

Wiersma, W. (2000). *Research methods in education: An introduction* (7th ed.). Boston: Allyn and Bacon.

Williams, G. H., & Wood, M. M. (1977). *Developmental art therapy.* Baltimore: University Park Press.

Yakman, G. (2008). STΣ@M Education: An overview of creating a model of integrative education. Unpublished manuscript, Virginia Polytechnic and State University, Pulaski, VA.

Chapter 12

EVALUATION AND ASSESSMENT IN DANCE/MOVEMENT THERAPY

Among the creative arts therapies, dance/movement therapy (DMT) is unique – therapists' and clients' bodies – are the medium for therapy. The fact that therapist and client are mobile and active in the therapy space, lends immediacy to the work. The therapist's observation skills are an important key to managing this immediacy. In addition to managing important issues of safety in the session, the observation of clients' changes in movement, posture, integration of body parts, et cetera, create and guide the interventions the therapist uses. Observing movement and the body is so important to the practice DMT that it has been described this way: "the ongoing assessment of the client's movement is the counterpart of 'listening' by traditional verbal psychotherapists" (Cruz, 2006, p. 133).

This ongoing assessment of movement in sessions and the more formal assessment of movement for evaluation purposes in DMT are different, but quite related issues as this chapter will reveal. At the heart of both are reliability and validity challenges that can have very different arguments and outcomes. While formal analysis systems that can be used clinically or for research in DMT are rather few, this chapter will address issues around observation and interpretation of movement, brief reviews of movement observation tools, and in-depth description of several selected assessment and evaluation tools.

MOVEMENT OBSERVATION TRAINING

Underscoring the importance of movement observation to the practice of DMT, movement observation courses are required in both types of training vetted by the Dance/Movement Therapy Certification Board (DMTCB) for the initial credential, Registered Dance/Movement Therapist (R-DMT). The two types of training are American Dance Therapy Association approved training programs and training via Alternate Route courses and programs. Alternate Route courses and programs are not required to be housed within accredited universities. Regardless of the type of training, the required movement observation courses take place over the equivalent of two semesters and instructors are not specifically required by DMTCB to teach any particular movement observation system. However, most movement observation courses use elements of Laban Movement Analysis (LMA) to some extent. Laban Movement Analysis is the modern term for a system originally devised by Rudolph Laban for describing the visible dynamics of movement. Over the years, it was developed further by a number of Laban's students, most notably Warren Lamb and Irmgard Bartenieff.

> Laban's system was influential in the development of assessment in DMT in that it provides both a vocabulary and a lens for focusing on the dynamic qualities of movement. Laban, a dancer and architect developed an elaborate theory of movement, techniques of movement observation, and a system of notating movement that spread through Europe after World War II. He had many students who carried his work to England and America where his theories had a profound effect on dance and dance education (Thornton, 1971). His system of observation and notation makes a key distinction between describing the spatial and dynamic aspects of movement apart from the actions performed, seeking to convey the qualities with which movement is performed. These qualities in turn impart feeling tones to movement. This distinction between spatial/dynamic aspects and action is important because it allows analysis of movement behavior apart from action so it can be used to describe functional and expressive movement as well as posture and the body at rest. (Cruz, 2006, p. 135)

LMA was introduced as an important tool early on in the professionalization of the field of DMT (Bartenieff, 1972). A description of LMA will be presented later in this chapter, yet for now it suffices to say that LMA offers a shared movement language for dance/movement therapists. As Bartenieff described it, "it compares to the *jargon* of craftsmen who can understand each other about the intricacies of their particular medium and the technicalities to handle crude and subtle detail by having their specific terms," (p. 69). While "The basic concepts of the LMA system including effort, shape, space, and body context serve as a basis for diverse movement observation scales created by dance/movement therapists" (p. 135) not all movement assessments used in DMT were influenced by this system.

ASSESSMENT IN PROFESSIONAL DMT PRACTICE

Definitions of the terms assessment and evaluation can be found in several places in this volume. For the purposes of this chapter brief definitions are that the term *evaluation* is usually used to refer to a process aiming to determine growth or development as a result of treatment; *assessment* describes a process that takes place prior to treatment. In the case of DMT, assessment actually takes place in every session as described briefly above, and guides what transpires in sessions.

In addition to training requirements of the Dance/Movement Therapy Certification Board, the American Dance Therapy Association holds dance/movement therapists to several principles about assessment beginning with the Code of Ethical Practice which states: "A dance/movement therapist is qualified to engage in assessment of clients for the purpose of diagnosis, treatment planning, and/or research," (http://www.adta.org/Resources/Documents/ADTA%20Code%20of%20Ethics%202010.pdf; p. 1). The code of ethics is used with the Ethical Standards of Practice which includes the following information relevant to assessment.

> PRINCIPLE 11: EVALUATION/ASSESSMENT: For the purposes of diagnosis, treatment planning, and/or research, a dance/movement therapist may engage in assessment of clients utilizing only those instruments and techniques for which he or she has been trained.
>
> A. Assessment instruments and assessment practices may include verbal or nonverbal techniques, or a combination of both.
>
> B. Research must be conducted in a manner that abides by the basic elements of informed consent including disclosure of purpose, duration and nature of the research, participation incentives, the right

> to participate or withdraw, identified informational contact person and confidentiality procedures.
>
> Research must be conducted in compliance with all applicable legal and professional guidelines and in full compliance with institutional review board or governmental regulations.
>
> Research data must be maintained, stored, and used in a manner which fully maintains participant's anonymity and must be reported in a manner which minimizes the possibility of misinterpretation. (http://www.adta.org/Resources/Documents/ADTA%20Code%20of%20Ethics%202010.pdf; p. 4)

In addition to the Code of Ethics and Ethical Standards of Practice, the American Dance Therapy Association's Approval Committee specifies that students attending approved programs be taught methods for observing, analyzing, and assessing movement as part of the curriculum. The DMTCB similarly specifies that students using the alternate route to DMT train (90 hours) in a systematized method of observing, assessing and evaluating movement and list this as a basic DMT competency (http://www.adta.org/Resources/Documents/R-DMT%20Applicant%20Handbook%2012.21.11.pdf). While training in a specific system is not required, instructors are expected to have expertise in a movement observation system.

The inclusion of movement observation in required training and ethical standards of professional practice is interesting in the lack of specificity of the requirements. While some ADTA approved programs offer in-depth LMA-based movement observation programs in addition to their DMT programs, the ADTA curricular requirements for approved programs are nonspecific. This allows graduate programs to describe and deliver their movement observation courses in terms that go beyond LMA. Powell (2008) listed several examples taken from available course syllabi across academic programs. Two sample descriptions are reproduced below for comparison and the differences between them are notable.

> In this course students look at how the mind is expressed through the body. The focus is placed on gathering the basic terms and concepts necessary to cultivate the skill of seeing the body descriptively both in stillness as well as in motion. A range of observation and assessment models specific to dance/movement therapy and body psychotherapy is introduced: including morphological, developmental, energetic, segmented, process-oriented and archetypal frameworks. (Powell, 2008, p. 33)

> This course introduces students to movement observation and analysis within the framework of Laban Movement Analysis. In experiential and didactic frameworks, students will examine personal, relational, cultural, and societal dynamics as manifested in movement behavior. Therapeutic implications for both individuals and groups will be discussed. (Powell, 2008, p. 33)

Given the professional focus on using observational assessment and the variation possible in training programs and courses it is relevant to ask what dance/movement therapists actually use in practice and how they use it. But data are limited on the clinical use of assessments by dance/movement therapists. One study from the U.K. (Karkou & Sanderson, 2001) found that 41 respondents surveyed reported not using established movement analysis tools such as the Kestenberg Movement Profile and criticized such tools as too complicated for clinical practice. Powell (2008) surveyed U.S. and international dance/movement therapists, and while a low response rate (6%; $N = 62$) resulted, respondents largely reported using a LMA-based formal assessment tool and about half reported also using tools that they developed themselves. Interesting in these studies was the implied difference between formal and informal assessments by respondents. Formal assessments were criticized in the U.K. study, but were reported to be used in the U.S. study. Dance/movement therapists who responded to these surveys seemed to make a very realistic distinction between what is possible in practice and formal tools that are available.

It is difficult to draw any conclusions from either study due to the low response rates of both, but it is interesting to speculate about why surveys on practice and assessment in particular fail to garner sufficient samples when such data could provide useful information for the profession. Powell (2008) pointed out the need for standardized methods of movement analysis in DMT related to establishing it as an evidence-based practice, and Karkou and Sanderson (2001) also framed their discussion around the issue of evidence-based practice. The call for more research leading to more recognition of DMT is common in the literature and certainly standardizing how assessment is used and what assessments are used can be seen as a key to moving the profession forward. However assessment in DMT is complex because of what is being assessed (body and movement), informal versus formal assessment, and a range of issues related to the objectivity, reliability, and validity of movement assessments. Some of these issues have been noted historically and more recently (McCoubrey, 1987; Chang, 2006; Chang, 2009; Caldwell & Johnson, 2012; Cruz & Koch, 2012) and will be explored in this chapter.

THE LANGUAGE OF MOVEMENT

As mentioned previously, Laban provided descriptive language for movement that has provided a base for many of the observation systems used in DMT. As described by Feder and Feder (1998):

> Of far more interest to dance/movement therapists is Laban's work in the qualitative analysis of movement in terms of how movement is performed and how effort can be analyzed in terms of its components: space, weight, time, and flow. The system has been modified by a number of others, particularly Irmgard Bartenieff, who combined Laban's analysis of effort with Warren Lamb's (1965) concept of shaping. The resultant blend is known as Laban Movement Analysis (LMA). . . . (p. 288)

Bartenieff (1972) described effort/shape as a "group of concepts that deal with movement process, with fluctuations and modifications of the stream of movement events or rather movement behavior" (p. 69). Laban's distinction between action and dynamics helps to convey the qualities with which movement is performed (Foroud & Whishaw, 2006). These qualities in turn impart feeling tones to movement. This distinction between spatial and/or dynamic aspects and action allows a broad analysis of movement behavior that can be used to describe functional and expressive movement (Foroud & Whishaw, 2006) as well as posture and the body at rest. As theorized by Lamb (1965) and Bartenieff (1980), there are common features to all movement that fall into four broad categories, effort, shape, body, and space. These categories make up the basic components of LMA that are useful for dance therapists.

Effort Elements. The effort elements are flow, weight, time, and space. Each element represents a continuum with two polarities as anchors described below. No value judgments are attached to any descriptors.

- Flow – aliveness, variations in bodily tension, ease or restraint of movement
  - Free: going with, allowing energy to go through and beyond body boundaries.

- Bound: restricted, controlled; keeping energy flow within body boundaries.
- Weight – sense of self, assertion of self – force or pressure exerted in movement.
  - Light: rarified, delicate, fine touch, overcoming one's weight.
  - Strong: having impact, penetrating, getting behind one's weight; (distinguished from passive giving into gravity or heaviness).
- Time – compensation to outward time demands, attitude toward duration of action.
  - Sustained: stretching out time, leisurely, actively indulging in time; decision in time (distinguished from slow motion or evenness of bound flow).
  - Sudden: urgent, instantaneous, a sense of urgency recreated each time; decision in time (distinguished from fast or tempo increase).
- Space – attention or orientation to reality – how energy is focused in action.
  - Indirect: multi-overlapping foci, multi-faceted attention, active meandering.
  - Direct: channeled, pin-pointing.

Shape Elements. These elements are organized in a developmental progression of increasing adaptability to and access to space.

- Shape flow – body oriented shape change for example, the movement of a newborn.
- Directional movement – environment oriented shape change that is goal oriented, going to a location or final end point, for example, locomotion of toddlers beginning to walk.
- Shaping – environment oriented shape change that is process oriented and forms the space or adapts to space and the environment, carving, molding, and sculpting.

Body. Coordination of body parts and sequencing of movement through the body from initiation to completion are noted in this category.

Space. In this category a mover's pathways through space both in terms of form and design are noted.

Supplemental concepts. A number of supplemental concepts may also be used such as planes, kinesphere, body attitude, proximity, eye contact, and facial expressivity.

Notation is available for these descriptors and one example, is depicted below.

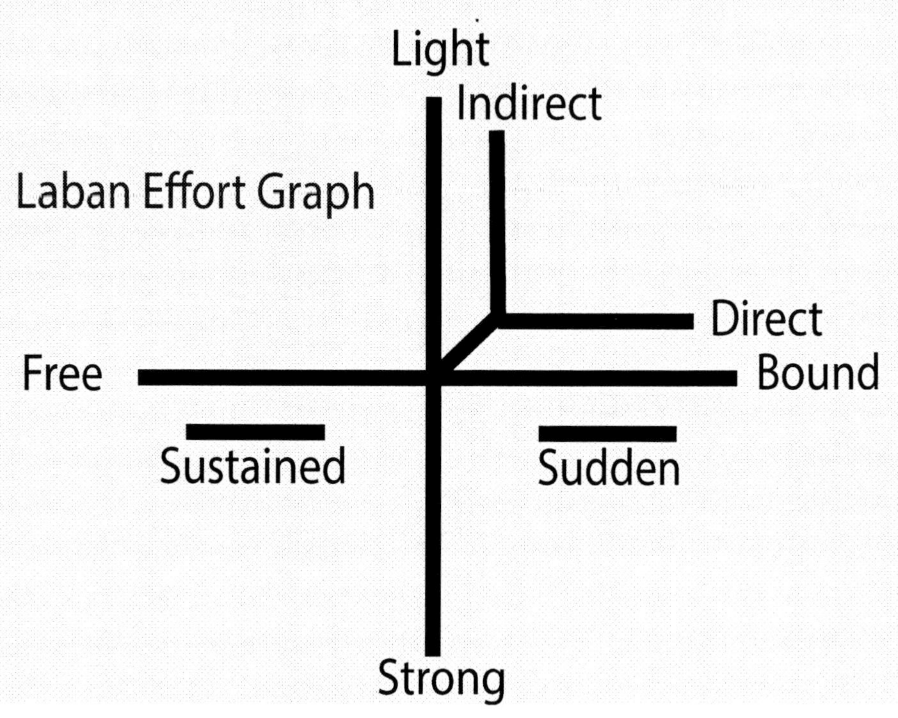

Fig. 12.1. Example of LMA Effort and Shape Notation.

As a basic system for describing movement, LMA has recently begun to be noticed outside dance and DMT in neurology and neuroscience (Foroud & Whishaw, 2006) where systems for describing movement rather than using set terms for particular types of movement disorder have been lacking (Cruz, 1995). Interestingly, even in nonverbal behavior research, an area that also studies movement, the "vast majority of nonverbal behavior research does not actually focus on movement, but on stable body positions such as postures and gestures (eyebrow lifts, eye contact, folded arms, nose wipe)," (Winter, 1992, p. 155). A possible sign of change is a recent study published in the *Journal of Nonverbal Behavior* focused on expression of emotion that used LMA (Gross, Crane, & Fredrickson, 2010). Nevertheless, the use of LMA in dance/movement therapy training, practice, and research remains fairly unique among behavioral and medical sciences.

LMA is accompanied by some theoretical formulations. Bartenieff (1980) theorized that access to the full continua of effort and shape elements was descriptive of healthy movement – preferred personal patterns of effort and shape elements notwithstanding, and judgments of effort elements as "good" or "bad" as irrelevant. There has been no definitive study to test Bartenieff's theory of healthy movement, although, certain practical arguments may be made. For example, it is as necessary to be able both to swing a rope up to a tree branch with free flow, as it is to carry a hot cup of liquid with bound flow in order not to spill it. Movement tasks in diverse living environments require access to the full range of shape and effort elements for success. However the forces of personal history and culture have impact on both expressive and functional movement, and in addition the body structure develops according to its use.

Cross-cultural applications for LMA were initially advanced by ethnologist Alan Lomax and his colleagues such as Ernestine Paulay and Bartenieff. They did this via Choreometrics, a dance movement analysis system they developed that included LMA, at Columbia University in the 1960s (Bartenieff, 1980). The purpose of the project was to identify cultural patterns in movement, both intra-cultural (individual differences) and styles that are part of a tradition. This work involved gathering and analyzing documentary film footage from many different sources and produced four films. However, this work was viewed as controversial by dance scholars, in particular, the conclusions and research methods Lomax used (Kealiinohomoku, 2003). It is unclear if Lomax's anthropological studies over time became confused with the potential of LMA to "universally" describe movement dynamics by dance/movement therapists, a postulation that has never specifically been examined. Yet, while systematic inquiries of cross-cultural applications are lacking, the topic has not been ignored in DMT (see for example, Kestenberg-Amighi, Pinder, & Kestenberg, 1992).

Considering Multiculturalism and Diversity

Of the many social changes that have taken place in the U.S. since DMT became professionalized, two are worth attention to add context and depth to this discussion on the language of movement and movement observation. The first is the spread of DMT from the U.S. and U.K. to countries around the world. Much of this growth has taken place as international students flocked to universities in the U.S. in particular, to study DMT and then returned to their home countries. Additional influence resulted from U.S. teachers who traveled to countries outside the U.S. to assist in developing DMT programs or to teach courses and workshops to interested individuals. Some have also cited the International Panel included at annual ADTA conferences since 1994 as an influence on the international growth of the profession (Berger & Dulicai, 2005). Berger and Dulicai (2005) documented the development of DMT in 37 countries and described a vibrant and diverse international scene for the profession. Related to this growth, the ways and degree to which DMT has been re-conceptualized to fit with non-Western cultures is currently unknown but of interest. As pointed out by Chang (2009), "historically, the clinical theories and models for dance/movement psychotherapy have been based on western European and North American concepts of mental health," (p. 301). This bears not only on international development, but also on the increased attention to multiculturalism in the U.S.

While cross-cultural counseling competencies were formally advised as early as 1982 by the American Counseling Association (Sue et al., 1998), as time has progressed and as the recognition of diversity in the U.S. has continued to expand, multicultural competencies have come to be viewed as a vital element of psychotherapy training and practice. In 2008, the Board of Directors of American Dance Therapy Association voted to include a new clause addressing commitment to diversity to the Code of Ethics. Then, in 2011 the Multicultural and Diversity Committee was formally added to the bylaws of ADTA and its chairperson to the Board of Directors, signifying new and renewed dedication on the part of members to addressing issues of multiculturalism and diversity in the profession. These formal acts of recognition reflect current discussions within the profession, a profession that in the U.S. has been historically largely composed of white, heterosexual women.

As stated by Caldwell and Johnson (2012), "People who embody social difference (such as class, gender identity, sexual orientation, ability, and ethnicity) have been systematically abused by the viewpoints of people who occupy the current social norms. In this discourse, 'difference' quickly becomes 'deficit'" (p. 122). They also point out that viewpoints that can be damaging to others can be so internalized in the observer as to be unconscious. In a similar vein, Chang (2006) pointed out that the social and cultural contexts for DMT treatment are "never neutral" (p. 193). Hanna (2012) suggested that research was needed to "moderate" misunderstandings that could result from using "traditional" DMT "perspectives" with individuals of other cultures and groups (p. 169). These perceptions have bearing on both how DMT is practiced and how movement observation as a part of practice and research need new illumination. "How the movement is seen by others and what meaning they and the mover attach to the movement" (Chang, personal communication June 18, 2012) becomes highlighted when social justice issues are brought to inform DMT. Further, differences in perception and attention, causal inference, and organization of knowledge – to name just a few aspects – between cultures (Nisbett, 2003) have implications for DMT. As Chang described it, "in my experience, Korean students in my case study literally saw dance differently than I did, and interpreted the dance/movement very differently" (personal communication, June 18, 2012).

Where does this leave DMT and movement observation? Possibly, rather than the LMA system itself which frankly consists of descriptive language for movement dynamics, problems arise cross-culturally and multiculturally both in what is observed and when interpretations are applied. The qualities described impart feeling tones to movement and while it is natural to interpret these feeling tones, it is the interpretations that may harbor judgments more related to the observer's 'difference' from the observed person. The assumption that access to the full continua of effort indicates health also falls into the traditional DMT perspectives described by Hanna. As attention to social difference has increased and as DMT has spread to countries around the world – questioning the assumptions, historical models, and tools for observing and interpreting movement are now more relevant and more urgent for this profession than ever before.

CLASSIC PROBLEMS AND PITFALLS IN MOVEMENT OBSERVATION

With specific reference to LMA, McCoubrey (1987) explained that the observer's own inner attitudes and preferences in movement can be provoked or get in the way of objectively observing others' movement. While McCoubrey related this to the issue of reliability, it also influences the validity of observations. Cruz and Koch (2012) offered these standard definitions of reliability and validity,

> What does it really mean to speak of the validity and reliability of movement observations and scales? In simple terms, *validity* is the de-

> gree to which an observation scale measures what it is supposed to measure (precision), while *reliability* is defined as the consistency or accuracy of the scores that result from the observation measurement process. (pp. 49–50)

They then went further by describing the subjectivity of movement observations, difficulties presented by the fleeting nature of movement, and the potential to enact perceptual biases, including the fact that humans have a tendency "to change patterns to fit what they are used to seeing or what they expect to see" (p. 50). While their focus was on addressing these issues to increase the reliability and validity of movement observations for research purposes, many aspects of their discussion are applicable to clinical observation.

In an expanded discussion on normative assumptions about the body, Caldwell and Johnson (2012) presented the validity issue in terms used by Davis and Markus (2006) – encoding and decoding – and offered this expansion on McCoubrey's (1987) point:

> There is a prevailing assumption, for instance, that the greatest movement repertoire correlates to the greatest psychological health, that simultaneous core and distal initiation is healthier, and that coordinated, complex, and coherently interrelated movement is associated with psychological health (Cruz, 2009; Davis, 1970; Burn, 1987). While these correlations may be robust, how we operationalize them and enact them clinically in diverse settings becomes crucial. Between an observation that a client is carving space or sinking in a certain plane, and a dance therapy intervention that relates to that observation, comes a decoding process that cannot avoid being filtered through both one's personal history as well as institutionalized biases internalized by the dance therapy field itself. (p. 128)

As should be obvious from the discussion so far, the need for dance/movement therapists to question assumptions and uncover unconscious assumptions about interpretations of movement behaviors and observations is critical. While asking clients to describe their subjective experiences of moving may be helpful (Caldwell & Johnson, 2012) the difficulty of finding words to describe one's experience may be the very thing that has led the client to DMT. In fact, the ability to work on inner material without initially having to find words for it is a well-known characteristic of DMT. Without claiming a solution to the problems described thus far with respect to movement observation, several relevant points can be made.

The first is that in DMT sessions, the therapist needs to be observing in order to respond therapeutically in the moment and maintain safety in the session. Clinical work has been compared with research in that the therapist develops "hypotheses" and tests these hypotheses in the session (Chaiklin & Chaiklin, 2012). The therapist's observations and the interventions they introduce (for example, complementing or contrasting the quality observed, or intensifying or lessening the quality) have results in the immediate response of the client that informs the therapist of the correctness or incorrectness of his or her formulation. These successes and failures, when noted by the therapist, create material for supervision and for future work with the client. It remains the responsibility of the therapist to work to uncover his or her assumptions (internalized and otherwise) to address work with the client to the best of his or her ability and to assist the client to describe his or her subjective experience of the work when possible. Specifically addressing clinical work Cruz and Koch (2012) stated,

> When working clinically, dance/movement therapists need to be especially aware of how their own biases affect their movement observations. In this situation the therapist usually has access to historical and other information about the client that can bias his or her judgments of their movement behaviors, or create *observer contamination* (Borg & Gall, 1983). (p. 55)

A second point is that research in the field is needed to probe assumptions and even address methods of assisting dance/movement therapists in uncovering internalized or unconscious perceptions that can negatively impact on clients. These methods need to be incorporated in training, and more attention likely needs to be paid to standardizing elements such as uncovering unconscious perceptions in movement observation training and after training when dance/movement therapists are working professionally. In an important early paper on dance therapy training, Schmais (1972) pointed out that students "must be fully aware of their own movement repertoire; the consistent features that cut across contexts, the movements that are just below the surface and crop out when defenses are dropped, the movements that occur when angry or depressed" (p. 84). This early advice is even more important to address in training and professional practice today.

A final point is that while there have been many efforts over time to use movement observations to diagnose or locate "patterns" of movement common to diagnostic groups (for example, Burn, 1987; Goodman, 1991), advances in neuroscience indicate that these have to be associated to motor system dysfunction rather than to patterns of voluntary movement. As stated by Cruz and Koch (2012),

> . . . understanding important distinctions about the motor system can be very helpful in making movement assessments (Ropper & Brown, 2005; Cruz, 2009). For example, the distinction between movement characteristics that are produced by dysfunction of the extrapyramidal motor system associated with psychopathology since the latter part of the 19th century (Cruz, 2009) and other types of movement. Distinguishing between abnormal voluntary and involuntary movements based in neurological dysfunction and other types of movement patterns is germane for all movement assessment. (p. 53)

A neuroscience focus on abnormal voluntary and involuntary movements may offer an area of clarity in movement observation. For example, Foroud and Wishaw (2006) were able to use LMA to characterize kinematic and nonkinematic movement changes in reaching in patients who had suffered a stroke. They found that LMA was "sensitive to both severity and the location of the stroke" (p. 146) and recommended it for diagnosis and assessment. They described the application of LMA in their research,

> During the reaching-to-eat task, the kinematic structure (Body and Space) of movements work to support the action while the non-kinematic movements (Effort and Shape) are economized so as to minimize work effort. The kinematic structure of movement is the movement of the body through space – this creates the 'scaffolding' for movement that is the functional element of any task. While non-kinematic features of movements appear to be more qualitative and expressive, there are actions that benefit from an increase in non-kinematic movements. (p. 146)

From the DMT perspective, currently only the Movement Psychodiagnostic Inventory (MPI; Davis, 1991), which will be described in some detail later in this chapter, has been specifically investigated with respect to the neurological system and movement disorder (Cruz, 1995, 2009).

OVERVIEW OF MOVEMENT ANALYSIS SYSTEMS

All of the movement assessment systems that will be discussed require training, and some require very intensive training from someone who is an expert in the system. Some analysis systems are more appropriate as clinical tools and others may be more appropriate for evaluation of the type used in research. Most of them have not been standardized or used with normative groups. Some systems are rather complex; for example, the Kestenberg Movement Profile (KMP) and the Movement Psychodiagnostic Inventory (MPI) demand quite a lot of the rater, even after the rater training is completed. In a study of novice KMP raters who had 45 hours of training, Koch, Cruz, and Goodill (2001) found that raters had more difficulty observing some rhythms over others. In another study, Cruz (1995) found that raters who differed in level of experience with the MPI (expert, experienced, and novice) showed marked differences in agreement indicating how level of training with an assessment tool can affect ratings. The KMP and the MPI are systems that are difficult to use clinically. For example, Davis, Lausberg, Cruz, Berger, and Dulicai (2007) estimated the time for a trained rater to complete the MPI via a 30-minute videotape of an individual at three to four hours; and Koch and Müller (2007) estimated the time to complete a KMP profile for one individual including interpretations at "a full working day" (p. 195). Shorter versions of both the KMP and MPI for some clinical uses have been developed and will be described below when each of these tools is described more fully. Of course, training in the system is required even for these brief versions, and they may not be applicable with all populations as will be discussed.

Few of the movement assessment systems presented here offer comparative data on the individual assessed with regard to others from the same group or population. That is because it requires extensive study with large groups of individuals to compare one individual's performance with what is "typical" of others. A listing of movement observation tools from the DMT literature is given in Table 12.1 (revised from Cruz, 2006). As stated earlier, not all DMT movement analysis systems are based on LMA and Table 12.1 indicates which systems have LMA influence and which do not. Of the assessments listed, only the Body Movement Scale of the Behavior Rating Instrument for Autistic and Atypical Children (Kalish, 1976) was developed with a relatively small sample of normative data. Mark Sossin (2002) reported working to create developmental norms for children on the KMP, but they not widely available yet. Developing large samples of individuals rated by more than one trained rater to examine validity and reliability features requires financial resources that can be scarce for dancc/movement therapists.

The listing in Table 12.1 is not exhaustive, but includes tools that have been published or used in research. The use of many of these tools requires a dedicated period of observation.

Table 12.1
Movement Assessment Tools for Dance/Movement Therapy

Movement Assessment Tool	*Author*	*Population/Use*	*LMA**
Children			
Body Movement Scale of the Behavior Rating Instrument for Autistic and Atypical Children (BRIAAC)	Kalish (1975)	Children with autism and other emotional/behavioral problems. Provides baseline for judging treatment progress.	yes
Personality Assessment Through Movement	North (1972)	Normal children. Used to determine personality characteristics.	yes
Psychiatric Movement Assessment Scale (PMAS)	Westbrook & Sing (1988)	Children. Psychiatric assessment.	yes
Kestenberg Movement Profile (KMP)	Kestenberg (1975)	Children, adults, dyads. (see text)	yes
Moving Story Effort Assessment	Dyanim, Goodill, & Lewis (2006)	Children 8-11. Psychiatric Assessment	yes
Adult Psychiatric			
Movement Psychodiagnostic Inventory (MPI)	Davis (1991)	Adults, children. (see text)	yes
Movement Observation Scale	Samuels (1972)	Adult psychiatric patients. Assesses movement repertoire and monitors changes in movement behaviors.	
Functional Assessment of Movement (FAM)	Schappin (in Sack & Bolster, 2009)	Adult psychiatric inpatients. Codes non-verbal interaction and interpersonal behavior. Also used outpatient adults with developmental delays (see Sack & Bolster, 2009).	yes

Table 12.1 *(Continued)*
Movement Assessment Tools for Dance/Movement Therapy

Movement Assessment Tool	*Author*	*Population/Use*	*LMA**
Adult General			
Functional Assessment of Movement and Perception (FAMP)	Berrol, Ooi & Katz (1997)	Individuals with brain trauma or injury, frail elders. Behavioral assessment to identify motor dysfunction that impairs psychosocial functions.	no
Movement Diagnostic Tests	Espenak (1981)	Adults. Body dysfunction and personality traits.	no
Nonverbal Tools			
Movement Signature Analysis (MSA)	Davis (1991)	Normal adults. Identifies individual 'signature' patterns of movement associated with speaking.	yes
Davis Nonverbal Communication Analysis System (DaNCAS)	Davis (1983)	Adults. Codes nonverbal aspects of psychotherapy.	yes
Nonverbal Interaction and States Analysis (NISA)	Davis (1991)	Adults. Codes nonverbal interaction and emotional states.	yes
Nonverbal Assessment of Family Systems (NVAFS)	Dulicai (1977)	Families, or child – caregiver constellations. Measures dynamics of interaction to guide treatment.	yes
Action Profiling	Lamb (1965)	Adults, management consulting (see Winter, 1992)	yes

*Note that any basis or use of LMA in the tool qualifies it as "yes"

Movement Assessment Tools for Children

Body Movement Scale for Autistic and Other Atypical Children

Developed by Beth I. Kalish-Weiss (Kalish, 1976), this scale was incorporated into the Behavior Rating Instrument for Autistic and Other Atypical Children (BRIAAC) as one of eight scales used to measure the functioning of young children. The BRIAAC is used to screen for autism and other emotional and behavioral problems and to measure the degree of impairment or dysfunction. Kalish-Weiss's Body Movement Scale measures the movement behavior of children and provides a baseline from which to judge the degree of regression or of progress during treatment.

The BRIAAC overall is a behavioral observation procedure that measures behaviors associated with autism. The scales are scored on the basis both of frequency of given behaviors and their adaptive values, or "levels." These levels are derived from long-term clinical observations of autistic children and consultation with professionals from different disciplines having to do with autism in children. The Body Movement Scale, was empirically derived and is not dependent on theoretical inferences or constructs.

The Body Movement Scale can be used as a separate assessment by dance/movement therapists and others who want to focus on movement behavior. It is designed somewhat differently from the other seven BRIAAC scales. The author found two patterns of autistic movement behavior. Therefore, the Body Movement Scale provides two classes of observation, one for passive and one for active behaviors. The decision to rate the child on the passive or active scale is made after observing the child's level of activity, level of exertion, and body tension. The author notes that when a child is on the higher levels, it is harder to find clear differentiations that suggest one or the other class, and the examiner must look for subtle signs of movement behavior. For example, on the passive scale for body movement, the child who is scored at level one has a limp body, and he or she may sit for long periods of time with little discernible movement, is impervious to painful stimuli and/or body functions, and fails to track visually, exhibiting a fixed gaze or blank stare. On the active scale, level one is used to describe the child whose body is rigid, who shows little or no ability to relax, and movements are repetitive or "driven" and are abrupt and disjointed. This child exhibits a high level of exertion, although body actions may stop abruptly. This child, like the one at level one on the passive scale, will not change facial expression and appears to be unaware of movements in the environment. He or she shows little orientation to space. At level 10, the movements of both active and passive children approach those of normal children. They utilize the whole body, or parts of the body, to do the task at hand. They have the normal repertory of movements, can recognize themselves in the mirror, and can incorporate fantasy into their actions ("move like an elephant, fly like a bird").

The BRIAAC manual (Ruttenberg, Kalish, Wenar, & Wolf, 1977) is quite comprehensive in its descriptions of the levels. It provides "scoring aids" that describe typical behavioral manifestations of the various levels, and cross-references to "major dimensions." In the case of movement, these include the body as a whole, body parts, child's involvement with body or body parts, exertion level, variety and types of movements, child's awareness of movements in the environment, and the child's orientation to space.

In a study of low-functioning, visually handicapped children (Kalish-Weiss, 1988), the concurrent validity of the Body Movement Scale was established by comparing scores on this scale and the rank ordering of clinicians who had no knowledge of the scores; the correlation was an impressive .94 (p. 103). While data are provided to support the construct validity of the instrument (evidence of contrasted groups), normative data are not provided in the manual (Ruttenberg, Kalish, Wenar, & Wolf, 1977). Those who want such data may refer to the original research (Kalish, 1976), which compared the movement functioning of both atypical and normal children in five different age groups.

The work done by Kalish-Weiss in her original development of the Body Movement Scale involved a study of 195 normal children aged one to five matched for sex, race, and age with a group of 75 autistic children. Four raters visited 11 different settings for the autistic children, and 15 settings for the normal group. There were significant differences between the two groups, demonstrating the ability of the procedure to discriminate between normal and autistic children. Kalish-Weiss found, also, that the scores for the normal children were correlated with age, whereas the scores for the autistic children were not (1976).

The Body Movement Scale, as the BRIAAC overall, requires intensive training to ensure satisfactory reliability in scoring. Reuter (1985) in a review of the BRIAAC manual pointed out that "It may not be obvious to the prospective purchaser that the test cannot be used without extensive observer/rater training" (p. 50).

However, the Body Movement Scale is a carefully researched, well-designed, and psychometrically sound instrument that can be useful in screening for autism and other emotional and behavioral problems, in monitoring change, and in training those who work with such children. Because it is not wedded to any particular theory, it avoids many of the thorny problems that are often associated with construct validation.

Personality Assessment Through Movement

This tool grew out of Marion North's doctoral research (1974) that was directed at discovering if newborns demonstrated movement patterns that continued and developed as they matured (Dulicai, personal communication June, 12, 2012). It has remained one of the most direct applications of LMA in personality assessment. North began with observing 31 newborns and then followed eight of these at three, nine, 15, 21, and 24 months.

North (1972) also studied 12 school-age children to investigate Laban's hypotheses associating LMA and personality. As reported in Goodill and Dulicai (2007), these children were randomly selected from a class of 26 and were equally divided between boys and girls. All came from a school in a low socioeconomic area in London. North compared her interpretations of movement analysis with the results of three other sets of data: an apperception test in which children were asked to tell a story; an intelligence test; and a teacher rating on children's behaviors in class. In chart form, North compared the results of her movement assessments for the children with those of the tests and teacher reports in such areas as relationships, adaptability, willpower and drive, alertness and practicality, anxiety, creativity, tolerance, enthusiasm, thinking and reasoning ability. She saw clearly isomorphic relationships between the quality of an individual's movement patterns and his or her personality.

In a further investigation that is pending publication, in 2000, North and Dulicai observed two of the participants in the original baby study who were then adults. With the death of Marion North in 2012, Dianne Dulicai, who has worked with North's system for many years, is a knowledgeable resource about North's work, its relation to Laban's theories, and training opportunities in this system. Note that this system is wedded to LMA and Laban's theories.

Psychiatric Movement Assessment Scale (PMAS)

During their internship at St. Elizabeth's Hospital, Westbrook and Sing (1988) became interested in developing a "practical" diagnostic scale. They circulated a questionnaire among dance/movement therapists, asking for information on the scales that were currently being used and solicited the opinions of the respondents about the utility of these scales in identifying pathology. Of the rather limited distribution of 24 questionnaires, half were returned.

On the basis of the responses, Westbrook and Sing (1988) modified movement categories that had been identified by Hanna (1979) as space, dynamics, rhythm, and characteristic use of the body. The movement categories they finally settled on were chosen in part due to the responses to the questionnaires, but also on the basis of their own clinical observations. These were: eye contact, rhythm in synchrony, posture/gesture, and the ability to self-regulate. Their findings based on the observation of an unspecified number of children at St. Elizabeth's Hospital and on the responses to the questionnaire, indicated differences in each category for patients with different psychiatric diagnoses. Their purpose was to produce a simplified assessment scale that could be used clinically with children. However, no further information than what is contained in the original publication is available on this scale.

The Kestenberg Movement Profile (KMP)

The Kestenberg Movement Profile (KMP) is the culmination of over 37 years of research and study by child psychiatrist Judith Kestenberg and her colleagues, originally at the Sands Point Movement Study Group. Dr. Kestenberg's primary interest, for many years, was the study of the movement interaction of mothers and infants, to identify dysfunctional interactions and to prevent later psychological problems (Kestenberg & Buelte, 1977). Dr. Kestenberg contended that "in a few weeks or months, we can identify and prevent potential problems or correct existing ones that might require years of psychotherapy later in life, and we can do much of it even before the child begins to speak" (Feder & Feder, 1981, p. 239).

Kestenberg and her associates developed the Kestenberg Movement Profile, a complex combination of systems for describing and recording movement patterns, for analyzing movement in terms of tension and flow, and for interpreting the patterns in terms of a specific psychoanalytic theory. "It graphically depicts 120 distinct movement factors (across 29 polar dimensions) and includes descriptions of body attitudes. . . . Data are derived and calculated from a notation system that has its roots in Laban Movement Analysis" (Sossin & Loman, 1992, p. 21). Interesting historical details on the development of the KMP are included in Sossin (2007) and in Sossin and Kestenberg-Amighi (1999).

In the KMP, effort and shape have evolved into two systems, termed tension-flow/effort and shape-flow/shaping. These dual systems are used to describe and notate bodily expressions from which states of affect are inferred; pleasure and displeasure, comfort and discomfort, repulsion and attraction, safety and danger. The first system, tension-flow/effort, is used to describe inner needs and affects, while the second deals with relationships with people and things.

The psychological interpretation of the KMP was originally based on Anna Freud's developmental psychoanalytic metapsychology and psychosexual development stages. However,

> Theoretical developments in both psychoanalysis and KMP evolution have created shifts in language and emphasis. Moreover, a reliance on direct observation for appraisal of infants and preverbal children, along with a nonverbal avenue of understanding, has led the KMP well beyond theoretically constructed views of development or psychodynamics. Kestenberg (1985) herself, used movement observation to base reformulations of psycho-sexual phase theory, leading to new developmental insights. This focus on observations as a method, and movement patterns as the focus of such observation, has meant that the KMP is not wedded to any one theoretical school of thought. . . . (Sossin, 1999, p. 266)

The profiles, such as those of a mother and of her child, can be compared with each other to provide information about areas of interpersonal conflict and harmony. "At the Center for Parents and Children, the profile was used to assess the interpersonal dynamics among family members, as well as to evaluate congenital movement preferences, levels of developmental achievement, levels of fixation or regression, and factors indicative of cognitive abilities" (Sossin & Loman, 1992, p. 23).

The KMP is a very complex system and requires extensive training as noted earlier in this chapter. Even after extensive training, raters can have difficulty demonstrating agreement of ratings (Koch, Cruz, & Goodill, 2001). However, the KMP is not restricted to children but can be used across the lifespan and can be used to examine dyads such as parent and child interaction. The KMP has been very useful in research, for example, research on toddlers and sleep patterns (Lotan & Yirmiya, 2002), studying stress and transmission patterns between parents and children (Sossin & Birklein, 2006; Birklein & Sossin, 2006), and examining gender and leadership in the workplace (Koch, 2006) among other studies.

Until recently, validity of the KMP rested largely on longitudinal studies of children, adolescents, and adults (Sossin & Loman, 1992) and on attempts to establish concurrent validation with other instruments.

Koch (2007) has taken a step-wise approach to providing some validation for the KMP focusing first on the basic dimensions of indulgent and fighting qualities, and growing and shrinking and their effects on "affect, attitudes, and cognition" (p. 235) using adult men and women. In two studies ($N = 60$ in each study) effects of indulgent and fighting rhythms were found only on affect. Two additional studies ($N = 40$; $N = 62$) investigated indulgent and fighting rhythms with respect to approach and avoidance behaviors and found "complex moderations between the factors of movement quality and movement shape" (p. 238). Another study ($N = 62$) examined the effects of growing and shrinking with respect again to affect, attitudes, and cognition including memory but found no clear statistically significant results. And a final study of this group ($N = 62$) examined quick and slow efforts with respect to approach and avoidance movements and again had no significant findings. "In terms of validation, results are mixed, and further research is clearly needed. While studies on the influence of rhythms continuously rendered effects on affect, shape exerted a greater influence on attitudes" (p. 246). Since 2007, Koch has conducted 12 more similar studies aimed at validation, but they have yet to be published (personal communication, June, 8, 2012).

Due to the difficulty of using the KMP in clinical practice because of the lengthy time frame of completing a profile, mentioned earlier in this chapter, Koch attempted to create a brief, questionnaire tool that could be used with adults. The Brief KMP-based Affect Scale was developed from the earlier KMP Questionnaire that Koch created from extracting interpretive information from KMP publications. The questionnaire in English and German is available in Koch and Müller (2007) and the Affect Scale was used in the studies cited above is available from the first author.

At present, a major contribution of the KMP rests on its application in research. Continued research findings and the conclusions that flow from them can then constitute a solid base on which to refine (and perhaps simplify) the KMP for evaluation.

Moving Story Effort Assessment (MSEA)

This tool was developed and published in Dyanim, Goodill, and Lewis (2006) for use with children aged 8–11 years in clinical settings "to meet the demands of managed care" (p. 87). Based on the first author's field tests, the MSEA involves four interactive stories that each include eight images designed to elicit LMA effort movement responses from children as they "act out" the stories. Explored with 31 children in individual sessions, it is designed to provide initial assessment data for the therapist who has LMA training, and so is a "true" assessment. The stories are included in full in the cited publication and this may be a promising tool for therapists working with children in this age group (Dyanim, Goodill, & Lewis, 2006).

Assessments for Adults (Psychiatric and Other Uses)

The Movement Psychodiagnostic Inventory

The development of the MPI began in the 1960s when Davis started working as research assistant to Irmgard Bartenieff in the public mental health system in the Bronx, New York. Observing individuals with serious and persistent mental disorders, they identified a number of specific patterns in the abnormal movements of patients with schizophrenia that Davis developed into the MPI and continued to develop and revise over time (Davis, 1970, 1974, 1991). Although initially live observation was used, as videotape technology evolved, it began to be used because it allowed replaying segments so that very subtle movements could be detected.

Davis, Lausberg, Cruz, Berger, and Dulicai (2007) defined the MPI as "a method for assessing patterns of movement disorder" (p. 119). The MPI rates abnormal voluntary and involuntary movements associated with psychopathology. The movements are described in terms of their dynamic, spatial, rhythmic, and muscular involvement, rather than in terms of the traditional disease-symptom terms, such as chorea (involuntary muscular contractions and irregular jerky movements) or parkinsonism (the rhythmic tremors and muscular rigidity associated with Parkinson's disease).

The MPI has two parts. In the Primary Inventory, 52 items are grouped into 10 subscales that note abnormal movement. In the Action Inventory, 14 items describe nonverbal communication behaviors that usually accompany speech organized into seven subscales. It is important to note that the Action Inventory items are appropriate for use with interviews but not with dance therapy sessions (Davis, Lausberg, Cruz, Berger, & Dulicai, 2007), and that that the Primary Inventory items may be used with children when psychopathology is suspected.

> An example of an item in the Primary Inventory designed to record motor disorder is item 7 in the Disorganization subscale, "as two limbs move, changes in their directions are unsynchronized and/or there is not clear bilateral organization." An example of an item in the Action Profile is item 10, "head movements with speech." (Cruz, 2009, p. 126)

The Action Inventory uses specific codes for each of the 14 items that reflect relative frequencies of occurrences. Later, all codes are converted to a "Communicative Repertoire" scale, with 0 indicating no problem in obvious conversational behaviors and 2 or 3 suggesting a problem. On the Primary Inventory, observers code each of the 52 items as present or absent, then these scores are converted into 0-3 scales for each of the ten categories. These ratings and the composite Communicative Repertoire rating create the total MPI profile. Because the effects of antipsychotic medications are either to produce specific movement disorders such as tardive dyskinesia or parkinsonian signs, the MPI allows raters to note if these signs are suspected as they might introduce a confound to some of the Primary Inventory ratings (Cruz, 2009).

The MPI requires training as many of the items on the Primary Inventory can be subtle to detect. Davis and her colleagues began providing training sessions to groups internationally in 2006, and these have continued supplemented by video training sessions. As a result of group training sessions, Davis introduced an MPI Shortform published in Davis, Lausberg, Cruz, Berger, and Dulicai (2007). It was designed for trained observers to provide a tool "they can fill out after a session" that is "clinically useful and sufficiently accurate to monitor the patient's progress" (p. 122). It is constructed to assist clinicians "in organizing their impressions after a session, to review . . . what is noteworthy in the person's movement" (p. 122). The reliability and efficiency of the form has not been tested to date.

Research with the MPI includes two studies focused on its validity with a sample of 62 psychiatric patients in Sweden and the U.S. (Cruz, 1995; Berger, 1999) and a third case study (Lausberg, 1995). These studies also reported data on rater agreement for the MPI which will be briefly described. The first study examined the relationships of the Primary Inventory variables to each other, and found that the hyperkinetic to hypokinetic forms traditionally associated with abnormal involuntary movements were detected. This evidence indicated that the Primary Inventory items represent a finer level of observation of movement disorders than traditional neurological measures (Cruz, 2009). In addition, the first study found different patterns of co-occurring abnormal involuntary movements between patients with schizophrenia and those with personality disorders (Cruz, 1995) indicating the diagnostic potential of the MPI. Three independent raters with varying levels of expertise were used with the data. Analysis of rater agreement in the study showed that there was closer agreement for raters with more experience with the instrument, confirming the importance of training.

In the second study (Berger, 1999), a focus on the patients with personality disorders found that scores on only six Primary Inventory categories distinguished between the groups with borderline personality disorder and narcissistic personality disorder with 87 percent accuracy. The MPI categories that separated these groups were Disorganization, Immobility, Diffusion, Low Spatial Complexity, Flaccidity, and Hyperkinesis (see Cruz, 1995 for the complete inventory).

Lausberg (1995) used the MPI to assess a patient with irritable bowel syndrome before and after 10 sessions of verbal psychotherapy. Two independent raters coded the two 50-minute interview videos and produced an average Kappa coefficient of $\kappa = .76$, indicating good agreement. The MPI was found to be useful in showing improvement and may indicate that the MPI can be useful for monitoring treatment progress.

Of note is that in the studies above, modifications were made to the scoring of the MPI Primary Inventory items. Severity ratings were extrapolated using the original coding. Items were scored as never occurring, mild in severity, or moderate in severity. Then the item with the most severe rating within each Primary Inventory category was used to represent the category. Action Inventory items were coded as either absolute or relative frequency counts. However, some items were confounded with the length of the observation and others were confounded with known cultural parameters of nonverbal communication and were not used in analysis. As later described by Cruz (2009), "For example, rate and use of eye contact differs among Latin-Americans, African-Americans, and Caucasian-Americans and the Action Inventory item rating frequency of eye contact was not included" (p. 127).

The MPI is a useful research tool and with use and study, the Shortform may show potential as a clinical assessment. However, as with any tool used in DMT, it requires much more research.

The Functional Assessment of Movement (FAM)

Developed by Nathan Schappin and published in 2009 by Sack and Bolster, the Functional Assessment of Movement was based on concepts from LMA, the KMP, Action Profiling, and indices of nonverbal communication (Sack & Bolster, 2009). It was conceived as "a moderately complex assessment tool and outcome monitor of treatment responses to be used in a short-term adult psychiatric in-patient service" (p. 171). The ideas behind the scale were that "physical movement patterns correlate to psychological states and that emotional illness was characterized by an imbalance in a person's repertory and range of movement" (p. 171). The scale is composed of 16 factors that are divided into two categories for observation, motion and stillness. Sack and Bolster applied the scale to a longitudinal treatment program project involving adults with developmental disabilities and their extensive report is the only published use of the scale. They have included the scale and its training manual in an appendix which is very useful for dance/movement therapists who may wish to use the FAM. Sack and Bolster include group and case data in their results that demonstrate that the scale was useful in tracking progress and "variations in the functional ability" (p. 180) of clients who were participating in a multimodal arts program over time. Rater agreement for scale ratings was calculated at .85 prior to beginning the study. While this is a single application of the scale and more research is needed, the Sack and Bolster report is detailed and recommended to interested readers.

The Functional Assessment of Movement and Perception (FAMP)

The Functional Assessment of Movement and Perception (FAMP) was developed by Cynthia F. Berrol and Stephanie S. Katz (1985, 1991) for the assessment of individuals with severe neurotrauma – injury to the brain or nervous system. Because the assessment is concerned with the physiological manifestations of neurotrauma and not with diagnosis, the FAMP is fundamentally a behavioral assessment.

The categories that were incorporated into the FAMP are body scheme, spatial orientation and judgment, rhythmic discrimination, perceptual motor abilities, motor planning and sequencing, timed motor activity and delayed motor activity.

While there are common dysfunctions that result from neurotrauma, each victim manifests a different pattern, so the assessment involves the identification of the problems and an estimate of the severity of each. In the motor realm, for example, dysfunctional behaviors may include paresis (severe muscle weakness); ataxia (inability to coordinate movement and loss of balance); spasticity (abnormal increase in muscle tone that interferes with voluntary movement); and apraxia (the inability to organize the body for purposeful voluntary movement).

The scale includes similar taxonomies of dysfunction in the area of perceptual motor difficulties and in the cognitive domain. However, as Berrol and Katz point out, problems often become apparent in the psychosocial behavior of victims of neurotrauma. Most rehabilitation programs focus on the return of function and the modification of abnormal behaviors, but often neglect the emotional problems of the victim. Dealing with practical life issues that confront patients – job, school, family relationships – is essential to the resolution of many of the emotional difficulties. Presumably, the identification of such problems is part of the assessment process in order to help plan and guide the treatment program. The FAMP contains 30 items divided into 10 areas: Total Body Scheme, Spatial Orientation, Perceptual Motor Ability, Range of Motion, Sit/reach Crossing Midline, Rhythmic Discrimination, Motor Planning, Timed Motor Activity, Delayed Repetition, and Activities of Daily Living Summary Index.

The scale was used in research on DMT with individuals ($N = 107$) who had non progressive neurotrauma in a pre-test and post-test design with experimental and control groups (Berrol, Ooi, & Katz (1997). They reported rater agreement ranging from .71 to .95 for the FAMP ratings, and factor analysis of ratings established an eight-factor structure of the 30 items of the FAMP that explained 78.7 percent of the variance. Positive, statistically significant differences between the treatment and control groups were detected with the FAMP, specifically on the Perceptual Motor Ability, Range of Motion, and Body Scheme categories of items. Although a single study, the reliability and validity information as well as the fact that it discriminated between experimental and control groups indicates potential for the scale for this population. Dance/movement therapists interested in the FAMP should contact the first author (Berrol) regarding training requirements.

Nonverbal Tools

Dulicai's Nonverbal Family Assessment

Dianne Dulicai's interest in nonverbal family assessment began in the 1960s, when she was a dance/movement therapist at the Bronx State Hospital and had received training in family therapy. In 1976, she developed her Nonverbal Family Systems Assessment (1977, 1992) and conducted a series of validation and reliability studies on the use of the system. In an attempt to incorporate the identification and description of behaviors and the interpretation of these behaviors in terms of family dynamics, Dulicai drew from a number of sources. Of these, the most important were the research of Albert Scheflen on kinesics, or "body language," and Marion North's hypothesis of an isomorphic relationship between the qualities of movement and aspects of personality.

Similarly, the scoring system combines a behavioral frequency count, a qualitative description of movement qualities, and an interpretation of the emotional content of the movements.

According to Dulicai, the instrument yields three types of information, individual data on the developmental levels of the child and on the reciprocal behavior of the caregiver. A series of charts indicate age-appropriate behaviors and the appropriate role of the caregiver in response to each underlying function. These are based on norms developed on the basis of clinical observation by a number of researchers and observers including Judith Kestenberg.

Family dynamics descriptions, in terms of the interactions between family members, are couched in terms of both kinesics and LMA elements. However, juxtaposed on these descriptions are implicit judgments about interactional qualities; these are interpreted in terms of those that support and those that restrict further development in family relationships.

Dulicai states that the observed patterns – a father blocking any initiative from his son, for example, or a mother failing to respond directly to her child's efforts to communicate – offer guidance for the forms and levels of intervention that may be called for. "Ratings can be obtained in structure, goal-directed negotiations, autonomy, responsibility of action, invasiveness, permeability, expressiveness, mood and tone, presence and degree of conflict and degree of empathy" (1992, p.

2). The norms for each category are presented in chart form.

Changes in both the behaviors manifested in interactions and the perceived qualities of these interactions are noted as guides to the clinician for treatment options. Dulicai (1992) cited some preliminary evidence that medium or high scores in the affective movement qualities indicate the family's potential for change.

On a time-indicated form, the examiner indicates the frequency of 11 movement items: blocking, approach, molding, gestures towards or away, postures toward or away, full or partial body action, eye contact, bonding behavior, separating behavior, shared focus and the efforts used in each behavior. In summary, the examiner indicates the presence and frequency of these behaviors and the qualities associated with each. The resulting data collection presents a coded description of each behavior, its quality, and the time and sequence. So, for a single movement, a mother's gesture toward a child might be noted, the quality of the movement rated as strong and single-focused, and the time indicated as 10 seconds into the session.

This is an unstructured clinical assessment. The behavioral patterns used to ascertain normality or dysfunction are drawn largely from clinical observations reported in the literature and from isomorphic assumptions such as those suggested in Marion North's personality assessment. An unstructured clinical assessment is inherently intuitive and subjective in nature. However, Dulicai has attempted to establish the instrument's construct validity and inter-rater reliability on an empirical basis.

Her original study (1977) found movement differences between four "dysfunctional" families and four "normal" families. The designations of the sample families were supported by psychiatric interviews with the families.

Subsequently, the instrument was tested with an additional 215 families but not published. Dulicai reported that correlations were found for nine of the 11 items at the .01 level of significance. She further reported that "inter-rater reliability has been established with raters having 2 years experience with Laban analysis and clinical work" (Dulicai, personal communication, 1997). For the kinesic, or descriptive categories, reliabilities ranged from .77 (accommodation) to .97 (exploratory behavior). For the interpretations of quality, the range was from .78 (accommodation) to .96 (blocking behavior). For an exploratory study, these reliabilities are within the range of acceptability. The Nonverbal

Family Assessment is a potentially valuable instrument for the assessment of family dynamics. It has the advantage of flexibility and ease of use. This flexibility rides on the unstructured nature of the procedure.

Movement Signature Analysis (MSA)

The Movement Signature Analysis was developed by Martha Davis (1991) and uses notation systems or terms that derive, in part, from LMA along with pictographs or letter symbols for specifics that are not addressed in LMA. The criteria for coding and scaling in both these systems are based on the author's own research observations and focus. As the title suggests, the MSA is based on the assumption that individuals have unique ways of moving that pervade various contexts. Davis refers to these as "signature patterns" rather than personality traits or even tendencies, thereby avoiding the pitfalls associated with indirect assessment. The MSA is a microanalytic procedure, focusing more on the approach to the identification and recording of the individual's signature patterns than on the mechanics of coding. Training is required for MSA.

Action Profiling (AP)

Developed by Warren Lamb (1965), Action Profiling has been used in management and business settings. Deborah Du Nann Winter (1992) gives a good description of AP and reported on a series of four studies investigating the reliability of profiles, "the assumption that movement is simultaneously related to different thinking responses" (p. 167) concurrent validity with the Myers-Briggs Type Indicator (MBTI), and "if AP describes meaningful differences in cognitive style" it should "differentiate between different occupational groups" (p. 189). Results supported "the validity of the AP scores as a reflection of ongoing cognitive style," appeared to be consistent and related to the MBTI, and occupational groups. Unfortunately, sample sizes and sample demographics were not consistently presented to allow ideas about representativeness that might allow generalization. Winter herself described these efforts as a beginning validity investigation. However, for specific purposes, AP may have promise.

Alternative Movement Assessment Techniques

Bojner-Horwitz, Theorell, and Anderberg (2003; 2004) used an innovative technique in studying changes in patients with fibromyalgia who were treated with DMT that is worth mention here. Instead of employing raters to assess movement behavior of participants, they asked participants to rate videotapes of themselves. Participants were asked to perform the same movement sequence, and later rated baseline and treatment performance of the movements using a five-point scale to rate change in "mobility, perception of movement pain, and life energy" (p. 257) based on viewing their own movement. While this technique was developed for research purposes and was useful, as significant differences in movement perceptions were documented between experimental and control participant groups, it is intriguing for other purposes also. As noted earlier, Caldwell and Johnson (2012) recommended investigating clients' subjective responses to moving as a way to avoid negative consequences of interpretation bias. This video rating process, described by Bojner-Horwitz et al., has the potential for development into clinical and other research tools and deserves study for other purposes.

SUMMARY

Before the language of the body can be used in assessment, it must first be translated into the verbal language of description or the coded language of notation, if it is to be analyzed or communicated to others. The best-known system for dance/movement therapy is LMA, based on the work of Rudolf Laban and modified by some of his students and colleagues. While LMA has been used in a variety of ways, not all movement analysis systems used in DMT are complex systems based in part on LMA.

Regardless of the language used to describe movement and movement analysis systems, the validity and reliability of movement observations are of the utmost importance. While training of dance/movement therapists requires specific instruction in movement observation, new training techniques and priorities may be needed to uncover internalized and unconscious assumptions on the part of both instructors and students. Challenges presented by differences between the observer and the observed affect both reliability and validity and require extensive awareness, research, and sensitivity on the part of dance/movement therapists. Highlighting social justice issues as they affect clinical practice in working with clients who represent diverse cultures and backgrounds is a current focus of American Dance Therapy Association. In addition, the exporting of DMT to cultures that do not share the worldview, perceptual, and cognitive perspectives of the North American and western European roots of DMT needs to be studied and addressed. As introduced and discussed in this chapter, the time is ripe for attending to social and cultural difference and questioning the theoretical assumptions, historical models, and how this impacts tools for observing and interpreting movement. These fascinating challenges and their potential to affect this profession which is inextricably linked to movement assessment, make the present and the future exciting times to be a dance/movement therapist.

REFERENCES

Bartenieff, I. (1972). Effort/shape as a tool in dance therapy. *Proceedings, 7th Annual American Dance Therapy Association Conference.*

Bartenieff, I., & Lewis, D. (1980). *Body movement: Coping with the environment.* New York: Gordon and Breach.

Berger, M. R. (1999). Movement patterns in borderline and narcissistic personality disorders. *Dissertation Abstracts International: Section B: The Sciences & Engineering Vol. 60*(9-B), April 2000, 4875.

Berger, M. R., & Dulicai, D. (2005). Global dance/movement therapy growth and development. *The Arts in Psychotherapy, 32*(3), 205–216.

Berrol, C. F., & Katz, S. S. (1985). Dance/movement therapy individuals surviving severe head injury. *American Journal of Dance Therapy, 8,* 46–66.

Berrol, C. F., & Katz, S. S. (1991). A working model of a functional assessment in the rehabilitation setting. *Proceedings, 26th Annual Conference of the ADTA,* pp. 154–158. Columbia, MD: ADTA.

Berrol, C. Ooi, W. L., & Katz, S. (1997). Dance/movement therapy with older adults who have sustained neurological insult: A demonstration project. *American Journal of Dance Therapy, 19*(2), 135–154.

Birklein, S., & Sossin, K. M. (2006). Nonverbal indices of stress in parent-child dyads: Implications for individual and interpersonal affect regulation and intergenerational transmission. In S. C. Koch & I. Braeuninger (Eds.), *Advances in dance-movement therapy* (pp. 128–141). Berlin: Logos.

Bojner-Horwitz, E., Theorell, T., & Anderberg, U. (2003). Dance/movement therapy and changes in stress-related hormones: A study of fibrobyalgia patients with video-interpretation. *The Arts in Psychotherapy, 30*(5), 255–264.

Bojner-Horwitz, E., Theorell, T., & Anderberg, U. (2004). New technique for assessment of self-perception in fibromyalgia patients: A pilot study with video-interpretation. *The Arts in Psychotherapy, 31*(3), 153–164.

Burn, H. (1987). The movement behavior of anorectics: The control issue. *American Journal of Dance Therapy, 10*(1), 54–76.

Caldwell, C., & Johnson, R. (2012). Embodying difference: Addressing issues of diversity and social justice in dance/movement therapy research. In R. Cruz & C. Berrol (Eds.), *Dance/movement therapists in action* (2nd ed) (pp. 121–140). Springfield, IL: Charles C Thomas.

Chaiklin, H., & Chaiklin, S. (2012). The case study. In R. Cruz & C. Berrol (Eds.), *Dance/movement therapists in action* (2nd ed) (pp. 75–101). Springfield, IL: Charles C Thomas.

Chang, M. (2006). How do dance/movement therapists bring awareness of race, ethnicity, and cultural diversity into their practice? In S. C. Koch & I. Braeuninger (Eds.), *Advances in dance-movement therapy* (pp. 192–205). Berlin: Logos.

Chang, M. (2009). Cultural consciousness and the global context of dance/movement therapy. In S. Chaiklin & H. Wengrower (Eds.), *The art and science of dance/movement therapy: Life is dance* (pp. 299–316). New York: Routledge.

Cruz, R. F. (1995). An empirical investigation of the Movement Psychodiagnostic Inventory (Doctoral dissertation, The University of Arizona). *Dissertation Abstracts International (2B), (UMI No.AAM962042257).*

Cruz, R. F. (2009). Validity of the Movement Psychodiagnostic Inventory: A pilot study. *American Journal of Dance Therapy, 31*(2), 122–135.

Cruz, R.F. (2006). Assessment in dance/movement therapy. In S. Brooke (Ed.), *Creative arts therapies manual: A guide to the history, theoretical approaches, assessment, and work with special populations of art, play, dance, music, drama and poetry therapies* (pp. 133–143).

Cruz, R. F., & Koch, S. (2012) Issues of validity and reliability in the use of movement observations and scales. In R. Cruz & C. Berrol (Eds.), *Dance/movement therapists in action: A working guide to research options* (2nd ed.). Springfield, IL: Charles C Thomas.

Davis, M. (1970). Movement characteristics of hospitalized psychiatric patients. *Proceedings, Fifth Annual Conference of the ADTA,* pp. 25–45. Columbia, MD: ADTA.

Davis, M. (1974). *Analysis of movement styles and interaction in psychotherapy.* Paper presented at the First International Symposium on Nonverbal Aspects and Techniques of Psychotherapy, Vancouver, BC.

Davis, M. (1983). An introduction to the Davis Nonverbal Communication Analysis System (DaNCAS). *American Journal of Dance Therapy, 6,* 49–73.

Davis, M. (1991). *Guide to Movement Analysis Methods.* New York: Author.

Davis, M., Lausberg, H., Cruz, R. F., Berger, M., & Dulicai, D. (2007) The Movement Psychodiagnostic Inventory. In S. C. Koch & S. Bender (Eds.), *Movement analysis: The legacy of Laban, Bartenieff, Lamb & Kestenberg* (pp. 119–129). Berlin: Logos Verlag Berlin.

Davis, M., & Markus, K. (2006). Misleading cues, misplaced confidence: An analysis of deception in detection patterns. *American Journal of Dance Therapy, 28*(2), 107–126.

Dulicai, D. (1977). Nonverbal assessment of family systems: A preliminary study. *The Arts in Psychotherapy, 4*(2), 55–62.

Dulicai, D. (1992). Nonverbal family therapy assessment: Evaluation and application. *Proceedings, 27th Annual Conference of the ADTA,* pp. 1–4. Columbia, MD: ADTA.

Dayanim, S., Goodill, S. W., & Lewis, C. (2006). The moving story effort assessment as a means for the movement assessment of preadolescent children. *American Journal of Dance Therapy, 28,* 87–106.

Foroud, A., & Whishaw, I. Q. (2006). Changes in the kinematic structure and non-kinematic features of movement during skilled reaching after stroke: A Laban Movement Analysis in two case studies. *Journal of Neuroscience Methods, 158,* 137–149.

Feder, E., & Feder, B. (1981). *The expressive arts therapies: Art, music and dance as psychotherapy.* Englewood Cliffs, NJ: Prentice-Hall;

Feder, B., & Feder, E. (1998). *The art and science of evaluation in the arts therapies.* Springfield, IL: Charles C Thomas.

Goodill, S., & Dulicai, D. (2007). Dance/movement therapy for the whole person. In I. Serlin (Ed.), *Whole person healthcare Vol. 3 the arts and health* (pp. 121–142). Westport, CT: Praeger.

Goodman, L. S. (1991). Movement behavior of hyperactive children: A qualitative analysis. *American Journal of Dance Therapy, 13,* 19–31.

Gross, M., Crane, E., & Fredrickson, B. (2010). Methodology for assessing bodily expression of emotion. *Journal of Nonverbal Behavior, 34,* 223–248.

Hanna, J. L. (1979). *To dance is human.* Austin, TX: University of Texas Press.

Kalish, B. I. (1976). Body movement scale for autistic and other atypical children: An exploratory study using a normal group and an atypical group. Doctoral dissertation, Bryn Mawr College. *Dissertation Abstracts International, VI,* No. 10, 1977.

Kalish-Weiss, B. I. (1988). Born blind and visually handicapped infants: Movement psychotherapy and assessment. *The Arts in Psychotherapy, 15,* 101–108.

Karkou, V., & Sanderson, P. (2001). Report: Theories and assessment procedures used by dance/movement therapists in the UK. *The Arts in Psychotherapy, 28,* 197–204.

Kestenberg, J. S., & Buelte, A. (1977). Prevention, infant therapy and the treatment of adults: 1. Toward understanding mutuality. *International Journal of Psychoanalytic Psychotherapy, 6,* 339–366.

Kestenberg, J. S. (1975). *Children and parents.* New York: Jason Aronson.

Kestenberg-Amighi, J., Pinder, I., & Kestenberg, J. (1992). Nonverbal communication of affect in Bali: Movement in parenting and dance. In Susan Loman (Ed.), *The body-mind connection in human movement analysis* (pp. 121–134) Keene, NH: Antioch Institute.

Kealiinohomoku, J. W. (2003, Spring). Choreometrics revisited. *Cross-Cultural Dance Resources Newsletter,* 21.

Koch, S. C. (2007). Basic principles of movement analysis: Steps toward validation of the KMP. In S. C. Koch & S. Bender (Eds.), *Movement analysis: The legacy of Laban, Bartenieff, Lamb & Kestenberg* (pp. 119–129). Berlin: Logos Verlag Berlin.

Koch, S., & Müller (2007). Assessments with the KMP Questionnaire and the KMP-based Affect Scale. In S. C. Koch & S. Bender (Eds.), *Movement analysis: The legacy of Laban, Bartenieff, Lamb & Kestenberg* (pp. 195–202). Berlin: Logos Verlag Berlin.

Koch, S. (2006). Gender and leadership at work: Use of rhythms and movement qualities in team communication. In S. C. Koch & I. Braeuninger (Eds.), *Advances in dance-movement therapy* (pp. 116–127). Berlin: Logos.

Koch, S., Cruz, R. F., & Goodill, S. (2001). The Kestenberg Movement Profile: Performance of novice raters. *American Journal of Dance Therapy, 23,* 71–87.

Lamb, W. (1965). *Posture and gesture: An introduction to the study of physical behavior.* London: Gerald Duckworth.

Lausberg, H. (1995). Bewegungsverhalten als Prozeßparameter in einer kontrollierten Therapiestudie mit funktioneller Entspannung (Movement behaviour as process parameter in a controlled therapy study with functional relaxation). Paper presented at the 42nd Annual meeting of the Deutschen Kollegiums für Psychosomatische Medizin (German Committee of Psychosomatic Medicine).

Lotan, N., & Yirmiya, N. (2002). Body movement, presence of parents, and the process of falling asleep in toddlers. *International Journal of Behavioral Development, 26*(1), 81–88.

McCoubrey, C. (1987). Intersubjectivity vs. objectivity: Implications for effort observation and training. *Movement Studies: A Journal of the Laban/Bartenieff Institute of Movement Studies, 2,* 3–6.

Nisbett, R. (2003). *The geography of thought: How Asians and westerners think differently. . . and why.* New York: The Free Press.

North, M. (1972). *Personality assessment through movement.* London: MacDonald and Evans.

North, M. (1974). *The emergence of purposive movement patterns in babies.* Unpublished doctoral dissertation, University of London.

Powell, M. (2008). *Assessment in dance/movement therapy practice: A state of the field survey.* Unpublished master's thesis, Drexel University, Philadelphia, PA.

Reuter, J. (1985). Review of BRIAAC. In D. J. Keyser & R. C. Sweetland (Eds.), *Test critiques,* Vol. VI. Kansas City, MO: Test Corp. of America.

Ruttenberg, B. A., Kalish, B. I., Wenar, C., & Wolf, E. G. (1977). *Behavior Rating Instrument for Autistic and Other Atypical Children: Manual.* Philadelphia: Developmental Center for Autistic Children.

Sack, J., & Bolster, G. (2009). The Functional Assessment of Movement (FAM) Scale in multimodal creative arts therapies research. In S. Snow & M. D'Amico (Eds.), *Assessment in the creative arts therapies* (pp. 163–218). Springfield, IL: Charles C Thomas.

Samuels (1972). Movement change through dance therapy – A study. *American Dance Therapy Association Monograph* No. 2, 50–77.

Schmais, C. (1972). Looking in – reaching out: Learning to be a dance therapist. *Proceedings, 7th Annual American Dance Therapy Association Conference.*

Sossin, K. M., & Birklein, S. (2006). Nonverbal transmission of stress between parent and young child: Considerations and psychotherapeutic implications of a study of affective movement patterns. *Journal of Infant, Child, and Adolescent Psychotherapy, 5*(1), 46–69.

Sossin, K. M., & Loman, S. (1992). Clinical applications of the Kestenberg Movement Profile. In S. Loman with R. Brandt (Eds.), *The body-mind connection in human movement analysis* (pp. 21–55). Keene, NH: Antioch New England Graduate School.

Sossin, M. (October, 2002). *Recent statistical and normative findings regarding the KMP: Implications for theory and application.* Paper presented at the 37th annual conference of the American Dance Therapy Association, Burlington, VT.

Sossin, K. M. (2007). History and future of the Kestenberg Movement Profile. In S. C. Koch & S. Bender (Eds.), *Movement analysis: The legacy of Laban, Bartenieff, Lamb & Kestenberg* (pp. 103–118). Berlin: Logos Verlag Berlin.

Sossin, K. M., & Kestenberg Amighi, J. (1999). Introduction. In J. Kestenberg Amighi, S. Loman, & P. Lewis (Eds.), *The meaning of movement: Developmental and clinical perspectives of the Kestenberg Movement Profile* (pp. 1–20). Amsterdam: Gordon and Breach.

Sossin, K. M. (1999). The KMP and infant-parent psychotherapy. In J. Kestenberg Amighi, S. Loman, & P. Lewis (Eds.), *The meaning of movement: Developmental and clinical perspectives of the Kestenberg Movement Profile* (pp. 191–209). Amsterdam: Gordon and Breach.

Sue, D. W., Carter, R. T., Casas, J. M., Fouad, N. A., Ivey, A. E., Jensen, M., ...Vazquez-Nutall, E. (1998). Multicultural counseling competencies. *Multicultural aspects of counseling series 11.* Thousand Oaks, CA: Sage.

Westbrook, B. K., & Sing, M. (1988). A psychiatric movement assessment scale with developmental considerations. *The Arts in Psychotherapy, 15,* 37–46.

Winter, D. D. (1992). Body movement and cognitive style: Validation of Action Profiling. In S. Loman (Ed.), *The body-mind connection in human movement analysis* (pp. 153–201). Keene, NH: Antioch Institute.

Chapter 13

MUSIC THERAPY ASSESSMENT

BARBARA WHEELER

The process of conducting music therapy involves a number of phases. According to Gfeller and Davis (2008), these include: (a) referral, (b) assessment, (c) treatment planning, (d) documentation of progress, and (e) evaluation and termination of treatment. Assessment for music therapy is aimed at understanding the client's unique strengths and challenges and determining whether the client may benefit from music therapy treatment. Once it is determined that music therapy is appropriate for the client, assessment also provides a guideline for treatment planning. Assessment may take many forms. Sometimes it is systematic, in which the client engages with music so that the therapist can observe and evaluate his or her responses. Assessment may also include less formal inquiry such as observation, a verbal interview, speaking with others who know the client, or reading the medical or educational records including the referral to music therapy. The first type of assessment, where specific procedures are set up to assess the client's responses to music, is the focus of this chapter.

Because assessment occurs in so many ways, it would be more accurate to label the process that uses specific procedures to assess the client's responses to music as a *test/measurement* than as *assessment*. However, this chapter will follow conventional usage and refer to the specific process as *assessment*.

Music therapists generally make a distinction between assessment and evaluation. Assessment refers to what occurs prior to treatment to determine what will be done. An assessment documents the initial contact with a client, the client's caregiver or significant other and provides a means of accountability. Evaluation is aimed at determining client progress or effectiveness of the therapy method after a given period of treatment. Evaluation is ongoing and may occur prior to, during, and at the end of therapy.

PURPOSES OF ASSESSMENT

Several music therapists (Bruscia, 1988; Wigram, 1999) have categorized assessments by their purpose. Bruscia suggests that there are five reasons for doing an assessment: (a) diagnostic, where efforts are made to identify and understand the client's condition or problem, then to see if that condition or problem will lead to safety or abreaction issues given the method to be used (K. Bruscia, personal communication, Feb. 20, 2012); Wigram suggests that this type of assessment seeks to support a diagnostic hypothesis; (b) prescriptive, intended to determine treatment needs of the client and to provide a database for formulating goals, placing the client in the appropriate programs, and identifying the most effective methods of treatment; Wigram calls this general assessment; (c) interpretive, aiming to explain the client or condition in terms of a particular theory; (d) descriptive, in which efforts are made to understand the client and the client's world only in reference to self; and (e) evaluative, where efforts are made to determine the status of the client's condition prior to treatment so that it will be possible to document evidence of treatment effectiveness.

Examples of each type of assessment, according to Bruscia's (1988) categories, follow. A diagnostic assessment is done as part of an intake for the Bonny Method of Guided Imagery and Music (BMGIM) to understand the condition of the client and then to determine whether BMGIM is appropriate for that client. Bruscia (2002a) suggests that a diagnostic assessment in BMGIM is always to determine whether BMGIM is indicated or contraindicated. An example of a prescriptive assessment is the Special Education Music Therapy Assessment Process (SEMTAP, Brunk & Coleman, 2000; Coleman & Brunk, 2003), which compares a child's performance on musical and nonmusical tasks that are part of the Individual Education Plan (IEP) goals and objectives. An example of an interpretive assessment is an assessment by Rider (1981) in which he sought to discover if the ages at which children could perform musical tasks that involved increasingly complex levels of cognitive functioning correlated with the difficulty of the tasks. This was related to Piaget's theory of development and the musical tasks were modeled after nonmusical tasks that Piaget used. An example of a descriptive assessment is the music psychotherapy assessment that Loewy (2000) developed, described later in this chapter. The three scales used in Nordoff-Robbins music therapy, also described later in the chapter, are examples of evaluative assessments.

STANDARDS OF PRACTICE REGARDING ASSESSMENT

The first Standards of Practice of the National Association for Music Therapy (1983) were adopted in 1982, a time when music therapists were focusing increasingly on developing assessment measures and tools. The Standards of Practice of the American Music Therapy Association (AMTA) includes a section on Assessment:

> A client will be assessed by a Music Therapist at the onset of music therapy services.
>
> 2.1 The music therapy assessment will include the general categories of psychological, cognitive, communicative, social, and physiological functioning focused on the client's needs and strengths. The assessment will also determine the client's responses to music, music skills and musical preferences.
>
> 2.2 The music therapy assessment will explore the client's culture. This can include but is not limited to race, ethnicity, language, religion/spirituality, social class, family experiences, sexual orientation, gender identity, and social organizations.
>
> 2.3 All music therapy assessment methods will be appropriate for the client's chronological age, diagnoses, functioning level, and culture(s). The methods may include, but need not be limited to, observation during music or other situations, interview, verbal and nonverbal interventions, and testing. Information may also be obtained from different disciplines or sources such as the past and present medical and social history in accordance with HIPPA permission regulation.
>
> 2.4 All interpretations of test results will be based on *appropriate norms or criterion referenced data.
>
> 2.5 The music therapy assessment procedures and results will become a part of the client's file.

2.6 The results, conclusions, and implications of the music therapy assessment will become the basis for the client's music therapy program and will be communicated to others involved with provision of services to the client. When appropriate, the results will be communicated to the client.

2.7 When assessment indicates the client's need for other services, the Music Therapist will make an appropriate referral. (AMTA, 2011)

These assessment standards lead to the next standard, Program Planning, where the music therapist is directed to "prepare a written individualized program plan based upon the music therapy assessment, the client's prognosis, and applicable information from other disciplines and sources. The client will participate in program plan development when appropriate" (AMTA, 2011). Later in the Standards of Practice, under Documentation, the document links treatment to clinical outcomes and evaluation as it states: "The Music Therapist will periodically document the client's level of functioning with regard to the goals and objectives."

NEED FOR MUSIC THERAPY ASSESSMENT

Some may wonder whether a music therapy assessment is necessary. Would it not be just as effective – and save time and resources – to rely on assessments from related professions?

While existing assessments for learning and psychological development, for example, can be helpful, it is only through *music therapy* assessment that we can know the strengths and needs of the music therapy client. Music therapy assessment has a twofold advantage. First, it enables the music therapist to observe and interpret the ways in which the client uses musical media and consequently identify treatment goals from within the musical media themselves. Second, it allows the therapist to make some determination about the actual music therapy experiences that will be most beneficial for the client.

There are other benefits to undertaking a music therapy assessment with a client. Clients may perform differently under music conditions compared to their performance in other modalities (Bruscia, 1988; Coleman & Brunk, 2003). Michel and Rohrbacher (1982) state:

> Why should a separate type of assessment be conducted for music therapy? . . . Music is a form of human behavior which is unique from

> other forms. *Clients react differently within musical situations, listening to, moving to, or performing music.* It is generally recognized that clients may be seen from a different perspective – sometimes radically different – when under music stimuli conditions. Thus, special assessment by music therapists of clients under music conditions is important. (italics in original; p. iii)

One advantage of a music-based assessment is that it may tap into areas of functioning not easily accessible through other means. Bruscia (1988) suggested that music and other arts-based assessments could bypass many motivational problems, as clients can be easily engaged in the arts/musical experience. He also suggested that "because of their symbolic and nonverbal facets, the arts often provide easier access to inner or hidden aspects of the client's world, particularly when the client is resistant or highly defended" (p. 7). Sometimes music can tap into emotional areas more directly than verbal means (Zwerling, 1979). Music-based assessment can also provide useful information in situations where nonverbal means of assessment are needed. Many individuals with dementia are labeled *untestable* on standard mental status exams, primarily because these tests rely heavily on verbal communication. Children and others who have not developed verbal language may become involved in music when they cannot express themselves verbally. It is useful to consider what unique information can be added to a treatment team's assessment process by the music therapist.

OVERVIEWS OF ASSESSMENT

An Institute on Music Therapy Assessment was held at the World Congress of Music Therapy in Washington, DC, in 1999, chaired by Brian Wilson and Elizabeth York. In addition, assessment was the focus of a special issue of *The Journal of Music Therapy* (2000) and of *Music Therapy Perspectives* (2000). These were all intended to highlight current work in music therapy assessment and to promote consideration of future needs for assessment.

Two published studies in the U.S. surveyed the assessments or measures that have been used by music therapists and others in assessing responses (Gregory, 2000; Wilson & Smith, 2000). These were not actual assessments as used by music therapists in clinical practice, as many of them were used in research studies rather than clinically, but they are useful because they provide an overview of the types of measures that were being used at the time to assess responses in music therapy-related situations. In addition, Sabbatella (2004) conducted an overview of assessment and clinical evaluation from 1985–2001, based on literature in English, Spanish, and Portuguese, including conference presentations. Most of what she found was in English and related to assessment and evaluation of clients as part of the treatment process. Chase (2002) compiled information on assessment, including a number of music therapy assessments, in an easily readable handbook.

Wilson and Smith (2000) surveyed the literature to determine the assessments that were used by music therapists working in school settings and the feasibility of standardizing an assessment instrument for music therapists to use in school settings. As stated, many of the assessments that they found were used by researchers rather than clinicians. Music preferences were assessed in only 12 percent of the 41 studies reviewed. Approximately half of the assessment tools being used were *named* or *titled,* and the rest were untitled, usually researcher-designed. Of the 16 named assessments, only three were used in more than one research study. These were the Primary Measures of Music Audiation (Gordon, 1979), used three times; Continuous Response Digital Interface (CRDI; Robinson, 1988), used twice; and "Toney Listens to Music," computer software (Williams & Fox, 1983), used twice. The most frequent purpose of the assessments (16, or 39%) was to compare the assessment with data from other measures or other populations. The next most frequent use of music therapy assessments (12, or 29%) was to establish a baseline or as a pretest. The other uses, with far fewer responses, were to determine eligibility for treatment or services, to determine the psychometric properties of the assessment, to determine the appropriateness of an assessment instrument for a particular population, or to establish musical preferences. Music perception, musical aptitude, musical preferences, and attention to/enjoyment of music were among the elements that were assessed. Clientele addressed, from most to least, included those with intellectual and developmental disabilities (18, or 44%), emotional disturbances (9, or 22%), hearing impairments (7, or 17%), and autism (4, or 10%), with several other groups of clientele being assessed in fewer studies.

Gregory (2000) reviewed issues of the *Journal of Music Therapy* to investigate test instruments used in music therapy research. Of 183 experimental or descriptive research studies that were published in the

Journal of Music Therapy from 1984–1997, 92 (50%) included a test instrument. She reviewed the method section of these articles, resulting in a listing of 115 different test instruments. Of these, 40 percent were published tests, 35 percent were unpublished tests, and 25 percent were researcher-constructed tests. Music responses were tested in 25 of the 115 tests, primarily in the researcher-constructed tests (17 of 29). Very few of the published tests (2 of 46) or the unpublished tests (6 of 40) measured music or music-related responses. The published test instruments cited in two or more articles included: State-Trait Anxiety Inventory (9 studies; Spielberger, Gorsuch, & Lushene, 1970), Peabody Picture Vocabulary Test (4; Dunn & Dunn, 1981), Mini-Mental Status Examination (4; Folstein, Folstein, & McHugh, 1975), Vineland Social Maturity Scale (3; Doll, 1953), Multiple Affect Adjective Checklist (3; Zuckerman & Lubin, 1985), Hamilton Rating Scale for Depression (3; Hamilton, 1967), Image-CA (2; Achterberg & Lawlis, 1978), Primary Measures of Music Audiation (2; Gordon, 1979), Maslach Burnout Inventory (2; Maslach & Jackson, 1981).[1] Four unpublished tests were used in more than one study, with one of these, the Global Deterioration Scale (Reisberg, Ferris, DeLeon, & Crook, 1982) being used in seven studies, almost all to screen people for Alzheimer's disease.

Quantitative and Qualitative Approaches to Assessment

Music therapy assessment can be approached from either a quantitative or a qualitative perspective. Both types of assessment focus on either the musical or nonmusical responses of the client. Similar to the considerations of whether to pursue quantitative or qualitative research designs (Wheeler, 2005), the assumptions underlying qualitative versus quantitative assessment approaches are different, as are the procedures used. Many assessments include both quantitative and qualitative features. Bruscia's (1993) development of these two perspectives forms much of the basis of this section.

Quantitative assessment is used when the music therapist systematically gathers information about various aspects of the client's behavior or condition and measures these attributes, skills, or responses using numbers, inventories, or other numerical means of analysis. The ther-

[1] In some cases, studies used different sources for the test instruments. The citations given here were each used in at least one of the articles.

apist determines the scope of the assessment and defines the specific domain areas to be assessed. The target areas are then further represented by a number of tasks, and the responses to the tasks are weighted and scored. Specific assessment questions are advanced (either explicitly or implicitly) to determine how the tasks relate to the overall construct being assessed. Attempts are made to collect the assessment data in consistent and standardized ways. The music therapist attempts to remain objective during the data collection, allowing the client to respond with minimal interaction with the person conducting the assessment. The outcome of quantitative assessment is numeric data that summarize the information. Reliability and validity are computed for quantitative assessments.

A qualitative assessment is concerned with describing the ways in which clients respond to or are engaged in various music or nonmusic experiences provided by the therapist. This may also include interpreting the client's music making according to nonmusical theories or constructs. In some qualitative approaches, the therapist allows the objectives and target areas to emerge as the assessment proceeds, defining and limiting them according to whatever the assessment reveals. No attempts are made to reduce what is being examined to numerical measures of operationally defined variables, unless there is some evidence that this is appropriate. Efforts are made to understand rather than explain or prove the significance of the findings.

ISSUES IN MUSIC THERAPY ASSESSMENT

There are several areas in which music therapists' understanding of assessment lacks clarity. It is likely that this lack of clarity impedes progress in the development of music therapy assessment tools.

Assessment versus Evaluation

Music therapists often confuse assessment and evaluation of treatment. Assessment is focused on meeting the client and planning treatment, while evaluation is aimed at determining client progress or the effectiveness of the therapy method. According to Radocy (1999), "Evaluation is a procedure for making a judgment; assessment is a means for making judgments about a current state" (p. 5). Both assessment and evaluation can be conducted throughout the therapy process – assessment is not just prior to therapy, and evaluation is both before and after any period of therapy. Sometimes this confusion occurs only in the use of the words; although it might be quite clear that the person is referring to assessment, the word *evaluation* is used, leading to a lack of clarity about the topic.

Professional Identity and Assessment

In an article that has influenced thinking about music therapy assessment since its publication in 1988, Isenberg-Grezda spoke of the relationship of music therapy assessment to the professional identity of the music therapist. She suggested:

> The nature of the therapist's relationship with music largely determines the manner in which music, as a tool, will be employed in assessment. The therapist's philosophical stance, world view and resulting theoretical framework will be instrumental in determining what, (i.e., which area of functioning) is to be assessed. The therapist's perception and understanding of various client populations may lead to a decision regarding who will be assessed with the aid of a particular assessment tool, that is, whether or not an assessment instrument will be population specific. The therapist's role within the institution and response to the institutional culture may help determine the format and structure of the assessment tool. (p. 161)

Reliability and Validity

The need for assessments that meet psychometric standards is receiving more attention in music therapy assessment. Reliability and validity are important indicators that determine the technical quality of quantitative assessments and can only be determined if numeric data are collected (Walsh & Betz, 1990). Reliability and validity have not been adequately addressed in music therapy assessment, although the need for assessments to be reliable and valid was pointed out by Bruscia (1988), by Scalenghe (1999), and by Lipe and York (2000). It continues to be a concern of authors (see Gfeller & Davis, 2008). Information on reliability and validity is presented briefly in this chapter and more extensively in Chapter 3 of this book.

Reliability refers to the consistency with which a measuring instrument measures a construct (Boyle & Radocy, 1987). That is, does the measure provide an accurate and consistent way of collecting quantitative data on the variables of interest? Will different versions or different administrations of the same test provide similar information over time? Do the test items/tasks relate to each other and to the overall construct under investigation? Will the selected tasks provide the therapist an accurate and consistent representation of the strengths and challenges of the clients with similar diagnoses? Reliability is determined by the strength of relationship between aspects of the assessment, and is usually calculated statistically via correlational analysis and measures of internal consistency like coefficient Alpha. Test-retest reliability, item discrimination analysis (relationship between items in a test with the overall test score), and interrater reliability (relationships between different raters' scores) are examples. Correlation numbers range from -1 to +1, with, positive values indicating a positive relationship between variables. Values in test statistics above .80 are generally accepted as significant (Walsh & Betz, 1990).

Validity is the second requirement for a high quality test and refers to the extent to which the assessment measures the variable under investigation or, in other words, whether it measures what it purports to measure (Boyle & Radocy, 1987). There are several types of validity, but we will be concerned here with content validity, criterion-related validity, and construct validity. *Content validity* looks at how well a test or assessment measures what it claims to measure, or whether assessment items provide adequate coverage of what is being assessed. Lipe (2005; personal communication, Feb. 9, 2012) sought to establish content validity for the Music-Based Evaluation of Cognitive Functioning (MBECF) by examining the literature on music therapy with older adults to determine what types of music tasks were being used successfully with this population, questioning colleagues on their work, and evaluating her own practice. *Criterion-related validity* (also called *predictive validity*) exists when performance on an assessment predicts performance in a real-life situation. In Lipe's (2005) work to develop the MBECF, criterion-related validity was estimated by computing Pearson product-moment correlations among the MBECF and the MMSE, the Brief Cognitive Rating Scale, and the Severe Impairment Battery. Finally, a test has *construct validity* if there is an association between the test scores and the theoretical trait or construct that it purports to measure. Lipe, York, and Jensen (2007) also reported on construct validity, which they established for the construct of *music cognition* by comparing scores on York's (1994) Residual Music Skills Test (RMST), Lipe's (1995) MBECF, and the Mini-Mental Status Examination (MMSE; Folstein, Folstein, & McHugh, 1975) and finding the relationships that would be expected if they were all measuring music cognition. When seeking to establish the validity of assessment tools, it is important to directly relate and operationally define how specific music responses are related to broader, overarching constructs such as *music cognition* or *emotional expression* (A. Lipe, personal communication, Dec. 22, 2011).

It is encouraging that music therapy assessments increasingly include information on reliability and validity. It is important that music therapy assessments meet psychometric standards in order to establish the credibility of music therapy clinical practice.

Norm-Referenced and Criterion-Referenced Assessment

Another ongoing issue in music therapy assessment is the extent to which assessments need to be norm referenced or criterion referenced[2] (Coleman & Brunk, 2003). These issues relate only to some types of assessments. For example, it would be inappropriate to norm-reference any assessments in which the individual is compared to him- or herself, such as interpretive or descriptive assessments or some evaluative assessments. *Norm-referenced* tests (assessments) "describe a student's performance in comparison to some known group. For example, a 6 year-old student might be compared to other 6 year-old students" (Coleman & Brunk, p. 21). "*Criterion-referenced* tests describe a student's performance in terms of specific behaviors or skills. The objective of a criterion-referenced test is not to determine a mental age or IQ, but rather to evaluate the student's ability to perform particular skills in a particular setting" (Coleman & Brunk, p. 21).

There are no norm-referenced music therapy assessments, although music therapists use some norm-referenced assessments from other fields, including music. An example is the Primary Measures of Music Audiation (Gordon, 1979), found by Wilson and Smith (2000) and Gregory (2000) to be among the most-used published assessments in the ar-

[2] The use of *criterion-referenced* by Coleman and Brunk refers to criterion-related validity, as discussed earlier.

ticles that they surveyed. As described above, norm-referenced assessments allow comparison to some known group. Large numbers of people are tested with the tool in order to get data for norm-referenced assessments. Information is then provided as to how various portions of the group scored on the assessment. This information can then be used to compare the performance of an individual or group to the larger group that was tested. There are some areas, particularly those in which music therapy assessments are used for diagnostic purposes, in which norm-referenced assessment data would be strongly indicated, allowing comparisons of the performance of a client that one music therapist assesses with others who have similar diagnoses or characteristics. Since many tests in psychology are norm referenced, it may be important for music therapists to consider the need for more norm-referenced music therapy assessments.

General or Domain-Specific Assessment

Many music therapy assessments are general assessments that assess multiple domains. The AMTA Standards of Practice, Standard 2.1, encourage global assessments: "The music therapy assessment will include the general categories of psychological, cognitive, communicative, social, and physiological functioning focused on the client's needs and strengths. The assessment will also determine the client's responses to music, music skills and musical preferences" (AMTA, 2011).

Lipe has expressed concerns about the impracticality of establishing construct and criterion validity for global assessments and also the degree to which music therapists might duplicate the work of other professionals while attempting global assessments. With this in mind, she encourages music therapists to develop domain-specific (i.e., music based) assessments (A. Lipe, personal communication, Dec. 20, 2011; Jan. 12, 2012). She suggests that the focus of music therapy assessment should be to offer unique information on a client's functional ability based on responses to designated music tasks. After assessments using music-based protocols are developed, validity testing can be done using established tests that assess motor, communication, or other skills that are the focus of assessment. Music therapists do not have to replicate what the physical or speech therapist is doing (A. Lipe, personal communication, Feb. 9, 2012, Feb. 20, 2012).

Need for Protocols for Music Therapy Assessments

Few protocols have been developed for music therapy assessments, leaving what is done in the assessment session to the judgment of the music therapist. This is indefensible psychometrically (A. Lipe, personal communication, Dec. 20, 2011). It is important to establish protocols to provide guidance for how to conduct an assessment while still allowing for some flexibility. Specific music activities/tasks that will elicit desired behaviors to be assessed will need to be developed. Lipe (2005) and York (2005) provide general guidelines for gathering the information needed for the MBECF and the RMST. Regarding the guidelines provided for the MBECF, Lipe says, "What I've tried to do is to offer some balance [between the creativity of the therapist and psychometric demands]: I provide some directions for selecting a *greeting song* – what types of musical characteristics it should contain. This allows some flexibility but hopefully provides enough information to allow me to collect good data on how the task is functioning" (A. Lipe, personal communication, Dec. 20, 2011).

EARLY MUSIC THERAPY ASSESSMENT

Published work about early music therapy seldom speaks of formal assessment. Feder and Feder (1998), in the first edition of this book, identified some of the assessments that were developed in the early years of music therapy in the U.S., including several projective tests and some assessments that attempted to determine who might benefit most from music therapy. Many of these were not formulated by music therapists.

It seems likely, though, that music therapists did assess their clients in some way in these early days of music therapy. Michel (1965) reported on a survey of music therapists in which he found that most patients (40%) were selected or referred by a physician or as a cooperative effort among the physician, ward personnel, and music therapists. They were selected or assigned/prescribed both because of patient interest (26%) and for therapeutic reasons (25%). Music therapists received the following types of information on prescription forms: diagnosis, case history, music background, treatment goals, forms of musical activity, and miscellaneous other areas. All of this information was probably considered as part of an informal (and unlabeled) assessment process.

It appears from looking at case studies that were published at this time that some music therapists did assess clients to determine what type or scope of treatment they needed. Lathom (1968), for instance, speaking of a child with intellectual and developmental disabilities (labeled *retarded* at the time) who was new to an institution, said, "It is important that the therapist be skilled in observing the patient and in reporting his observations objectively" (p. 66). She then describes of a variety of situations in which the music therapist might observe the child and things to look for. It is clear that she was assessing the child and that this was an important part of her treatment planning. Michel (1968) described the use of a musicality test, pitch matching, and a general assessment of the musical potential of children with cleft palates, although it is not clear what was done with this information. Many of the cases reported from this time were referred by physicians, and it is possible that it was left to the physician to focus the treatment in terms of the goals for the patient; this, of course, does not address their musical responses. Lathom reported:

> Assessment has always been done, since I have been in music therapy. Even in my internship at Topeka State Hospital in 1960-61, we evaluated each client before they were assigned to a group. That was a psychiatric setting, and the psychiatrists did give us a referral that might say "Increase ego strength" or "provide emotional expression." We then had to translate that into music therapy goals and objectives. When I worked at Parsons [State Hospital and Training School, Parsons, Kansas], we had psychiatrists who gave similar referrals, but we also had psychologists who tended to be humanists. We had a large group doing some of the important early work in behavior modification, using Skinner's techniques and others who followed. It was interesting to attend team meetings with all of these diverse schools of thought, and then to communicate in terms all could understand and accept.
>
> Assessment was being done when I started my first job at Parsons in 1961. I was told that my responsibility would include assessing every new client in the school (about 650 retarded children, 6-18, who were educable or trainable). I devised my own instrument and revised it many times over the five years I worked there. It was not very different, in final form, from the form found in my book *Pediatric Music Therapy* [Lathom-Radocy, 2002]. Over the five years I was there, I as-

> sessed almost all of the children, since the population turned over weekly. I always had a group of about 6-10 children. At that time, we had the luxury of taking three months for assessment and every area of the facility assessed every child. At the end of three months, we had a meeting to share our observations and plan a program for that specific child. I did receive some recommendations (e.g., provide socialization, provide experience in structure with the long-term goal of internalization of structure, etc.), but could make my own recommendations to the team. After the child was in the program, each cottage had weekly meetings and every child was followed through periodic meetings and progress reports. It was an excellent program with every form of therapy and special education that each child needed. (W. Lathom, personal communication, Dec. 28, 2011)

The Categories of Response developed by Nordoff and Robbins (1965/1971), in which they used children's drum beating to understand their pathology, was an important early assessment tool. The categories were developed from observations of work done with 145 children. Nordoff and Robbins described the child coming into the room, being seated at a drum, and being encouraged to beat the drum and to make music. The quality of the child's drumming was thought to be an indicator of his or her pathology. They said, "The initial aims of the therapist will be to discover to what extent the child can make music, how he makes it, and what music-making means to him" (1971, pp. 61–62). The 13 Categories of Response include: complete rhythmic freedom, unstable rhythmic freedom, limited rhythmic freedom, compulsive beating, disordered beating, evasive beating, emotional-force beating, chaotic-creative beating, piano playing, responses by singing, responses to singing, responses to specific musical idioms, and responses to mood or changes of mood in music, with subcategories under many (p. 63).

Alvin's pioneering music therapy work in the United Kingdom (Alvin, 1965, 1975) did not include formal assessment, but Bruscia (1987) analyzed her work and suggested that she included three stages of assessment: Stage 1, relating self to objects; Stage 2, relating to self and therapist; and Stage 3, relating self to others; and that she assessed the child's responses in listening, improvising freely on instruments, and singing (Bruscia, 1987, pp. 103–107).

EXAMPLES OF MUSIC THERAPY ASSESSMENT

Numerous assessments were developed and published following the early assessment work that was just described. Music therapy assessment has become more sophisticated, often with attention paid to psychometric standards for assessment.

Children with Disabilities

Nordoff and Robbins (1977, 2007) developed two scales to assess musical responses of children with disabilities. The scales were based on the study of improvisational music therapy of approximately 1050 sessions with 52 children, half of whom were diagnosed as having autism. They were developed and refined beginning in 1964 and with extensive additional revision beginning in 1992. Scale I, Child-Therapist Relationship in Coactive Music Experience, rates the client-therapist relationship in musical activity in two areas: Levels of Participation and Qualities of Resistiveness. Scale II, Musical Communicativeness, rates the child's musical communicativeness in three areas of activity: instrumental, vocal, and body movement. A third scale, Musicing: Forms of Activity: Stages and Qualities of Engagement, was added in the revision of their book (2007). In using this scale, each response rating combines an assessment of the level of complexity of its musical form with an assessment of the stage or quality of engagement that it expresses. This is done for instrumental rhythmic activity and singing. All three scales are used regularly in Nordoff-Robbins music therapy work and have been revised as necessary. Responses of various raters are compared as part of this process. A formal reliability study was conducted on Scale 1 (Mahoney, 2010). Interobserver reliability was computed among experienced clinicians trained in Nordoff-Robbins music therapy and among those not trained in this approach. He found that 78 percent of the entire group of 34 participants obtained mean scores that were within one point of the total group mean, with 82 percent of those with Nordoff-Robbins training and 74 percent of those without Nordoff-Robbins training obtaining scores within one point of the group mean (all at $p < .05$). An additional scale, the *Music Therapy Communication and Social Interaction* scale (*MTCSI;* Hummel-Rossi et al., 2008) is designed to measure the communication and social interaction behaviors that a child demonstrates during a music therapy session.

Videotaped sessions are coded with the MTCSI in one-minute intervals. Coded behaviors include an individual's simultaneous or sequential participation in musical activity with the therapists or peers; joint attention and turn-taking; reciprocal verbal exchange and reciprocal musical exchange, either instrumental or vocal; communication of affect via facial expression, gesture, movement, or touch; and other indicators of the client's response to or initiation of communication and interaction. This scale is still being developed, but correlations that have been found between subscales of the MTCSI and non-music tests related to similar areas support the concurrent validity of the MTCSI (Guerrero & Turry, 2012).

A major effort that was part of a Federal grant to the National Association for Music Therapy was to develop an assessment tool that could be used for students with severe and profound disabilities. The Music Therapy Assessment Profile for Severely/Profoundly Handicapped persons, Research Draft III (0-27 Months Level; Michel & Rohrbacher, 1982) incorporated developmental scales used by physical therapists, occupational therapists, and speech therapists as the basis for music therapy programming. This assessment tool was intended for early stages of development, up to 27 months, with each stage presented in two- to three-month increments. Behaviors observed under music conditions were matched with norms of development across communicative, cognitive, motor, social, and affective domains. Programmatic goals could then be developed by identifying the stage of development that immediately followed the student's current level across each of the domains. This assessment was distributed to approximately 500 music therapists nationwide as part of the outcomes of this grant, but not published further in the years to follow (M. Rohrbacher, personal communication, Feb. 17, 2012).

The Special Education Music Therapy Assessment Process or SEMTAP (Brunk & Coleman, 2000; Coleman & Brunk, 2003) was developed in response to the need for an assessment process that could provide evidence that music therapy, as a *related service,* is required for certain students to benefit from public school special education programs. In this sense, it is considered an *eligibility assessment.* The emphasis is on testing a student's response to certain tasks that are specifically connected to already-existing objectives in the IEP. This assessment has been extremely influential and helpful in establishing the need for music therapy services for students and getting it included on their Individualized Education Programs (IEPs).

The Individualized Music Therapy Assessment Profile or IMTAP (Baxter et al., 2007) was designed to assess the skills of children and adolescents with multiple severe physical disabilities, communication disorders, autism, severe emotional disturbances, social impairments, and learning disabilities. Eleven domains are assessed: gross motor, fine motor, oral motor, sensory, receptive, communication/auditory perception, expressive communication, cognitive, social, emotional, and musicality, plus sub-domains for each. It was developed through a systematic literature review of various standardized assessments in music therapy and across a range of allied health and child development fields. The test items were reviewed and tested by a field of experts including music therapists.

The Music Therapy Diagnostic Assessment (MTDA) was developed by Oldfield (2006) to assist the diagnosis of children's difficulties at the Croft Unit for Child and Family Psychiatry, U.K. The MTDA consists of two half-hour sessions with a specific but flexible structure depending on the child's preferences, strengths, and weaknesses. It typically includes a hello song, an opportunity for the child to choose what to do, the child playing one or more instruments alone and also improvising with the therapist, an improvised story, and a goodbye song, although the exact contents is flexible and varies from child to child. Oldfield conducted research study to determine whether the MTDA could highlight important aspects of behavior that might help to determine whether a child had autism. In a study of 30 children with possible autistic disorders aged 4-12, primarily boys, the results of the MTDA were compared to the Autistic Diagnostic Observation Schedule (ADOS). The method also included questionnaires for each performed test either MTDA or ADOS and a structured interview with the child after each assessment type. The MTDA had a 72 percent agreement with the ADOS regarding the diagnosis for a child, indicating that the MTDA found similar information to the well-established ADOS. The MTDA and ADOS also showed significant differences in their scores, implying that they were picking up different information on the children.

The Individual Music-Centered Assessment Profile for Neurodevelopmental Disorders (IMCAP-ND) examines and evaluates a client's ability to relate musically and communicate in musical play (Carpente, 2011b). The IMCAP-ND is comprised of two rating scales (Musical

Emotional Assessment Rating Scale and Musical Perception Scale), the Musical-Emotional Profile (narrative), and the individualized treatment and intervention plan, each of which targets and conceptualizes a client's strengths and challenges in musical-play within the context of relating and communicating, while considering individual-differences and supportive interventions (i.e., modeling, positioning, verbal cuing) used to foster musical interaction. Informed by Greenspan's DIR®/Floortime™ Model (Greenspan & Weider, 2006), the IMCAP-ND is based on six music domain areas: (a) Musical Attunement, (b) Musical Mutuality and Relatedness, (c) Musical-Affect, (d) Musical Dialoguing, (e) Musical Adaptation, and (f) Musical Interrelatedness (Carpente, 2009; 2011a). Each of the six areas is evaluated by clinical listening and observation, focusing on a client's musical responses in musical-play through any or all of four modes of musical expression: (a) instruments, (b) voice, (c) movement, and (d) gestures. The IMCAP-ND is currently being tested for reliability. The disciplines included in the reliability testing are: music therapy, psychology, speech and language pathology, and education.

Layman, Hussey, and Laing (2002) piloted an assessment instrument for children with severe emotional disturbances in four domains: (a) behavioral/social functioning, (b) emotional responsiveness, (c) language/communication abilities, and (d) music skills. Included under music skills were musical awareness, response to music, response to cue, imitation, and vocal inflection. Functioning is measured "along a continuum anchored by defensive/withdrawn behavior on one pole, and disruptive/intrusive behavior at the other pole" (p. 173). The authors measured responses along a continuum that ranged from defensive/withdrawn to disruptive/intrusive, with target behaviors assuming the middle range of the continuum. Overall interrater reliability for the assessment tool was .915, with reliability in the four domains ranging from .90 to .94. Cohen's kappa measures how much better than chance the agreement is between a pair of coders and was found to be 0.81, a very good level of agreement.

The analysis system to Assess the Quality of Relationship (AQR) during music therapy (Schumacher, 1999, 2004; Schumacher & Calvet-Kruppa, 2007) was developed for the evaluation and documentation of music therapy with children with profound disturbances within the autistic spectrum. The AQR-Instrument includes four different scales: Scale 1, Instrumental Quality of Relationship (IQR); Scale 2, Vocal Pre-

Speech Quality of Relationship (VQR); Scale 3, Physical-Emotional Quality of Relationship (PEQR), and Scale 4, Therapeutic Quality of Relationship (TQR). The first three scales assess the quality of relationship of the child, while the fourth focuses on the therapist and his or her interventions. Based on developmental psychological knowledge, especially infancy research, the authors identify seven levels of contact/relationship: 0 = lack of contact/contact refusal, 1 = sensory contact/contact-reaction, 2 = functionalizing contact, 3 = contact to oneself/ self-awareness, 4 = contact to others/inter-subjectivity, 5 = relationship to others/interactivity, 6 = joint experience/interaffectivity. This analysis system can be applied to confirm the qualities in a relationship (diagnostic) as well as the presentation of a course of therapy (evaluation). It can answer the question of whether the therapist offers an intervention appropriate to the client's state of development (method) and helps to work out an appropriate aim for the therapy (prognosis). The reliability of the AQR-Instrument was analysed in 2005 (Schumacher, Calvet, & Stallmann, 2005). Raters from different countries have been trained in assessing video sequences with the AQR-scales. The results of the reliability analysis showed the following intraclass correlations (ICC) for the various scales:

Table 13.1
Intraclass Correlations for AQR Scales

Scale	*n video sequences; n raters*		*ICC*	*95% Confidence interval*
IQR	9	52	0.82	0.67 – 0.94
VQR	9	52	0.83	0.68 – 0.95
PEQR	8	58	0.75	0.56 – 0.93
TQR	9	63	0.78	0.62 – 0.93

The AQR-Instrument is published in a revised version in German (Schumacher, Calvet, & Reimer, 2011). The newer version incorporates the latest research into preverbal development. An English translation is in preparation.

The Music Therapy Assessment Tool for Emotionally Disturbed Children (Goodman, 1989) offers choices to children, including various instruments and activities. The choices are considered representative of the child's personality and lead to a clinical picture that assists in planning music therapy sessions. Administration and scoring of the assessment are up to the individual therapist.

People with Intellectual and Developmental Disabilities

Published assessments for people with intellectual and developmental disabilities include one by Cohen and Gericke (1972), whose assessment combined clinical observation with information on musical ability, leading to recommendations about treatment. Cohen, Averbach and Katz (1978) identified four parameters that should be included in assessment of clients with intellectual and developmental disabilities that: (a) responding to program identified problems; (b) determining social/psychological/medical needs of a general order; (c) determining specific habilitation/educational needs; and (d) determining specific music therapy needs. Wasserman, Plutchik, Deutsch, and Taketomo (1973) developed three rating scales for musical aptitude and social behavior in adult patients with intellectual and developmental disabilities and emotional illness. Individual participation was rated by independent observers in all three components of the sessions: (a) rhythm group participation, (b) singing group, and (c) vocal dynamics. Bitcon (1976) used an assessment that measured attention span, retention, awareness of self and others, and attitudes. Boxill (1985) provided detailed information on assessment in adaptive behavior and the motor, communication, cognitive, affective, and social domains. She emphasized the need to understand normal development in order to judge the child's delayed development in each of these domains.

Snow (2009) developed a Music Therapy Assessment for adults with developmental disabilities. She piloted her assessment with eight adults, ages early twenties to early forties. The steps in the assessment session include: (a) participant is invited to explore and play a larger instrument, chosen by the therapist, by him or herself; (b) participant and therapist dialogue, each using separate but identical instruments (e.g., two conga drums); (c) participant plays the bass drum with therapist at the piano, playing a four-beat pattern with clearly accented beats; (d) therapist makes some changes in music (specified as part of the assessment protocol), asking participant to follow; and (e) participant chooses one of five instrument and plays, then answers questions (specified in the assessment protocol) from the music therapist. An additional qualitative section is also included. Nine scales were developed for scoring: Interactional I and II, Mobility, Rhythmic Synchrony, Engagement, Attention, Length of Playing, Boundary, and Following Changes. Reliability was computed on those scoring the assessment and changes made based on initial results. After the revision of the tasks and scales, interrater reliability (based on percentage of agreements of ratings of 25% of the scores) was .85-.90. The author suggests that these results are promising because higher intellectually functioning participants had higher scores on assessment, and the majority of scores improved over time in the same direction observed through information gained in music therapy groups.

People with Psychiatric Disorders

In 1981, the Joint Commission on Accreditation of Hospitals (JCAH) required that activity services do an "assessment of the patient's needs, interests, life experiences, capacities, and deficiencies" (p. 126; in Feder & Feder, 1998, p. 245). After this directive was issued, a number of hospitals prepared their own activity intake assessments, which often included music therapy (Feder & Feder). This no doubt influenced other aspects of music therapy assessment in this setting.

Braswell et al. (1983, 1986) used the Music/Activity Therapy Intake Assessment for Psychiatric Patients to examine the attitudes of clients with psychiatric problems, examining self-concept, interpersonal relationships, and altruism/optimism. Wells' (1988) Music Therapy Assessment for Disturbed Adolescents utilizes a specific protocol with clients (a) selecting a song, (b) composing a written story to background music, and (c) improvising instrumentally, each intended to elicit information in a particular area. The assessment is done as clients participate in a designated activity. Crowe (2007), in an overview of assessment for adults, adolescents, and children with psychiatric problems also includes the Hamilton Rating Scale for Depression and Rhythmic Competency (Migliore, 1991), the Music Therapy Effects Scale (Thaut, 1989), and the Patient Evaluation of Treatment (Heaney, 1992), as well as several assessments that will be presented later in this chapter.

The Psychiatric Music Therapy Questionnaire (PMTQ) was developed by Cassity and Cassity (1994), who surveyed clinical training directors for information to find out what areas of nonmusic behavior they assessed and treated most frequently during music therapy sessions. They then asked them to write two client problems assessed and treated most often for each area, and two music therapy interventions used for each of these problems. They developed and organized this into a comprehensive manual, *Multimodal Psychiatric Music Therapy for Adults, Adolescents, and Children: A Clinical Manual* (Cassity & Cassity, 1991, 2006), based on Lazarus' (1976, 1989) Multimodal Therapy model. Reliability was assessed by calculating test-retest reliability of the PMTQ with undergraduate students at an interval of three weeks and was found to be: Part I: Music, $r_S = .79$, $p < .01$; Part II: Multimodal Problem Analysis, $r_S = .90$, $p < .001$; and Part III: Post-Interview Observations, $r_S = .83$, $p < .001$, with reliability scores also available for Part II subtests (Blodgett & Davis, 1994). Test-retest reliability for the same subtests (for adults, adolescents, and children) was also computed by administering them at a three-week interval to 12 people with psychiatric disorders of various ages (or their parents, for the children). It was found to be: Part I, $r_S = .77$, $p < .01$; Part II, $r_S = .90$, $p < .001$; and Part III, $r_S = .92$. For this computation, also, reliability scores are available for the Part II subtests (Murray, 1994). Interrater reliability was computed as: Part I, $r_S = .92$, $p < .001$; Part II, $r_S = .94$, $p < .001$ (Blodgett & Davis). Validity was assessed by Anderson and Krebaum (1998), who conducted an exploratory study comparing the PMTQ scores of adult psychiatric clients with their scores on the Beck Depression Inventory (BDI; Beck, Ward, Mendelson, Mock, & Erbaugh, 1961), the Symptom Checklist-90-R (Derogatis, Lipman, & Covi, 1973), and the Millon Clinical Multiaxial Inventory-III (MCMI-III; Millon, Millon, & Davis, 1994). The highest validity coefficients obtained were: .70 between the BDI total score and the Cognitive subscale of the PMTQ, .76 between the Drug Dependence subscale of the MCMI-III and the Drugs subscale of the PMTQ, and .74 between the Aggressive/Sadistic subscale of the MCMI-III and the Behavior subscale of the PMTQ [no significance level given]. Anderson and Krebaum concluded that the PMTQ appeared to correlate with other psychometric instruments that assess symptoms and underlying personality constructs. Haegg (2012) used the BDI short form (BDI-SF), the PMTQ Cognitive subtest (PMTQ-C), and a visual analogue scale (VAS) to measure the effect of brief structured improvisation upon mood among people with chemical dependency. All three tests indicated significant increases in mood. Concurrent validity coefficients were .72 ($p < .01$) between the BDI-SF and the PMTQ-C, .64 ($p < .05$) between the BDI-SF and the VAS-M, and .63 ($p < .05$) between the VAS-M and the PMTQ-C.

Older Adults

An assessment developed by Hintz (2000) addresses client strengths, needs, and functioning levels, and can be utilized in both long-term care and rehabilitation settings. The tool targets the following skills: expressive musical, receptive musical, behavioral/psychosocial, motor, and cognitive/memory. Results of the testing are then interpreted and used in making treatment and program recommendations. The Musical Assessment of Gerontologic Needs and Treatment, the MAGNET Survey (Adler, 2001), was designed to correlate with the Minimum Data Set (MDS), a multidisciplinary assessment used for treatment planning in long-term care facilities. Background information, musical preferences, and observable behaviors are collected in the initial part of the survey. The following areas are assessed in the session and lead to a treatment plan: cognition; emotional status; memory; motor skills; musical participation; musical preferences; musical skills; observable behaviors; reality orientation; sensory processing, planning, and task execution; singing; social interactions; and speech and communication.

Two assessments have been developed to evaluate aspects of music therapy for people with dementia. York (1994) developed the Residual Music Skills Test (RMST) for people with probable Alzheimer's disease to assess musical behaviors acquired over a lifetime (residual skills) without the benefit of musical training. It includes the following categories: Musical Memory/Recall of Song; Instrument Identification; Tonal Memory/Pitch Discrimination; Short Term Recall of Instrument Names and Song; Musical Language; Rhythm Tasks. York initially tested 37 people with probable Alzheimer's disease using both the RMST and Folstein's Mini-Mental Status Examination (MMSE; Folstein, Folstein, & McHugh, 1975), seeking to determine: (a) internal consistency (using several aspects of item analysis), (b) interrater reliability for both the RMST and the MMSE, and (c) the relationships between language and non-language sub-scores as well as total scores between the two tests. She found: (a) stronger correlations for items that required singing, and that Total Musical Language sub-scores were also strongly correlated with total scores of the RMST ($r = .82$), using Pearson r for items 1-6(continuous variables) and point-biserial for items 7-10 (dichotomous variables); (b) interrater reliability of $r = .96$ for the RMST and $r = .98$ for the MMSE; and (c) highly correlated language scores between the RMST and MMSE ($r = .72$), with correlations between total scores of the two tests producing an r of .61, suggesting that RMST may be measuring unique musical behaviors as compared to the MMSE. In later testing, York (2000) calculated test-retest reliability (after two weeks), using Pearson's product-moment correlation, and found significant relationships between scores from the two administrations of the test ($r = .92$, $p < .000$, N = 95). Lipe, York, and Jensen (2007) also reported on construct validity (i.e., the construct of *music cognition*), assessed through comparisons between the RMST, Lipe's Music Based Evaluation of Cognitive Function (MBECF, 1995), and MMSE scores. The RMST was found to have a higher correlation with the musical MBECF ($r = .83$), but, again, a less positive relationship to the MMSE ($r = .76$). Since the RMST was developed to specifically assess residual *music* skills in persons with probable Alzheimer's disease, these findings confirm that the RMST is measuring what it purports to measure and that it is a reliable and stable instrument. The RMST "may provide additional information in understanding musical responses in persons with probable AD" (York, 1994, p. 294).

Lipe (1995) used music task performance to assess cognitive functioning of older adults with dementia in her Music-Based Evaluation of Cognitive Functioning (MBECF). The MBECF includes 19 tasks that require singing, as well as melodic, rhythm, movement, and verbal responses. In developing the MBECF, Lipe did an initial evaluation, then another evaluation 10-14 days later. She tested 32 people, 16 with and 16 without dementia. She found overall rater agreement of $r = .92$, test-retest reliability (using the Pearson product-moment correlation) of $r = .93$, and internal consistency (Cronbach's alpha) of .95 (Lipe, 2005). Cronbach's alpha coefficients were computed for the verbal, singing, and rhythm items, averaging scores from both testings, at .88 for verbal, .98 for singing, and .85 for rhythm items. To assess validity, Lipe (2005) compared scores of people with and without dementia and found that those without dementia scored significantly higher than those with dementia. Criterion-related validity was estimated using Pearson product-moment correlations among the MBECF and the MMSE ($r = .93$, $p < .01$), Brief Cognitive Rating Scale ($r = -.83$, $p < .01$), and Severe Impairment Battery ($r = .98$, $p < .01$), with the latter being used only with 16 participants with dementia (Lipe, 2005). In later testing of 16 people (Lipe, 2005), a correlation of $r = .86$ was obtained between the revised version (based on revision of items that were not performing well) of the MBECF and MMSE scores. The face validity of the revised protocol was evaluated by the music therapy staff in a state hospital and found to be satisfactory (Lipe, 2005). The strong correlations between the MBECF and the established measures of cognitive functioning indicate that the MBECF is achieving its purpose of assessing cognitive functioning in this population using music tasks.

To substantiate the usefulness of the tasks of the RMST and the MBECF and to add to the understanding of the nature of the construct of music cognition and its relationship to general cognition, the MMSE, the MBECF, and the RMST were given to 50 individuals with dementia (Lipe, York, & Jensen, 2007). The MBECF, after some revisions, and the MMSE were correlated using the Pearson product-moment correlation at $r = .89$, $p < .01$, indicating that the MBECF can serve as a valid measure of cognitive functioning. The RMST was found to correlate at $r = .76$ with the MMSE, supporting the use of the RMST to discern music skills rather than cognitive skills. A correlation of $r = .83$, $p < .01$, was found between the MBECF and RMST, indicating that there are strong similarities between the two tests, although they take different approaches to measuring music cognition. The authors concluded that the pattern of correlations between the tasks on the three assessments indicates that, while there are strong relationships between music cognition and general cognition, rhythmic, singing, and melodic abilities may represent unique aspects of cognitive ability.

Medical and Rehabilitation Settings

Thompson, Arnold, and Murray (1990) describe an assessment for people who recently suffered a cerebrovascular accident (CVA). Their assessment covers six major areas of functioning: (a) orientation (self-recognition and memory), (b) visual (memory, perception, discrimination), (c) auditory (identification of sounds, discrimination of sounds, abstract thinking related to songs, counting, and spelling), (d) motor (identification of body parts, sensory awareness, body integration, body use; musical and nonmusical), (g) communication (presence of various communication disorders such as aphasia and agnosia, articulation, respiration, phonation, vocal range), and (e) social (affect, range of social behaviors, self-control, self-concept). Scalenghe and Murphy's (2000) music therapy assessment in the managed care environment provides a comprehensive descriptive assessment of clients, divided into nine major areas: history of present illness, behavioral observations, motor skills, communication skills, cognitive skills, auditory perceptual skills, social skills, specific musical behaviors, and summary and recommendations. The assessment is intended to describe the skills of the client in these areas and consequently identify therapeutic goals, as well as to meet the assessment requirements of the managed care setting and, in so doing, advocate for the inclusion of music therapy in the therapeutic milieu.

Douglass (2006) developed an assessment tool for hospitalized children. She initially assessed the needs of the target population by reviewing the literature and interviewing other professionals who worked with these clientele, examined existing assessment tools used by music therapists and other professionals, planned the format and content, piloted the form with patients and revised initial drafts based on feedback, and determined the validity and reliability of the form. The assessment tool includes the following categories: background information, referral information, physiological information, physical/motor skills, cognitive skills, social and emotional behaviors, communication skills, and musical behaviors. Content validity was established by soliciting input from music therapists who worked in hospital settings as to whether the assessment instrument met the objectives that had been established for it. This was done twice, once with an initial form and a second time with a revised form. All of them felt that the revised form met the objectives. Preliminary work to develop interrater reliability was done by having a music therapist watch a video of work with a client who had been assessed previously using the form and rate the session using the form, then comparing those ratings with the original ratings. Following this, questions about responses that were intended were discussed. Music therapy sessions were then jointly facilitated by two music therapists, with each filling out the form at the end of the session. This was followed by a comparison of the number of agreements and disagreements on the checklist portion of the form. At this point, the raters agreed on all of the ratings, leading to interrater reliability of 1.0 (E. Douglass Espinoza, personal communication, Feb. 10, 2012).

Loewy (2000) developed a music psychotherapy assessment with 13 areas of inquiry: (a) awareness of the self, others, and the moment; (b) thematic expression; (c) listening; (d) performing; (e) collaboration/relationship; (f) concentration; (g) range of affect; (h) investment/motivation; (i) use of structure; (j) integration; (k) self-esteem; (l) risk taking, and (m) independence. These areas of inquiry evolved from Loewy's research that incorporated a music psychotherapy investigation involving survey and hermeneutic inquiry. The 13 areas interconnect to address four core themes that are important to her findings and that integrate music and verbal evaluation within a music psychotherapy context: relationship, dynamics, achievement, and cognition. Loewy emphasizes that the format of an assessment session is critical. She combines structured and free-flowing experiences and finds that this combination may provide for the optimal experience of assessing the therapeutic needs of a new client. She developed a *Tour of the Room* model in which each instrument is played and the client is encouraged to relay memories or in-the-moment experiences that are associated with the sounds played. Loewy finds that one's culture, experience of sound, and symbolic association of instrument(s) is best understood within a cultural context and should be invited prior to using structured or improvisational play in therapy.

Loewy also developed a music therapy pain assessment, which she says is to "understand and feel the pain of the patient as well as it can be defined by him or her" (1999, p. 195). In addition to asking patients to comprehensively describe their pain, she encourages them to improvise their pain, because these improvisations "provide clues on how to address physical aspects of the tension" (p. 195). By playing with her patients, Loewy is also able to assess the types of interventions needed to ameliorate the patient's pain and define the therapist's role in doing so. Loewy and her team also use a color analysis scale (CAS) that was developed by Loewy at Beth Israel Medical Center, as well as the Wong-Baker Faces Scale (Wong & Baker, 1988) and 0-10 ratings, which are part of standard nursing flow sheets. Music therapists at Beth Israel Hospital assess pain as part of their general assessment evaluation.

The Music-Based Attention Assessment (MAA; Jeong & Lesiuk, 2011) was designed for patients with traumatic brain injuries (TBI). It is a melodic-contour identification test with three subtests designed to assess three types of auditory attention: sustained, selective, and divided. The 48-item test was piloted with 15 patients with TBI to evaluate preliminary psychometric properties. It was found that: (a) Test items had an easy to moderate level of item difficulty and an acceptable to high level of item discrimination; (b) the musical characteristics were associated with the level of item difficulty; and (c) the internal consistency, as computed by Cronbach's alpha, was .95. The authors felt that the high Cronbach's alpha provided support for the construct validity of the test, since it indicates the degree to which the test items measure underlying latent constructs that are consistent.

The Music Therapy Assessment Tool for Low Awareness States (MATLAS; Magee, 2007) includes 14 items that are systematically categorized to cover five behavioral domains: motor responses, communication, arousal, auditory responsiveness, and visual responsiveness. The MATLAS has a defined protocol with operationalized procedures that include presenting familiar salient and unfamiliar music, visual, and simple auditory stimuli, using primarily live music, or recorded music where the idiom demands (Magee, Lenton-Smith, & Daveson, 2012). Its purpose is to measure behavioral responses in music therapy intervention and to assess awareness of patients in low awareness states. A pilot study demonstrated significant correlations between the MATLAS and two other validated non-music therapy scales suggesting concurrent validity (Daveson, Magee, Crewe, Beaumont, & Kenealy, 2007). Further research using intraclass correlations has demonstrated good levels of interrater reliability (.65-1.00) and intrarater reliability (.77-.90; Magee, Siegert, Lenton-Smith, & Daveson, 2012). The MATLAS provides a newly standardized tool for assessing patients in low awareness states with particular sensitivity for the auditory modality. It produces outcomes that are comparable with those produced by other specialist validated tools for this population and has a good level of interrater agreement (Magee, Lenton-Smith, Daveson, Siegert, & O'Kelly, 2012).

Additional Clientele and Areas

Bruscia (2000) developed the Guided Imagery and Responsiveness Scale (GIMR), which uses a five-point scale to rate the responsiveness of the traveler (client) in Guided Imagery and Music (GIM) in the following areas: relaxation, imagery, music, guiding, verbal processing, and general. Bruscia suggested that responsiveness to the GIM experience was an indication of psychological health and that scores on the GIMR should therefore be positively related to other measures of health and negatively related to measures of psychological defensiveness. Meadows (2000) conducted three studies to assess the validity and reliability of the GIMR. The first study, for content-related validity, was a literature review in which the dimensions of the GIMR were examined in relation to self-report inventories of imagery experience, with the finding that the GIMR accounted for the major dimensions of imagery that had been previously studied. The second study, for construct validity, looked for relationships of scores within the GIMR and among the GIMR, Sense of Coherence (SOC; from the Orientation to Life Questionnaire), and Defense Mechanisms Inventory (DMI). This study found that the various sub-scores were correlated and were components of the total score, suggesting that each area of responsiveness measured by the GIMR is an interdependent part of the total score and that together they provide a valid measure of the single construct, responsiveness. The third study compared therapist ratings on the same session and found that 92.4 percent were identical or within one rating, indicating that the GIMR has a satisfactory level of interrater reliability.

Jacobsen (2012) developed a music therapy assessment tool, the Assessment of Parenting Competencies (APC), to evaluate parent-child interaction and parental capacity (including the parents' resources and potential as well as their weaknesses and inappropriate interaction patterns) prior to music therapy to inform the music therapy treatment and also during the music therapy as a measure of change. The scale yields five scores: Autonomy, Turn Analysis, Negative Response, Positive Response, and a total score for Parent-Child Interaction in Music. Interrater reliability for APC scores ranged from .73 to .89 and test-retest reliability ranged from .70 to. 89. Internal consistency had an alpha level of .93, with correlations between APC scores ranging from .57 to .91. Results indicated that the APC had a high level of reliability and was administered and scored in a consistent and stable manner. Furthermore, results of validity testing suggest that the APC measured what it attempted to measure, as is could distinguish between clinical and nonclinical groups, and it correlated mildly with similar variables from the Parenting Stress Index and the Parent-Child Relationship-Inventory, standardized questionnaires of parenting competencies.

Moreau (2003) began developing the Scale for Measurement of Expressive and Musical Behavior (MAKS) in 1994. The MAKS includes two subscales, the Expression scale, with 14 items for rating a solo improvisational musical performance, and the Communication scale, with 13 items for rating improvisational musical performance in duo playing with the therapist. In 2003, Moreau reported on a reliability study, using video episodes of adolescents who had psychiatric problems, playing solo or in dyads, in which they were rated by 52 trained raters, with measures for objectivity, reliability (interrater and test-test), and validity. It was evaluated again (Moreau, Ellgring, Goth, Poustka, & Aldridge, 2010), with some revisions, using a sample of 62 children from a psychiatric unit and primary schools, with measures at three points during the therapy process. Reliability was assessed by computation of Cronbach's alpha which, after some revision of the items, was found to be $> .75$. Objectivity was assessed by including items with acceptable discriminatory power and that loaded on a stable factor in a factor analysis. Based on these selection criteria and using the Pearson product-moment correlation, an interrater correlation of $r = .90$ was found for the total score of the Expression scale and of $r = .70$ for the Communication scale. Sensitivity for change was tested using a MANOVA analysis with the factors Psychopathology and Time of Measurement and using the MAKS Expression total score Communication total score. The analysis of the solo improvisations showed significant changes over time in musical expression (within-subject factor time: $p = .02$), while the duo improvisations showed significant changes in musical communication (within-subject factor time: $p = .001$), leading to the conclusion that the MAKS is sensitive to discrete changes in musical expression and communication.

The Improvisation Assessment Profiles (IAPs) were developed by Bruscia (1987, 1994, 2002b) to provide a comprehensive model of client assessment and evaluation. To use the IAPs, the therapist (a) observes the client improvising under various conditions; (b) analyzes the improvisations musically, according to the profiles and subscales provided; and (c) interprets the findings according to a psychological theory that is relevant to the client's problem. The IAPs consist of six profiles that have subscales for each musical element. Each profile focuses on a particular musical process (e.g., integration) and provides a continuum of five gradients ranging from one extreme to its opposite (e.g., undifferentiated – fused – integrated – differentiated – over-differentiated). Each subscale focuses on how that process is manifested in a specific musical element (e.g., rhythmic integration, harmonic integration). The six profiles are: (a) integration (how simultaneous aspects of each element are organized); (b) variability (how sequential aspects of each element are organized); (c) tension (how each element accumulates, sustains, modulates, or releases tension); (d) congruence (whether simultaneous feeling states and role relationships are consistent among each element); (e) salience (how much prominence and control each element is given); and (f) autonomy (the kinds of relationships formed between the improvisers through each element). The IAPs are used widely around the world. Wigram (2000, 2004) adapted the IAPs into a quantitative format for event-based analysis of musical improvisations. This abbreviated version of the IAPs is based on the profiles of autonomy and variability, which Wigram found most relevant for diagnostic assessment of communication disorders. Bruscia (2002b) stated that, although they were developed for qualitative research, the IAPs can be used fruitfully also in quantitative research if measurable events are defined carefully.

SUMMARY AND RECOMMENDATIONS

This chapter has presented an overview of music therapy assessment, including information on the purposes of assessment, AMTA Standards of Clinical Practice for assessment, the need for assessment specific to music therapy, a summary of assessment overviews, a comparison of quantitative and qualitative approaches, and issues in music therapy assessment including the desirability of clarifying the purpose of assessment, assessment versus evaluation, professional identity and assessment, reliability and validity, norm-referenced and criterion-referenced assessment, general or domain-specific assessment, and the need for protocols. A number of music therapy assessments were also presented.

It is clear from the assessments described in this chapter that music therapist have made considerable progress in developing assessments in recent years. It is encouraging that many of those developing assessments are aware of the need to meet psychometric standards for assessment and attempting to do so.

In spite of the progress, many challenges still exist. Suggestions that were made regarding domain-specific assessment and the need for protocols to guide what is done in the assessment session can help music therapists as they develop these areas. Attention needs to be paid to improving psychometric qualities such as reliability and validity. These issues can help to focus music therapist as improvements are made in the assessments that currently exist and additional assessments are developed.

Author Acknowledgments

The author wishes to thank the following colleagues for their feedback on this chapter: Anne Lipe, Kenneth Bruscia, Debra Burns, Susan Gardstrom, Stine Lindahl Jacobsen, Eric Waldon, Elizabeth York, and the authors of many of the assessments that are discussed.

REFERENCES

Achterberg, J., & Lawlis, G. F. (1978). *Imagery of cancer: A diagnostic tool for the process of disease.* Champaign, IL: Institute for Personality and Ability Testing.

Adler, R. (2001). *Musical Assessment of Gerontologic Needs and Treatment: The MAGNET Survey.* St. Louis, MO: MMB Music.

Alvin, J. (1965). *Music for the handicapped child.* London: Oxford University Press.

Alvin, J. (1975). *Music therapy.* New York: Basic Books.

American Music Therapy Association. (2011). *AMTA Standards of Practice.* http://www.musictherapy.org/about/standards/.

Anderson, C. L., & Krebaum, S. R. (1998, November). An analysis of the Psychiatric Music Therapy Questionnaire (PMTQ) and standard personality questionnaires. Paper presented at the annual conference of the AMTA, Cleveland, OH.

Baxter, H. T., Berghofer, J. A., MacEwan, L., Nelson, J., Peters, K., & Roberts, P. (2007). *The Individualized Music Therapy Assessment Profile, IMTAP.* London: Jessica Kingsley.

Beck, A. T., Ward, C. H., Mendelson, M., Mock, J., & Erbaugh, J. (1961). An inventory for measuring depression. *Archives of General Psychiatry, 4,* 561–571.

Bitcon, C. (1976). *Alike and different: The clinical and educational uses of Orff-Schulwerk* (2nd Ed.). Gilsum, NH: Barcelona.

Blodgett, G., & Davis, D. (1994, Nov.). Reliability of the Psychiatric Music Therapy Questionnaire for Adults: A pilot study. Paper presented at the annual conference of the National Association for Music Therapy, Orlando, FL.

Boyle, J. D., & Radocy, R. E. (1987). *Measurement and evaluation of musical experiences.* New York: Schirmer Books.

Boxill, E. H. (1985). *Music therapy for the developmentally disabled.* Rockville, MD: Aspen Systems.

Braswell, C., Brooks, D. M., DeCuir, A., Humphrey, T., Jacobs, K. W., & Sutton, K. (1983). Development and implementation of a music/activity therapy intake assessment for psychiatric patients. Part I: Initial standardization procedures on data from university students. *Journal of Music Therapy, 20,* 88–100.

Braswell, C., Brooks, D. M., DeCuir, A., Humphrey, T., Jacobs, K. W., & Sutton, K. (1986). Development and implementation of a music/activity therapy intake assessment for psychiatric patients. Part II: Standardization procedures on data from psychiatric patients. *Journal of Music Therapy, 23,* 126–141.

Brunk, B., & Coleman, K. (2000). Development of a special education music therapy assessment process. *Music Therapy Perspectives, 18,* 59–68.

Bruscia, K. (1988). Standards for clinical assessment in the arts therapies. *The Arts in Psychotherapy, 15,* 5–10.

Bruscia, K. E. (1987). *Improvisational models of music therapy.* Springfield, IL: Charles C Thomas.

Bruscia, K. E. (1993). *Client assessment in music therapy.* Unpublished manuscript.

Bruscia, K. E. (1994). *IAP. Improvisational Assessment Profiles. Kartlegging gjennom musikkterapeutisk improvisation* [Improvisation Assessment Profiles: Assessment through improvisational music therapy]. Sandane, Norway: Høgskula på Sandane.

Bruscia, K. (2000). A scale for assessing responsiveness to Guided Imagery and Music. *Journal of the Association of Music and Imagery, 7,* 1–7.

Bruscia, K. E. (2002a). Client assessment in the Bonny Method of Guided Imagery and Music (BMGIM). In K. E. Bruscia & D. E. Grocke (Eds.), *Guided imagery and music: The Bonny method and beyond* (pp. 273–295). Gilsum, NH: Barcelona.

Bruscia, K. E. (2002b). Response to the Forum discussion of the "IAPs" in the *Nordic Journal* website. *Nordic Journal of Music Therapy, 11,* 72–82.

Carpente, J. (2011a). Addressing core features of autism: Integrating Nordoff-Robbins Music Therapy within the developmental, individual-difference, relationship-based (DIR®/Floortime™) model. In A. Meadows (Ed.), *Developments in music therapy practice: Case study perspectives* (pp. 134–149). Gilsum, NH: Barcelona.

Carpente, J. (2011b). *The individual music-centered assessment profile for neurodevelopmental disorders (IMCAP-ND®) for children, adolescents, and adults: A clinical manual.* Manuscript submitted for publication.

Carpente, J. (2009). *Contributions of Nordoff-Robbins Music Therapy within the developmental, individual differences, relationship (DIR) based model in the treatment of children with autism: Four case studies.* Unpublished Doctoral Dissertation, Temple University. Ann Arbor: ProQuest/UMI, publication number AAT 3359621.

Cassity, M. D., & Cassity, J. E. (1991). *Multimodal psychiatric music therapy for adults, adolescents, and children: A clinical manual.* St. Louis, MO: MMB Music.

Cassity, M., & Cassity, J. E. (1994). Psychiatric music therapy assessment and treatment in clinical training facilities with adults, adolescents, and children. *Journal of Music Therapy, 31,* 2–20.

Cassity, M. D., & Cassity, J. E. (2006). *Multimodal psychiatric music therapy for adults, adolescents, and children: A clinical manual* (3rd ed.). London: Jessica Kingsley.

Chase, K. M. (2002). *The music therapy assessment handbook.* Columbus, MS: SouthernPen.

Cohen, G., & Gericke, O. L. (1972). Music therapy assessment: Prime requisite for determining patient objectives. *Journal of Music Therapy, 9,* 161–189.

Cohen, G., Averbach, J., & Katz, E. (1978). Music therapy assessment of the developmentally disabled child. *Journal of Music Therapy, 15,* 86–99.

Coleman, K. A., & Brunk, B. K. (2003). *SEMTAP: Special Education Music Therapy Assessment Process handbook* (2nd ed.). Grapevine, TX: Prelude Music Therapy.

Crowe, B. (2007). *Music therapy for children, adolescents, and adults with mental disorders.* Silver Spring, MD: AMTA.

Daveson, B. A., Magee, W. L., Crewe, L., Beaumont, G., & Kenealy, P. (2007). The Music Therapy Assessment Tool for Low Awareness States. *International Journal of Therapy and Rehabilitation, 14*(12), 545–549.

Derogatis, L. R., Lipman, R. S., & Covi, L. (1973). The SCL-90: An outpatient psychiatric rating scale – Preliminary report. *Psychopharmacology Bulletin, 9,* 13–28.

Doll, E. A. (1953). *The measurement of social competence: A manual for the Vineland Social Maturity Scale.* Minneapolis, MN: Educational Test Bureau Educational Publishers.

Douglass, E. (2006). The development of a music therapy assessment tool for hospitalized children. *Music Therapy Perspectives, 24,* 73–79.

Dunn, L. M., & Dunn, L. M. (1981). *Peabody picture vocabulary test.* Circle Pines, MN: American Guidance Service.

Feder, B., & Feder, E. (1998). *The art and science of evaluation in the arts therapies.* Springfield, IL: Charles C Thomas.

Folstein, M. F., Folstein, S. E., & McHugh, P. R. (1975) Mini-mental state: A practical method for grading the cognitive state of patients for the clinician. *Journal of Psychiatric Research, 12,* 189–198.

Gfeller, K. E., & Davis, W. B. (2008). The music therapy treatment process. In W. B. Davis, K. E. Gfeller, & M. H. Thaut, *An introduction to music therapy: Theory and practice* (3rd ed., pp. 429–486). Silver Spring, MD: AMTA.

Goodman, K. D. (1989). Music therapy assessment of emotionally disturbed children. *The Arts in Psychotherapy, 16*(3), 179–192.

Gordon, E. E. (1979). *Primary measures of music audiation.* Chicago: GIA Publications.

Greenspan, S. I., & Weider, S. (2006). *Engaging autism: Using the floortime approach to help children relate, communicate, and think.* New York: Da Capo Lifelong Books.

Gregory, D. (2000). Test instruments used by Journal of Music Therapy authors from 1984-1997. *Journal of Music Therapy, 37,* 79–94.

Guerrero, N., & Turry, A. (2012). Nordoff-Robbins Music Therapy: An expressive and dynamic approach for young children on the autism spectrum. Manuscript submitted for publication.

Haegg, R. (2012). The influence of brief structured improvisation upon mood among the chemically dependent. Manuscript submitted for publication.

Hamilton, M. (1967). A rating scale for depression. *Journal of Neurology, Neurosurgery, and Psychiatry, 23,* 56–62.

Heaney, C. J. (1992). Evaluation of music therapy and other treatment modalities by adult psychiatric inpatients. *Journal of Music Therapy, 29,* 70–86.

Hintz, M. (2000). Geriatric music therapy clinical assessment: Assessment of music skills and related behaviors. *Music Therapy Perspectives, 18,* 31–37.

Hummel-Rossi, B., Turry, A., Guerrero, N., Selim, N., Birnbaum, J., Ritholz, M., & Marcus, D. (2008). *Music Therapy Communication and Social Interaction scale.* Unpublished instrument, Nordoff-Robbins Center for Music Therapy, New York University.

Isenberg-Grzeda, C. (1988). Music therapy assessment: A reflection of professional identity. *Journal of Music Therapy, 25,* 156–169.

Jacobsen, S. (2012). *Music therapy assessment and development of parental competences in families with children who have experienced emotional neglect: An investigation of the reliability and validity of the tool, Assessment of Parenting Competencies (APC).* Aalborg, Denmark: Aalborg University.

Jeong, E., & Lesiuk, T. L. (2011). Development and preliminary evaluation of a Music-Based Attention Assessment for patients with traumatic brain injury. *Journal of Music Therapy, 48,* 551–572.

Journal of Music Therapy. (2000). Special issue on assessment. *37*(2).

Lathom, W. B. (1968). The use of music therapy with retarded patients. In E. T. Gaston (Ed.), *Music in therapy* (pp. 66–77). New York: Macmillan.

Lathom-Radocy, W. B. (2002). *Pediatric music therapy.* Springfield, IL: Charles C Thomas.

Layman, D. L., Hussey, D. L., & Laing, S. J. (2002). Music therapy assessment for severely emotionally disturbed children: A pilot study. *Journal of Music Therapy, 34,* 164–187.

Lazarus, A. A. (1976). *Multimodal behavior therapy.* New York: Springer.

Lazarus, A. A. (1989). *The practice of multimodal therapy.* Baltimore: John Hopkins University Press.

Lipe, A. (1995). The use of music performance tasks in the assessment of cognitive functioning among older adults with dementia. *Journal of Music Therapy, 32,* 137–151.

Lipe, A. (2005). The music-based evaluation of cognitive functioning. In A. Lipe & E. York, *Manual for administration.* Spartanburg, SC: Converse College.

Lipe, A., & York, E. (2000). Guest editorial: Special issue on assessment in music therapy. *Music Therapy Perspectives, 18,* 12.

Lipe, A. W., York, E., & Jensen, E. (2007). Construct validation of two music-based assessments for people with dementia. *Journal of Music Therapy, 44,* 369–387.

Loewy, J. (1999). The use of music psychotherapy in the treatment of pediatric pain. In C. Dileo (Ed.), *Music therapy and medicine: Theoretical and clinical applications* (pp. 189–206). Silver Spring, MD: American Music Therapy Association.

Loewy, J. (2000). Music psychotherapy assessment. *Music Therapy Perspectives, 18,* 47–58.

Magee, W. (2007). Development of a music therapy assessment tool for patients in low awareness states. *NeuroRehabilitation, 22,* 319–324.

Magee, W., Lenton-Smith, G., & Daveson, B. A. (2012). *The Music Therapy Assessment Tool for Low Awareness States manual.* London: Royal Hospital for Neuro-Disability.

Magee, W. L., Lenton-Smith, G., Daveson, B. A., Siegert, R. J., & O'Kelly, J. (2012). Music Therapy Assessment Tool for Low Awareness States (MATLAS): Establishing reliability and validity (Poster presentation). Ninth World Congress in Brain Injury, Edinburgh, Scotland, March 21-25.

Magee, W. L., Siegert, R. J., Lenton-Smith, G., & Daveson, B. A. (2012). Music Therapy Assessment Tool for Low Awareness States (MATLAS): Preliminary report on a subscale to assess awareness in patients in low awareness states. Manuscript submitted for publication.

Mahoney, J. (2010). Interrater agreement on the Nordoff-Robbins Evaluation Scale I: Client-Therapist Relationship in Musical Activity. *Music and Medicine, 2*(1), 23–28.

Maslach, C., & Jackson, S. (1981). *Maslach Burnout Inventory ("Human Services Survey").* Berkeley, CA: Consulting Psychologists Press.

Meadows, A. (2000). The validity and reliability of the Guided Imagery and Music Responsiveness Scale. *Journal of the Association for Music and Imagery, 7,* 8–33.

Michel, D. E., & Rohrbacher, M. J. (1982). *The music therapy assessment profile for severely/profoundly handicapped persons, Research draft III (0-27 months level).* Unpublished manuscript. Denton, TX: Texas Woman's University.

Michel, D. E. (1965). Professional profile: The NAMT member and his clinical practices in music therapy. *Journal of Music Therapy, 2,* 124–129.

Michel, D. E. (1968). Music therapy in speech habilitation of cleft-palate children. In E. T. Gaston (Ed.), *Music in therapy* (pp. 162–166). New York: Macmillan.

Migliore, M. J. (1991). The Hamilton Rating Scale for Depression and Rhythmic Competency: A correlational study. *Journal of Music Therapy, 28,* 211–221.

Millon, T., Millon, C., & Davis, R. (1994). *Millon Clinical Multiaxial Inventory-III (MCMI-III) Manual.* Minneapolis, MN: National Computer Systems.

Moreau, D. V. (2003). MAKS – A scale for measurement of expressive and musical behaviour. *Music Therapy Today* (online), *4*(4), available at http://musictherapyworld.net.

Moreau, D. V., Ellgring, H., Goth, K., Poustka, F., & Aldridge, D. (2010). Psychometric results of the Music Therapy Scale (MAKS) for measuring expression and communication. *Music and Medicine, 2*(1), 41–47.

Murray, A. (1994, Nov.). Reliability of the Psychiatric Music Therapy Questionnaire with psychiatric patients: A pilot study. Paper presented at the annual conference of the National Association for Music Therapy, Orlando, FL.

Music Therapy Perspectives. (2000). Special issue on assessment. *18*(1).

National Association for Music Therapy. (1983). Standards of Practice of the National Association for Music Therapy, Inc. *Music Therapy Perspectives, 1*(2), 13–27.

Nordoff, P., & Robbins, C. (1965/1971). *Therapy in music for handicapped children.* New York: St. Martin's Press.

Nordoff, P., & Robbins, C. (1977). *Creative music therapy.* New York: John Day.

Nordoff, P., & Robbins, C. (2007). *Creative music therapy: A guide to fostering clinical musicianship* (2nd ed.). Gilsum, NH: Barcelona.

Oldfield, A. (2006). *Interactive music therapy in child and family psychiatry.* London: Jessica Kingsley.

Radocy, R. (1999). Measurement traditions: May they facilitate music therapy assessments? In B. Wilson & E. York (Co-Chairs), *Proceedings of the Institute on Music Therapy Assessment* (pp. 4–8). Institute conducted at the World Congress of Music Therapy, Washington, DC.

Reisberg, B., Ferris, S. H., DeLeon, M. J., & Crook, T. (1982). The global deterioration scale for assessment of primary degenerative dementia. *American Journal of Psychiatry, 139,* 1136–1139.

Rider, M. (1981). The assessment of cognitive functioning level through musical perception. *Journal of Music Therapy, 18,* 110–119.

Robinson, C. R. (1988). Differential modes of choral performance evaluation using traditional procedures and a continuous response digital interface device (Doctoral dissertation, Florida State University). *Dissertation Abstracts International, 49*(10), 2859.

Sabbatella, P. E. (2004). Assessment and clinical evaluation in music therapy: An overview from literature and clinical practice. *Music Therapy Today* (online), *5*(1), available at http://musictherapyworld.net.

Scalenghe, R. (1999). The interface between music therapy assessments and managed care, accreditation and regulatory expectations. In B. Wilson & E. York (Co-Chairs), *Proceedings of the Institute on Music Therapy Assessment* (pp. 9–12). Institute conducted at the World Congress of Music Therapy, Washington, DC.

Scalenghe, R., & Murphy, K. M. (2000). Music therapy assessment in the managed care environment. *Music Therapy Perspectives, 18,* 23–30.

Schumacher, K. (1999, 2004). *Musiktherapie und Säuglingsforschung. Zusammenspiel. Einschätzung der Beziehungsqualität am Beispiel des instrumentalen Ausdrucks eines autistischen Kindes.* Frankfurt/M.: Peter Lang.

Schumacher, K., & Calvet-Kruppa, C. (2007). The AQR instrument (Assessment of the Quality of Relationship): An observational instrument to assess the quality of a relationship. In T. Wosch & T. Wigram (Eds.), *Microanalysis in music therapy* (pp. 49–91). London: Jessica Kingsley.

Schumacher, K., Calvet, C., & Reimer, S. (2011): Das EBQ-Instrument und seine entwicklungspsychologischen Grundlagen. [book with DVD]. Göttingen, Germany: Vandenhoeck & Ruprecht.

Schumacher, K., Calvet, C., & Stallmann, M. (2005) Zwischenmenschliche Beziehungsfähigkeit" – Ergebnisse der Reliabilitätsprüfung eines neu entwickelten Instrumentes zum Wirkungsnachweis der Musiktherapie. In B. Müller – Oursin (Ed.), *Ich wachse, wenn ich Musik mache. Musiktherapie mit chronisch kranken und von Behinderung bedrohten Kindern.* Wiesbaden: Reichert Verlag.

Snow, S. (2009). The development of a music therapy assessment tool: A pilot study. In S. Snow & M. D'Amico (Eds.), *Assessment in the creative arts therapies* (pp. 47–98). Springfield, IL: Charles C Thomas.

Spielberger, C. D., Gorsuch, R. L., & Lushene, R. E. (1970). *State-trait anxiety inventory.* Palo Alto, CA: Consulting Psychologists Press.

Thaut, M. H. (1989). The influence of music therapy interventions on self-rated changes in relaxation, affect, and thought in psychiatric prisoner-patients. *Journal of Music Therapy, 26,* 155–166.

Thompson, A. B., Arnold, J. C., & Murray, S. E. (1990). Music therapy assessment of the cerebrovascular accident patient. *Music Therapy Perspectives, 8,* 23–29.

Walsh, W. B., & Betz, N. E. (1990). *Tests and assessment* (2nd ed.). Englewood Cliffs, NJ: Prentice-Hall.

Wasserman, N. R., Plutchik, R., Deutsch, R., & Taketomo, Y. (1973). A music therapy evaluation scale and its clinical applications to mentally retarded adult patients. *Journal of Music Therapy, 10,* 64–77.

Wells, N. F. (1988). An individual music therapy assessment procedure for emotionally disturbed young adolescents. *The Arts in Psychotherapy, 15,* 47–54.

Wheeler, B. L. (2005). Introduction. In B. L. Wheeler (Ed.), *Music therapy research* (2nd ed.). (pp. 3–19). Gilsum, NH: Barcelona.
Wigram, T. (1999). Assessment methods in music therapy: A humanistic or natural science framework? *Nordic Journal of Music Therapy, 8*(1), 7–25.
Wigram, T. (2000). A method of music therapy assessment for the diagnosis of autism and communication disorders in children. *Music Therapy Perspectives, 18,* 13–22.
Wigram, T. (2004). *Improvisation. Methods and techniques for music therapy clinicians, educators and students.* London: Jessica Kingsley.
Williams, D. B., & Fox, D. B. (1983). *Toney listens to music* (computer program). Bellevue, WA: Temporal Acuity Products, Inc.
Wilson, B. L., & Smith, D. S. (2000). Music therapy assessment in school settings: A preliminary investigation. *Journal of Music Therapy, 37,* 95–117.
Wong, D., & Baker, C. (1988). Pain in children: Comparison of assessment scales. *Pediatric Nursing, 14*(1), 9–17.
York, E. (1994). The development of a quantitative music skills test for patients with Alzheimer's disease. *Journal of Music Therapy, 31,* 280–297.
York, E. (2000). A test-retest reliability study of the Residual Music Skills Test. *Psychology of Music, 28,* 174–180.
York, E. (2005). The Residual Music Skills Test (RMST, 1994). In A. Lipe & E. York, *Manual for administration.* Spartanburg, SC: Converse College.
Zuckerman, M., & Lubin, B. (1985). *Manual for the Multiple Affect Adjective Check List, Revised.* San Diego, CA: Educational and Industrial Testing Service.
Zwerling, I. (Dec. 1979). The creative arts therapist as "real therapies." *Hospital and Community Psychiatry, 30,* 841–844.

INDEX

C

M

N

Q

R

T